An Introduction
to the Theory of Numbers

Books by Ivan Niven

Calculus: An Introductory Approach (Van Nostrand)
Diophantine Approximations (Wiley)
Irrational Numbers (Wiley)
Mathematics of Choice (Random House)
Numbers: Rational and Irrational (Random House)

An Introduction
to the Theory of Numbers

Second Edition

IVAN NIVEN

University of Oregon

HERBERT S. ZUCKERMAN

University of Washington

John Wiley & Sons, Inc. NEW YORK · LONDON · SYDNEY

Preface

The second edition differs from the first in improved explanations in several places, the addition of many problems, and, especially in the first few chapters, a better transition from easy to hard problems. We express our thanks to Paul T. Bateman, Charles W. Curtis, Emma Lehmer, and Sigmund Selberg for helpful suggestions. We thank John Wiley and Sons for their sympathetic consideration of our wishes about format and typography.

March 1966

Preface to the First Edition

Our purpose is to present a reasonably complete introduction to the theory of numbers within the compass of a single volume. The basic concepts are presented in the first part of the book, followed by more specialized material in the final three chapters. Paralleling this progress from general topics to more particular discussions, we have attempted to begin the book at a more leisurely pace than we have followed later. Thus the later parts of the book are set forth in a more compact and sophisticated presentation than are the earlier parts.

The book is intended for seniors and beginning graduate students in American and Canadian universities. It contains at least enough material for a full year course; a short course can be built by the use of Sections 1.1 to 1.3, 2.1 to 2.4, 3.1, 3.2, 4.1, 5.1 to 5.3, 5.5, 6.1, and 6.2. Various other arrangements are possible because the chapters beyond the fourth are, apart from a very few exceptions, independent of one another. The final three chapters are entirely independent of each other.

To enable the student to deepen his understanding of the subject, we have provided a considerable number of problems. The variety of these exercises is extensive, ranging from simple numerical problems to additional developments of the theory. The beginner at number

v

theory should take warning that the subject is noted for the difficulty of its problems. Many an innocent-looking problem gives, by the very simplicity of its statement, very little notion of the considerable ingenuity or depth of insight required for its solution. As might be expected, the more difficult problems are placed toward the ends of the sets. In many instances three or four consecutive problems constitute a related series in which the last ones can be solved more readily by use of information from the first ones. As a matter of principle we have made the text itself entirely independent of the problems. In no place does the proof of a theorem depend on the results of any problem.

In choosing methods of proof, we have tried to include as many methods as possible. We have tried to state the proofs accurately, avoiding statements that could be misleading and also avoiding unduly long discussions of unimportant details. As the reader progresses he will become familiar with more and more methods, and he should be able to construct accurate proofs by patterning them after our proofs.

The reader interested in further exploration of the subject will find the bibliography at the end of the book of considerable use. In particular, anyone interested in the history of the subject should consult O. Ore, *Number Theory and Its History*, and, for more specific information, L. E. Dickson, *History of the Theory of Numbers*. Our approach is analytical, not historical, and we make no attempt to attribute various theorems and proofs to their original discoverers. However, we do wish to point out that we followed the suggestion of Peter Scherk that we use F. J. Dyson's formulation of the proof of Mann's $\alpha\beta$ Theorem. Our proof is based on notes graciously placed at our disposal by Peter Scherk. For permission to use several problems from the *American Mathematical Monthly*, we are indebted to the editors. We also appreciate the careful reading of the manuscript by Margaret Maxfield, whose efforts resulted in numerous improvements. Finally, we would like to record our deep appreciation of and our great debt to the mathematicians whose lectures were vital to our introduction to the theory of numbers: L. E. Dickson, R. D. James, D. N. Lehmer, and Hans Rademacher.

IVAN NIVEN
HERBERT S. ZUCKERMAN

June 1960

Contents

Chapter 1

Divisibility

1.1 Introduction

The theory of numbers is primarily concerned with the properties of the natural numbers, 1, 2, 3, 4, · · · , also called the positive integers. However, the theory is not strictly confined to just the natural numbers or even to the set of all integers: 0, ±1, ±2, ±3. · · · . In fact, some theorems of number theory are most easily proved by making use of the properties of real or complex numbers even though the statement of the theorems may involve only natural numbers. Also, there are theorems concerning real numbers that depend so heavily on the properties of integers that they are properly included in the theory of numbers.

An integer n greater than 1 is called a prime if it has no divisor d such that $1 < d < n$. The fact that for every given positive integer m there is a prime greater than m is stated in terms of integers, and it can be proved from the properties of the natural numbers alone. The fact that every natural number can be expressed as a sum of, at most, fifty-four fifth powers of integers is also stated in terms of natural numbers, but any known proof depends on properties of complex numbers. Finally, the question as to how many primes there are that do not exceed x clearly belongs to the theory of numbers but its answer involves the function $\log x$ and is well outside of the realm of the natural numbers. The last two examples are beyond the scope of this book. However, we do not restrict ourselves to the integers but will use real and complex numbers when it is convenient. The questions discussed in this book are not numerical computations or numerical curiosities, except insofar as

1

these are relevant to general propositions. Nor do we discuss the foundations of the number system; it is assumed that the reader is familiar not only with the integers, but also with the rational and real numbers. However, a rigorous logical analysis of the real-number system is not prerequisite to the study of number theory.

The theory of numbers relies for proofs on a great many ideas and methods. Of these, there are two basic principles to which we draw especial attention. The first is that any set of positive integers has a smallest element if it contains any members at all. In other words, if a set S of positive integers is not empty, then it contains an integer s such that for any member a of S, the relation $s \le a$ holds. The second principle, mathematical induction, is a logical consequence of the first.* It can be stated as follows: if a set S of positive integers contains the integer 1, and contains $n + 1$ whenever it contains n, then S consists of all the positive integers.

It may be well to point out that a negative assertion such as, for example, "Not every positive integer can be expressed as a sum of the squares of three integers," requires only that we produce a single example—the number 7 cannot be so expressed. On the other hand, a positive assertion such as "Every positive integer can be expressed as a sum of the squares of four integers," cannot be proved by producing examples, however numerous. This result is Theorem 5.6 in Chapter 5, where a proof is supplied.

Finally, it is presumed that the reader is familiar with the usual formulation of mathematical propositions. In particular, if A denotes some assertion or collection of assertions, and B likewise, the following statements are logically equivalent—they are just different ways of saying the same thing.

A implies B.
If A is true, then B is true.
In order that A be true it is necessary that B be true.
B is a necessary condition for A.
A is a sufficient condition for B.

If A implies B and B implies A, then one can say that B is a necessary and sufficient condition for A to hold.

* Compare G. Birkhoff and S. MacLane, *A Survey of Modern Algebra*, Macmillan, revised edition, 1953, pp. 10–13.

In general, we shall use letters of the roman alphabet, a, b, c, $\cdots$, m, n, $\cdots$, x, y, z, to designate integers unless otherwise specified.

1.2 Divisibility

Definition 1.1 *An integer b is divisible by an integer a, not zero, if there is an integer x such that $b = ax$, and we write $a|b$. In case b is not divisible by a we write $a \nmid b$.*

Other language for the divisibility property $a|b$ is that a divides b, that a is a divisor of b, and that b is a multiple of a. If $a|b$ and $0 < a < b$ then a is called a proper divisor of b. It is understood that we never use 0 as the left member of the pair of integers in $a|b$. On the other hand, not only may 0 occur as the right member of the pair, but also in such instances we always have divisibility. Thus $a|0$ for every integer a not zero. The notation $a^K\|b$ is sometimes used to indicate that $a^K|b$ but $a^{K+1} \nmid b$.

Theorem 1.1

(1) $a|b$ *implies* $a|bc$ *for any integer c;*
(2) $a|b$ *and* $b|c$ *imply* $a|c$;
(3) $a|b$ *and* $a|c$ *imply* $a|(bx + cy)$ *for any integers x and y;*
(4) $a|b$ *and* $b|a$ *imply* $a = \pm b$;
(5) $a|b$, $a > 0$, $b > 0$, *imply* $a \leqq b$.

Proof. The proofs of these results follow at once from the definition of divisibility. Property 3 admits an obvious extension to any finite set, thus:

$$a|b_1, \ a|b_2, \ \cdots, \ a|b_n \text{ imply } a \ \left| \ \sum_{j=1}^{n} b_j x_j \text{ for any integers } x_j. \right.$$

Property 2 can be extended similarly.

Theorem 1.2 *The division algorithm. Given any integers a and b, with $a > 0$, there exist integers q and r such that $b = qa + r$, $0 \leqq r < a$. If $a \nmid b$, then r satisfies the stronger inequalities $0 < r < a$.*

Proof. Consider the arithmetic progression

$$\cdots, \ b - 3a, \ b - 2a, \ b - a, \ b, \ b + a, \ b + 2a, \ b + 3a, \ \cdots$$

extending indefinitely in both directions. In this sequence, select the smallest non-negative member and denote it by r. Thus by definition r satisfies the inequalities of the theorem. But also r, being in the sequence, is of the form $b - qa$, and thus q is defined in terms of r, and the proof is complete.

We have stated the theorem with the assumption $a > 0$. However, this hypothesis is not necessary, and we may formulate the theorem without it: given any integers a and b, with $a \neq 0$, there exist integers q and r such that $b = qa + r$, $0 \leqq r < |a|$.

Theorem 1.2 is called the division algorithm. An algorithm is a mathematical procedure or method to obtain a result. We have stated Theorem 1.2 in the form "there exist integers q and r," and this wording suggests that we have a so-called existence theorem rather than an algorithm. However, it may be observed that the proof does give a method for obtaining the integers q and r, because the infinite arithmetic progression $\cdots$, $b - a$, b, $b + a$, $\cdots$ need be examined only in part to yield the smallest positive member r.

In actual practice the quotient q and the remainder r are obtained by the arithmetic division of a into b.

Definition 1.2 *The integer a is a* common divisor *of b and c in case $a|b$ and $a|c$. Since there is only a finite number of divisors of any non-zero integer, there is only a finite number of common divisors of b and c, except in the case $b = c = 0$. If at least one of b and c is not 0, the greatest among their common divisors is called the* greatest common divisor *of b and c and is denoted by (b, c). Similarly we denote the greatest common divisor g of the integers b_1, b_2, $\cdots$, b_n, not all zero, by $(b_1, b_2, \cdots , b_n)$.*

Thus the greatest common divisor (b, c) is defined for every pair of integers b, c except $b = 0$, $c = 0$, and we note that $(b, c) \geqq 1$.

Theorem 1.3 *If g is the greatest common divisor of b and c, then there exist integers x_0 and y_0 such that $g = (b, c) = bx_0 + cy_0$.*

Proof. Consider the linear combinations $bx + cy$, where x and y range over all integers. This set of integers $\{bx + cy\}$ includes positive and negative values, and also 0 by the choice $x = y = 0$. Choose x_0 and y_0 so that $bx_0 + cy_0$ is the least positive integer l in the set; thus $l = bx_0 + cy_0$.

Next we prove that $l|b$ and $l|c$. We establish the first of these, and the second follows by analogy. We give an indirect proof that $l|b$, that is, we assume $l \nmid b$ and obtain a contradiction. From $l \nmid b$ it follows that there exist integers q and r, by Theorem 1.2, such that $b = lq + r$ with $0 < r < l$. Hence we have $r = b - lq = b - q(bx_0 + cy_0) = b(1 - qx_0) + c(-qy_0)$, and thus r is in the set $\{bx + cy\}$. This contradicts the fact that l is the least positive integer in the set $\{bx + cy\}$.

Now since g is the greatest common divisor of b and c, we may write $b = gB$, $c = gC$, and $l = bx_0 + cy_0 = g(Bx_0 + Cy_0)$. Thus $g|l$, and so by part 5 of Theorem 1.1, we conclude that $g \leq l$. Now $g < l$ is impossible, since g is the *greatest* common divisor, and so $g = l = bx_0 + cy_0$.

Theorem 1.4 *The greatest common divisor g of b and c can be characterized in the following two ways: (1) it is the least positive value of $bx + cy$ where x and y range over all integers; (2) it is the positive common divisor of b and c which is divisible by every common divisor.*

Proof. Part 1 follows from the proof of Theorem 1.3. To prove part 2, we observe that if d is any common divisor of b and c, then $d|g$ by part 3 of Theorem 1.1. Moreover, there cannot be two distinct integers with property 2, because of Theorem 1.1, part 5.

Theorem 1.5 *Given any integers $b_1, b_2, \cdots, b_n$ not all zero, with greatest common divisor g, there exist integers $x_1, x_2, \cdots, x_n$ such that*

$$g = (b_1, b_2, \cdots, b_n) = \sum_{j=1}^{n} b_j x_j.$$

Furthermore, g is the least positive value of the linear form $\sum_{j=1}^{n} b_j y_j$ where the y_j range over all integers; also g is the positive common divisor of b_1, $b_2, \cdots, b_n$ which is divisible by every common divisor.

Proof. This result is a straightforward generalization of the preceding two theorems, and the proof is analogous without any complications arising in the passage from two integers to n integers.

Theorem 1.6 *For any positive integer m,*

$$(ma, mb) = m(a, b).$$

Proof. By Theorem 1.4 we have

$$(ma, mb) = \text{least positive value of } max + mby$$
$$= m \cdot \{\text{least positive value of } ax + by\}$$
$$= m(a, b).$$

Theorem 1.7 *If* $d|a$ *and* $d|b$ *and* $d > 0$ *then*

$$\left(\frac{a}{d}, \frac{b}{d}\right) = \frac{1}{d}(a, b).$$

If $(a, b) = g$, *then* $\left(\frac{a}{g}, \frac{b}{g}\right) = 1.$

Proof. The second assertion is the special case of the first obtained by using the greatest common divisor g of a and b in the role of d. The first assertion in turn is a direct consequence of Theorem 1.6 obtained by replacing m, a, b in that theorem by d, (a/d), (b/d) respectively.

Theorem 1.8 *If* $(a, m) = (b, m) = 1$, *then* $(ab, m) = 1$.

Proof. By Theorem 1.3 there exist integers x_0, y_0, x_1, y_1 such that $1 = ax_0 + my_0 = bx_1 + my_1$. Thus we may write $(ax_0)(bx_1) = (1 - my_0)(1 - my_1) = 1 - my_2$ where y_2 is defined by the equation $y_2 = y_0 + y_1 - my_0y_1$. From the equation $abx_0x_1 + my_2 = 1$ we note, by part 3 of Theorem 1.1, that any common divisor of ab and m is a divisor of 1, and hence $(ab, m) = 1$.

Definition 1.3 *We say that* a *and* b *are* relatively prime *in case* $(a, b) = 1$, *and that* $a_1, a_2, \cdots, a_n$ *are* relatively prime *in case* $(a_1, a_2, \cdots, a_n) = 1$. *We say that* $a_1, a_2, \cdots, a_n$ *are* relatively prime in pairs *in case* $(a_i, a_j) = 1$ *for all* $i = 1, 2, \cdots, n$ *and* $j = 1, 2, \cdots, n$ *with* $i \neq j$.

The fact that $(a, b) = 1$ is sometimes expressed by saying that a and b are coprime, or by saying that a is prime to b.

Theorem 1.9 *For any* x, $(a, b) = (b, a) = (a, -b) = (a, b + ax)$.

Proof. Denote (a, b) by d and $(a, b + ax)$ by g. It is clear that $(b, a) = (a, -b) = d$.

By application of Theorem 1.1, parts 3 and 4, we obtain $d|g$, $g|d$, and hence $d = g$.

Theorem 1.10 *If $c|ab$ and $(b, c) = 1$, then $c|a$.*

Proof. By Theorem 1.6, $(ab, ac) = a(b, c) = a$. But $c|ab$ and $c|ac$, and so $c|a$ by Theorem 1.4.

Given two integers b and c, how can the greatest common divisor g be found? Definition 1.2 gives no answer to this question, and neither does Theorem 1.3 which merely asserts the existence of a pair of integers x_0 and y_0 such that $g = ax_0 + by_0$. If b and c are small, values of g, x_0, and y_0 can be found by inspection. For example, if $b = 10$ and $c = 6$, it is obvious that $g = 2$, and one pair of values for x_0, y_0 is 2, -3. We now state an algorithm which gives a general method for finding the value of g and also values of x_0 and y_0. By Theorem 1.9, $(b, c) = (b, -c)$, and hence we may presume c positive, because the case $c = 0$ is very special: $(b, 0) = |b|$.

Theorem 1.11 *The Euclidean algorithm. Given integers b and $c > 0$, we make a repeated application of the division algorithm, Theorem 1.2, to obtain a series of equations*

$$b = cq_1 + r_1, \qquad 0 < r_1 < c,$$
$$c = r_1q_2 + r_2, \qquad 0 < r_2 < r_1,$$
$$r_1 = r_2q_3 + r_3, \qquad 0 < r_3 < r_2,$$
$$\cdots \qquad\qquad \cdots$$
$$r_{j-2} = r_{j-1}q_j + r_j, \qquad 0 < r_j < r_{j-1},$$
$$r_{j-1} = r_jq_{j+1}.$$

The greatest common divisor (b, c) of b and c is r_j, the last non-zero remainder in the division process. Values of x_0 and y_0 in $(b, c) = bx_0 + cy_0$ can be obtained by eliminating $r_1, r_2, \cdots, r_{j-1}$ from the set of equations.

Example. $b = 963$, $c = 657$.

$$963 = 657 \cdot 1 + 306$$
$$657 = 306 \cdot 2 + 45$$
$$306 = 45 \cdot 6 + 36$$
$$45 = 36 \cdot 1 + 9$$
$$36 = 9 \cdot 4$$

Thus $(963, 657) = 9$, and we can express 9 as a linear combination of 963 and 657 by eliminating the remainders 36, 45, and 306 as follows:

$$9 = 45 - 36$$
$$= 45 - (306 - 45 \cdot 6)$$
$$= -306 + 7 \cdot 45$$
$$= -306 + 7(657 - 306 \cdot 2)$$
$$= 7 \cdot 657 - 15 \cdot 306$$
$$= 7 \cdot 657 - 15(963 - 657)$$
$$= 22 \cdot 657 - 15 \cdot 963.$$

Proof. The chain of equations is obtained by dividing c into b, r_1 into c, r_2 into r_1, $\cdots$, r_j into r_{j-1}. The process stops when the division is exact, that is when the remainder is zero. Thus in our application of Theorem 1.2 we have written the inequalities for the remainder without an equality sign. Thus, for example, $0 < r_1 < c$ in place of $0 \leqq r_1 < c$, because if r_1 were equal to zero, the chain would stop at the first equation $b = cq_1$, in which case the greatest common divisor of b and c would be c.

We now prove that r_j is the greatest common divisor g of b and c. Since $g|b$ and $g|c$, we see that $g|r_1$ by the first equation of the chain. Since $g|c$ and $g|r_1$, we see that $g|r_2$ by the second equation. Continuing by mathematical induction we find that $g|r_j$. On the other hand, the final equation implies that $r_j|r_{j-1}$. This, together with the next to last equation, implies $r_j|r_{j-2}$. Continuing by mathematical induction, we conclude that $r_j|b$ and $r_j|c$. By Theorem 1.4, $r_j|g$. Hence $g = r_j$ by Theorem 1.1.

To see that r_j is expressible as a linear combination of b and c, we need merely eliminate r_1 from the first two equations of the chain, then eliminate r_2 from this and the third equation. Proceeding by successive eliminations of r_3, r_4, $\cdots$, r_{j-1}, we obtain r_j in the form $bx_0 + cy_0$.

Definition 1.4 *The integers a_1, a_2, $\cdots$, a_n, all different from zero, have a* common multiple *b if $a_i|b$ for $i = 1, 2, \cdots, n$. (Note that common multiples do exist; for example the product $a_1 a_2 \cdots a_n$ is one.) The least of the positive common multiples is called the* least common multiple, *and it is denoted by $[a_1, a_2, \cdots, a_n]$.*

Theorem 1.12 *If b is any common multiple of $a_1, a_2, \cdots, a_n$, then $[a_1, a_2, \cdots, a_n] | b$. This is the same as saying that if h denotes $[a_1, a_2, \cdots, a_n]$, then $0, \pm h, \pm 2h, \pm 3h, \cdots$ comprise all the common multiples of $a_1, a_2, \cdots, a_n$.*

Proof. Let m be any common multiple and divide m by h. By Theorem 1.2 there is a quotient q and a remainder r such that $m = qh + r$, $0 \leqq r < h$. We must prove that $r = 0$. If $r \neq 0$ we argue as follows. For each $i = 1, 2, \cdots, n$ we know that $a_i | h$ and $a_i | m$, so that $a_i | r$. Thus r is a positive common multiple of $a_1, a_2, \cdots, a_n$ contrary to the fact that h is the least positive of all the common multiples.

Theorem 1.13 *If $m > 0$, $[ma, mb] = m[a, b]$. Also $[a, b] \cdot (a, b) = |ab|$.*

Proof. Since $[ma, mb]$ is a multiple of ma, it is *a fortiori* a multiple of m, and so can be written in the form mh_1. Denoting $[a, b]$ by h_2, we note that $a | h_2$, $b | h_2$, $am | mh_2$, $bm | mh_2$, and so $mh_1 | mh_2$ by Theorem 1.12. Thus $h_1 | h_2$. On the other hand, $am | mh_1$, $bm | mh_1$, $a | h_1$, $b | h_1$ and so $h_2 | h_1$. We conclude that $h_1 = h_2$ and thus the first part of the theorem is established.

It will suffice to prove the second part for positive integers a and b, since $[a, -b] = [a, b]$. We begin with the special case where $(a, b) = 1$. Now $[a, b]$ is a multiple of a, say ma. Then $b | ma$ and $(a, b) = 1$, so by Theorem 1.10 we conclude that $b | m$. Hence $b \leqq m$, $ba \leqq ma$. But ba, being a positive common multiple of b and a, cannot be less than the least common multiple, and so $ba = ma = [a, b]$.

Turning to the general case where $(a, b) = g > 1$, we have $((a/g), (b/g)) = 1$ by Theorem 1.7. Applying the result of the preceding paragraph, we obtain

$$\left[\frac{a}{g}, \frac{b}{g} \right] \left(\frac{a}{g}, \frac{b}{g} \right) = \frac{a}{g} \frac{b}{g}.$$

Multiplying by g^2 and using Theorem 1.6 as well as the first part of the present theorem, we get $[a, b] (a, b) = ab$.

Problems

1. By using the Euclidean algorithm find the greatest common divisor (g.c.d.) of
   (a) 7469 and 2464; (b) 2689 and 4001;
   (c) 2947 and 3997; (d) 1109 and 4999.

2. Find the greatest common divisor g of the numbers 1819 and 3587, and then find integers x and y to satisfy
$1819x + 3587y = g$.

3. Find values of x and y to satisfy
   (a) $243x + 198y = 9$;
   (b) $71x - 50y = 1$;
   (c) $43x + 64y = 1$;
   (d) $93x - 81y = 3$;
   (e) $6x + 10y + 15z = 1$.

4. Find the least common multiple (l.c.m.) of (a) 482 and 1687, (b) 60 and 61.

5. How many integers between 100 and 1000 are divisible by 7?

6. Prove that the product of three consecutive integers is divisible by 6; of four consecutive integers by 24.

7. Exhibit three integers that are relatively prime but not relatively prime in pairs.

8. Two integers are said to be of the same parity if they are both even or both odd: if one is even and the other odd, they are said to be of opposite parity, or of different parity. Given any two integers, prove that their sum and their difference are of the same parity.

9. Show that if $ac|bc$ then $a|b$.

10. Given $a|b$ and $c|d$, prove that $ac|bd$.

11. Prove that $4 \nmid (n^2 + 2)$ for any integer n.

12. Given that $(a, 4) = 2$ and $(b, 4) = 2$ prove that $(a + b, 4) = 4$.

13. Prove that $n^2 - n$ is divisible by 2 for every integer n; that $n^3 - n$ is divisible by 6; that $n^5 - n$ is divisible by 30.

14. Prove that if n is odd, $n^2 - 1$ is divisible by 8.

15. Prove that if x and y are odd, then $x^2 + y^2$ is even but not divisible by 4.

16. Prove that if a and b are positive integers satisfying $(a, b) = [a, b]$ then $a = b$.

17. Evaluate $(n, n + 1)$ and $[n, n + 1]$ where n is a positive integer.

18. Find the values of (a, b) and $[a, b]$ if a and b are positive integers such that $a|b$.

19. Prove that any set of integers that are relatively prime in pairs are relatively prime.

20. Given integers a and b, a number n is said to be of the form $ak + b$ if there is an integer k such that $ak + b = n$. Thus the numbers of the form $3k + 1$ are $\cdots -8, -5, -2, 1, 4, 7, 10, \cdots$. Prove that every integer is of the form $3k$ or of the form $3k + 1$ or of the form $3k + 2$.

21. Prove that if an integer is of the form $6k + 5$ then it is necessarily of the form $3k - 1$, but not conversely.

22 Prove that the square of any integer of the form $5k + 1$ is of the same form.

23. Prove that the square of any integer is of the form $3k$ or $3k + 1$ but not of the form $3k + 2$.
24. Prove that no integers x, y exist satisfying $x + y = 100$ and $(x, y) = 3$.
25. Prove that there are infinitely many pairs of integers x, y satisfying $x + y = 100$ and $(x, y) = 5$.
26. Let s and $g > 0$ be given integers. Prove that integers x and y exist satisfying $x + y = s$ and $(x, y) = g$ if and only if $g|s$.
27. Find positive integers a and b satisfying the equations $(a, b) = 10$ and $[a, b] = 100$ simultaneously. Find all solutions.
28. Find all triples of positive integers a, b, c satisfying $(a, b, c) = 10$ and $[a, b, c] = 100$ simultaneously.
29. Let g and l be given positive integers. Prove that integers x and y exist satisfying $(x, y) = g$ and $[x, y] = l$ if and only if $g|l$.
30. Let b and $g > 0$ be given integers. Prove that the equations $(x, y) = g$ and $xy = b$ can be solved simultaneously if and only if $g^2|b$.
31. Let $n \geq 2$ and k be any positive integers. Prove that $(n - 1)|(n^k - 1)$.
32. Let $n \geq 2$ and k be any positive integers. Prove that $(n - 1)^2|(n^k - 1)$ if and only if $(n - 1)|k$. *Suggestion:* $n^k = \{(n - 1) + 1\}^k$.
33. Prove that $(a, b, c) = ((a, b), c)$.
34. Extend Theorems 1.6, 1.7, and 1.8 to sets of more than two integers.
35. Prove that if $(b, c) = 1$ and $r|b$, then $(r, c) = 1$.
36. Prove that if $m > n$ then $a^{2^n} + 1$ is a divisor of $a^{2^m} - 1$. Show that if a, m, n are positive integers with $m \neq n$, then

$$(a^{2^m} + 1, a^{2^n} + 1) = \begin{cases} 1 \text{ if } a \text{ is even,} \\ 2 \text{ if } a \text{ is odd.} \end{cases}$$

1.3   Primes

Definition 1.5 *An integer* $p > 1$ *is called a* prime number, *or a* prime, *in case there is no divisor d of p satisfying* $1 < d < p$. *If an integer* $a > 1$ *is not a prime, it is called a* composite *number.*

Thus, for example, 2, 3, 5, and 7 are primes, whereas 4, 6, 8, and 9 are composite.

Theorem 1.14 *Every integer n greater than 1 can be expressed as a product of primes (with perhaps only one factor).*

Proof. If the integer n is a prime, then the integer itself stands as a "product" with a single factor. Otherwise n can be factored into, say, $n_1 n_2$, where $1 < n_1 < n$ and $1 < n_2 < n$. If n_1 is a prime, let it stand; otherwise it will factor into, say, $n_3 n_4$ where $1 < n_3 < n_1$ and $1 <$

$n_4 < n_1$; similarly for n_2. This process of writing each composite number that arises as a product of factors must terminate because the factors are smaller than the composite number itself, and yet each factor is an integer greater than 1. Thus we can write n as a product of primes, and since the prime factors are not necessarily distinct, the result can be written in the form

$$n = p_1^{\alpha_1} p_2^{\alpha_2} \cdots p_r^{\alpha_r}$$

where p_1, p_2, $\cdots$, p_r are distinct primes and α_1, α_2, $\cdots$, α_r are positive.

This expression is called a representation of n as a product of primes, and it turns out that the representation is unique in the sense that, for fixed n, any other representation is merely a permutation of the factors. It may appear obvious to the reader that the representation of an integer as a product of primes is unique, but it is a fact requiring proof. Indeed there are mathematical situations where it might appear equally "obvious" that factorization will be unique, but where in fact it is not. We digress from our main theme to discuss two of these situations where factorization is not unique.

First consider the class E of positive even integers, so that the elements of E are 2, 4, 6, 8, 10, $\cdots$. Note that E is a multiplicative system, the product of any two elements in E being again in E. Now let us confine our attention to E in the sense that the only "numbers" we know are members of E. Then $8 = 2 \cdot 4$ is "composite," whereas 10 is a "prime" since 10 is not the product of two or more "numbers." The "primes" are 2, 6, 10, 14, $\cdots$, the "composite numbers" are 4, 8, 12, $\cdots$. Now the "number" 60 has two factorings into "primes," namely $60 = 2 \cdot 30 = 6 \cdot 10$, and so factorization is not unique.

A somewhat less artificial, but also rather more complicated, example is obtained by considering the class C of numbers $a + b \sqrt{-6}$ where a and b range over all integers. We say that this system C is closed under addition and multiplication, meaning that the sum and product of two elements in C are elements of C. By taking $b = 0$ we note that the integers form a subset of the class C.

First we establish that there are primes in C, and that every number in C can be factored into primes. For any number $a + b \sqrt{-6}$ in C it will be convenient to have a norm, $N(a + b\sqrt{-6})$, defined as

$$N(a + b\sqrt{-6}) = (a + b\sqrt{-6})(a - b\sqrt{-6}) = a^2 + 6b^2.$$

Thus the norm of a number in C is the product of the complex number $a + b\sqrt{-6}$ and its conjugate $a - b\sqrt{-6}$. Another way of saying this, perhaps in more familiar language, is that the norm is the square of the absolute value. Now the norm of every number in C is a positive integer greater than 1, except for the numbers 0, 1, -1 for which we have $N(0) = 0$, $N(1) = 1$, $N(-1) = 1$. We say that we have a factoring of $a + b\sqrt{-6}$ if we can write

(1.1) $a + b\sqrt{-6} = (x_1 + y_1\sqrt{-6})(x_2 + y_2\sqrt{-6}),$

where $N(x_1 + y_1\sqrt{-6}) > 1$ and $N(x_2 + y_2\sqrt{-6}) > 1$. This restriction on the norms of the factors is needed to rule out such trivial factorings as $a + b\sqrt{-6} = (1)(a + b\sqrt{-6}) = (-1)(-a - b\sqrt{-6})$. The norm of a product can be readily calculated to be the product of the norms of the factors, so that in the factoring (1.1) we have $N(a + b\sqrt{-6}) = N(x_1 + y_1\sqrt{-6})N(x_2 + y_2\sqrt{-6})$. It follows that

$$1 < N(x_1 + y_1\sqrt{-6}) < N(a + b\sqrt{-6}),$$

$$1 < N(x_2 + y_2\sqrt{-6}) < N(a + b\sqrt{-6}),$$

and so any number $a + b\sqrt{-6}$ will break up into only a finite number of factors since the norm of each factor is an integer.

We remarked above that the norm of any number in C, apart from 0 and ± 1, is greater than 1. More can be said. Since $N(a + b\sqrt{-6})$ has the value $a^2 + 6b^2$, we observe that

(1.2) $N(a + b\sqrt{-6}) \geq 6$ if $b \neq 0,$

that is, the norm of any complex number in C is not less than 6.

A number of C having norm > 1, but which cannot be factored in the sense of (1.1), is called a prime in C. For example 5 is a prime in C. For in the first place 5 cannot be factored into real numbers in C. In the second place, if we had a factoring $5 = (x_1 + y_1\sqrt{-6})(x_2 + y_2\sqrt{-6})$ into complex numbers, we could take norms to get

$$25 = N(x_1 + y_1\sqrt{-6})N(x_2 + y_2\sqrt{-6}),$$

which contradicts (1.2). Thus 5 is a prime in C, and a similar argument establishes that 2 is a prime.

We are now in a position to show that not all numbers of C factor uniquely into primes. Consider the number 10 and its two factorings:

$$10 = 2 \cdot 5 = (2 + \sqrt{-6})(2 - \sqrt{-6}).$$

The first product $2 \cdot 5$ has factors that are prime in C, as we have seen above. Thus we can conclude that there is not unique factorization of the number 10 in C. Note that this conclusion does not depend on our knowing that $2 + \sqrt{-6}$ and $2 - \sqrt{-6}$ are primes; they actually are, but it is unimportant in our discussion.

We now return to the discussion of unique factorization in the ordinary integers $0, \pm 1, \pm 2, \cdots$. It will be convenient to have the following result.

Theorem 1.15 *If $p|ab$, p being a prime, then $p|a$ or $p|b$. More generally, if $p|a_1a_2 \cdots a_n$, then p divides at least one factor a_i of the product.*

Proof. If $p \nmid a$, then $(a, p) = 1$ and so by Theorem 1.10, $p|b$. We may regard this as the first step of a proof of the general statement by mathematical induction. So we assume that the proposition holds whenever p divides a product with fewer than n factors. Now if $p|a_1a_2 \cdots a_n$, that is, $p|a_1c$ where $c = a_2a_3 \cdots a_n$, then $p|a_1$ or $p|c$. If $p|c$ we apply the induction hypothesis to conclude that $p|a_i$ for some subscript i.

Theorem 1.16 *The fundamental theorem of arithmetic. The factoring of any positive integer n into primes is unique apart from the order of the primes.*

First proof. Suppose that there is an integer n with two different factorings. Dividing out any primes common to the two representations, we would have an equality of the form

(1.3) $$p_1p_2 \cdots p_r = q_1q_2 \cdots q_s$$

where the factors p_i and q_j are primes, not necessarily all distinct, but where no prime on the left side occurs on the right side. But this is impossible because $p_1|q_1q_2 \cdots q_s$, and so by Theorem 1.15, p_1 is a divisor of at least one of the q_j. That is, p_1 must be identical with at least one of the q_j.

Second proof. Suppose that the theorem is false and let n be the smallest positive integer having more than one representation as the product of primes, say

$$(1.4) \qquad n = p_1 p_2 \cdots p_r = q_1 q_2 \cdots q_s.$$

It is clear that r and s are greater than 1. Now the primes $p_1, p_2, \cdots$, p_r have no members in common with $q_1, q_2, \cdots, q_s$ because if, for example, p_1 were a common prime, then we could divide it out of both sides of (1.4) to get two distinct factorings of n/p_1. But this would contradict our assumption that all integers smaller than n are uniquely factorable.

Next, there is no loss of generality in presuming that $p_1 < q_1$, and we define the positive integer N as

$$(1.5) \quad N = (q_1 - p_1) q_2 q_3 \cdots q_s = p_1 (p_2 p_3 \cdots p_r - q_2 q_3 \cdots q_s).$$

It is clear that $N < n$, so that N is uniquely factorable into primes. But $p_1 \nmid (q_1 - p_1)$, so (1.5) gives us two factorings of N, one involving p_1 and the other not, and thus we have a contradiction.

It can be noted that the second proof of Theorem 1.16 does not depend on Theorem 1.15 or indeed on any previous theorem. Thus it would be possible to put Theorem 1.16 nearer the beginning of the study of number theory, and to derive such results as Theorems 1.8, 1.10, and 1.15 as consequences. However, not all of our previous results are consequences of the fundamental theorem.

In the application of the fundamental theorem we frequently write any integer $a > 1$ in the form, sometimes called the "canonical form,"

$$a = p_1^{\alpha_1} p_2^{\alpha_2} \cdots p_r^{\alpha_r}$$

where the primes p_i are distinct and the exponents α_i are positive. However, it is sometimes convenient to use a slight variation of the canonical form and to permit some exponents to be zero. For example, if we want to describe the greatest common divisor g of a and b in terms of the prime factors of a and b, we would write

$$(1.6) \qquad a = p_1^{\alpha_1} p_2^{\alpha_2} \cdots p_r^{\alpha_r}, \qquad b = p_1^{\beta_1} p_2^{\beta_2} \cdots p_r^{\beta_r}$$

where $\alpha_i \geq 0$ and $\beta_i \geq 0$. Then the greatest common divisor is seen to be

$$g = (a, b) = p_1^{\min (\alpha_1, \beta_1)} p_2^{\min (\alpha_2, \beta_2)} \cdots p_r^{\min (\alpha_r, \beta_r)}$$

where $\min(\alpha, \beta)$ denotes the minimum of α and β. In case $a = 108$ and $b = 225$, we would have

$$a = 2^2 3^3 5^0, \quad b = 2^0 3^2 5^2, \quad g = 2^0 3^2 5^0 = 9.$$

Similarly the least common multiple of a and b is seen to be

$$[a, b] = p_1^{\max\,(\alpha_1,\,\beta_1)} p_2^{\max\,(\alpha_2,\,\beta_2)} \cdots p_r^{\max\,(\alpha_r,\,\beta_r)}$$

where $\max\,(\alpha, \beta)$ denotes the maximum of α and β. If no α_i is greater than 1, we say that a is square-free.

Theorem 1.17 *Euclid. The number of primes is infinite. That is, there is no end to the sequence of primes*

$$2,\ 3,\ 5,\ 7,\ 11,\ 13,\ \cdots.$$

Proof. Suppose there were only a finite number of primes $p_1, p_2, \cdots,$ p_r. Then form the number

$$n = 1 + p_1 p_2 \cdots p_r.$$

Note that n is not divisible by p_1 or p_2 or $\cdots$ or p_r. Hence any prime divisor p of n is a prime distinct from $p_1, p_2, \cdots, p_r$. Since n is either a prime or has a prime factor p, this implies that there is a prime distinct from $p_1, p_2, \cdots, p_r$.

Theorem 1.18 *There are arbitrarily large gaps in the series of primes. Stated otherwise, given any positive integer k, there exist k consecutive composite integers.*

Proof. Consider the integers

$$(k + 1)! + 2,\ (k + 1)! + 3,\ \cdots,\ (k + 1)! + k,\ (k + 1)! + k + 1.$$

Every one of these is composite because j divides $(k + 1)! + j$ if $2 \leq j \leq k + 1$.

The primes are spaced rather irregularly, as the last theorem suggests. If we denote the number of primes that do not exceed x by $\pi(x)$, we may ask about the nature of this function. Because of the irregular occurrence of the primes, we cannot expect a simple formula for $\pi(x)$. However, one of the most striking results in advanced number theory, the prime number theorem, gives an asymptotic approximation for

$\pi(x)$. It states that

$$\lim_{x \to \infty} \pi(x) \frac{\log x}{x} = 1,$$

that is, that the ratio of $\pi(x)$ to $x/\log x$ approaches 1 as x becomes indefinitely large.

Problems

1. In any positive integer, such as 8347, the last digit is called the units digit, the next the tens digit, the next the hundreds digit, etc. In the example 8347, the units digit is 7, the tens digit is 4, the hundreds digit is 3, and the thousands digit is 8. Prove that a number is divisible by 2 if and only if its units digit is divisible by 2; that a number is divisible by 4 if and only if the integer formed by its tens digit and its units digit is divisible by 4; that a number is divisible by 8 if and only if the integer formed by its last three digits is divisible by 8.

2. Prove that an integer is divisible by 3 if and only if the sum of its digits is divisible by 3. Prove that an integer is divisible by 9 if and only if the sum of its digits is divisible by 9.

3. Prove that an integer is divisible by 11 if and only if the difference between the sum of the digits in the odd places and the sum of the digits in the even places is divisible by 11.

4. Show that every positive integer n has a unique expression of the form $n = 2^r m$, $r \geq 0$, m a positive odd integer.

5. Let a/b and c/d be fractions in lowest terms, so that $(a, b) = (c, d) = 1$. Prove that if their sum is an integer, then $|b| = |d|$.

6. Prove that if a rational number r/s in lowest terms satisfies an equation $x^m = a$, where a is an integer, then $s = \pm 1$. Thus the only rational solutions, if any, of $x^m = a$ are integers.

7. Use the preceding problem to prove that $x^2 = 2$, $x^3 = 3$ and $x^4 = 7$ have no rational solutions. Thus $\sqrt{2}$, $\sqrt[3]{3}$, $\sqrt[4]{7}$ are irrational. In general prove that $x^m = a$ has no rational solutions unless a is the mth power of an integer.

8. Prove that any prime of the form $3k + 1$ is of the form $6k + 1$.

9. Prove that any positive integer of the form $3k + 2$ has a prime factor of the same form; similarly for each of the forms $4k + 3$ and $6k + 5$.

10. If x and y are odd, prove that $x^2 + y^2$ cannot be a perfect square.

11. If x and y are prime to 3, prove that $x^2 + y^2$ cannot be a perfect square.

12. Prove that $(a, b) = (a, b, a + b)$, and more generally that $(a, b) = (a, b, ax + by)$ for all integers x, y.

13. Prove that $(a, a + k)|k$ for all integers a, k not both zero.
14. Prove that $(a_1, a_2, \cdots, a_n) = ((a_1, a_2, \cdots, a_{n-1}), a_n)$.
15. Prove that $(a, a + 2) = 1$ or 2 for every integer a.
16. If $(a, b) = p$, a prime, what are the possible values of (a^2, b)? Of (a^3, b)? Of (a^2, b^3)?
17. Evaluate (ab, p^4) and $(a + b, p^4)$ given that $(a, p^2) = p$ and $(b, p^3) = p^2$ where p is a prime.
18. If a and b are represented by (1.6), what conditions must be satisfied by the exponents if a is to be a perfect square? A perfect cube? For $a|b$? For $a^2|b^2$?
19. Prove the second part of Theorem 1.13 by use of the g.c.d. and l.c.m. formulas following (1.6).
20. Prove that $(a^2, b^2) = c^2$ if $(a, b) = c$.
21. Let a and b be positive integers such that $(a, b) = 1$ and ab is a perfect square. Prove that a and b are perfect squares. Prove that the result generalizes to kth powers.
22. Given $(a, b, c) [a, b, c] = abc$, prove that $(a, b) = (b, c) = (a, c) = 1$.
23. Prove that $[a, b, c] (ab, bc, ca) = |abc|$.
24. Determine whether the following assertions are true or false. If true, prove the result, and if false, give a counterexample.

  (1) If $(a, b) = (a, c)$ then $[a, b] = [a, c]$.
  (2) If $(a, b) = (a, c)$ then $(a^2, b^2) = (a^2, c^2)$.
  (3) If $(a, b) = (a, c)$ then $(a, b) = (a, b, c)$.
  (4) If p is a prime and $p|a$ and $p|(a^2 + b^2)$ then $p|b$.
  (5) If p is a prime and $p|a^7$ then $p|a$.
  (6) If $a^3|c^3$ then $a|c$.
  (7) If $a^3|c^2$ then $a|c$.
  (8) If $a^2|c^3$ then $a|c$.
  (9) If p is a prime and $p|(a^2 + b^2)$ and $p|(b^2 + c^2)$ then $p|(a^2 - c^2)$.
  (10) If p is a prime and $p|(a^2 + b^2)$ and $p|(b^2 + c^2)$ then $p|(a^2 + c^2)$.
  (11) If $(a, b) = 1$ then $(a^2, ab, b^2) = 1$.
  (12) $[a^2, ab, b^2] = [a^2, b^2]$.
  (13) If $b|(a^2 + 1)$ then $b|(a^4 + 1)$.
  (14) If $b|(a^2 - 1)$ then $b|(a^4 - 1)$.
  (15) $(a, b, c) = ((a, b), (a, c))$.

25. For which positive integers n is it true that

$$\sum_{j=1}^{n} j \,\Big|\, \prod_{j=1}^{n} j ?$$

26. Given positive integers a and b such that $a|b^2$, $b^2|a^3$, $a^3|b^4$, $b^4|a^5$, $\cdots$, prove that $a = b$.

27. Given integers a, b, c, d, m, n, u, v satisfying $ad - bc = \pm 1$, $u = am + bn$, $v = cm + dn$, prove that $(m, n) = (u, v)$.

28. Prove that if n is composite it has a prime divisor p satisfying $p \leq \sqrt{n}$.

29. Obtain a complete list of the primes between 1 and n, with $n = 200$ for convenience, by the following method, known as the "sieve of Eratosthenes". By the "proper" multiples of k we mean all positive multiples of k except k itself. Write all numbers from 2 to 200. Cross out all proper multiples of 2, then of 3, then of 5. At each stage the next larger remaining number is a prime. Thus 7 is now the next remaining larger than 5. Cross out the proper multiples of 7. The next remaining number larger than 7 is 11. Continuing, we cross out the proper multiples of 11 and then of 13. Now we observe that the next remaining number greater than 13 exceeds $\sqrt{200}$, and hence by the previous problem all the numbers remaining in our list are prime.

30. Consider the set S of integers $1, 2, 3, \cdots, n$. Let 2^k be the integer in S which is the highest power of 2. Prove that 2^k is not a divisor of any other integer in S.

31. Prove that $\displaystyle\sum_{j=1}^{n} 1/j$ is not an integer if $n > 1$.

32. Consider the set T of integers $1, 3, 5, \cdots, 2n - 1$. Let 3^r be the integer in T which is the highest power of 3. Prove that 3^r is not a divisor of any other integer of T.

33. Prove that $\displaystyle\sum_{j=1}^{n} 1/(2j - 1)$ is not an integer if $n > 1$.

34. Say that a positive integer n is a sum of consecutive integers if there exist positive integers m and k so that $n = m + (m + 1) + \cdots + (m + k)$. Prove that n is so expressible if and only if it is not a power of 2.

35. If $2^n + 1$ is an odd prime, prove that n is a power of 2.

36. If $2^n - 1$ is a prime, prove that n is a prime.

37. If a and $b > 2$ are any positive integers, prove that $2^a + 1$ is not divisible by $2^b - 1$.

38. Let positive integers g and l be given with $g|l$. Prove that the number of pairs of positive integers x, y satisfying $(x, y) = g$ and $[x, y] = l$ is 2^k, where k is the number of distinct prime factors of l/g. (Count x_1, y_1 and x_2, y_2 as different pairs if $x_1 \neq x_2$ or $y_1 \neq y_2$.)

39. Let $k \geq 3$ be a fixed integer. Find all sets $a_1, a_2, \cdots, a_k$ of positive integers such that the sum of any triplet is divisible by each member of the triplet.

40. Prove that $2 + \sqrt{-6}$ and $2 - \sqrt{-6}$ are primes in the class C of numbers $a + b\sqrt{-6}$.

41. Prove Theorem 1.13 by use of the fundamental theorem.

42. Prove that every positive integer is uniquely expressible in the form

$$2^{j_0} + 2^{j_1} + 2^{j_2} + \cdots + 2^{j_m}$$

where $m \geq 0$ and $0 \leq j_0 < j_1 < j_2 < \cdots < j_m$.

43. Prove that any positive integer a can be uniquely expressed in the form

$$a = 3^m + b_{m-1}3^{m-1} + b_{m-2}3^{m-2} + \cdots + b_0,$$

where each $b_j = 0$, 1, or -1.

44. Prove that there are no positive integers a, b, $n > 1$ such that $(a^n - b^n) \mid (a^n + b^n)$.

45. Prove that no polynomial $f(x)$ with integral coefficients can represent a prime for every positive integer x. *Suggestion:* if $f(j) = p$ then $f(j + kp) - f(j)$ is a multiple of p for every k, and so $f(j + kp)$ has the same property.

46. Prove that there are infinitely many primes by considering the sequence $2^{2^1} + 1$, $2^{2^2} + 1$, $2^{2^3} + 1$, $2^{2^4} + 1$, $\cdots$. *Suggestion:* use Problem 36 of Section 1.2.

47. Prove that there are infinitely many primes of the form $4n + 3$; of the form $6n + 5$.

Remark. The last problem can be stated thus: each of the arithmetic progressions 3, 7, 11, 15, 19, $\cdots$, and 5, 11, 17, 23, 29, $\cdots$ contains an infinitude of primes. One of the famous theorems of number theory (the proof of which lies deeper than the methods of this book), due to Dirichlet, is that the arithmetic progression a, $a + b$, $a + 2b$, $a + 3b$, $\cdots$ contains infinitely many primes if the integers a and $b > 0$ are relatively prime, that is if $(a, b) = 1$.

Chapter 2

Congruences

2.1 Congruences

It is apparent from Chapter 1 that divisibility is a fundamental concept of number theory, one that sets it apart from many other branches of mathematics. In this chapter we continue the study of divisibility, but from a slightly different point of view. A congruence is nothing more than a statement about divisibility. However, it is more than just a convenient notation. It often makes it easier to discover proofs, and we will see that congruences can suggest new problems that will lead us to new and interesting topics.

Definition 2.1 *If an integer m, not zero, divides the difference $a - b$, we say that a is congruent to b modulo m and write $a \equiv b \pmod{m}$. If $a - b$ is not divisible by m, we say that a is not congruent to b modulo m, and in this case we write $a \not\equiv b \pmod{m}$.*

Since $a - b$ is divisible by m if and only if $a - b$ is divisible by $-m$, we can generally confine our attention to a positive modulus. Indeed, we shall assume throughout the present chapter that the modulus m is a positive integer.

Congruences have many properties in common with equalities. Some properties that follow easily from the definition are listed in the following theorem.

Theorem 2.1 *Let a, b, c, d, x, y denote integers. Then:*
(a) $a \equiv b \pmod{m}$, $b \equiv a \pmod{m}$, and $a - b \equiv 0 \pmod{m}$ are equivalent statements.

21

(b) *If $a \equiv b \pmod{m}$ and $b \equiv c \pmod{m}$, then $a \equiv c \pmod{m}$.*

(c) *If $a \equiv b \pmod{m}$ and $c \equiv d \pmod{m}$, then $ax + cy \equiv bx + dy$* *(mod m).*

(d) *If $a \equiv b \pmod{m}$ and $c \equiv d \pmod{m}$, then $ac \equiv bd \pmod{m}$.*

(e) *If $a \equiv b \pmod{m}$ and $d|m$, $d > 0$, then $a \equiv b \pmod{d}$.*

Theorem 2.2 *Let f denote a polynomial with integral coefficients. If $a \equiv b \pmod{m}$ then $f(a) \equiv f(b) \pmod{m}$.*

Proof. We can suppose $f(x) = c_0 x^n + c_1 x^{n-1} + \cdots + c_n$ where the c_i are integers. Since $a \equiv b \pmod{m}$ we can apply Theorem 2.1d repeatedly to find $a^2 \equiv b^2, a^3 \equiv b^3, \cdots, a^n \equiv b^n \pmod{m}$, and then $c_j a^{n-j} \equiv c_j b^{n-j} \pmod{m}$, and finally $c_0 a^n + c_1 a^{n-1} + \cdots + c_n \equiv c_0 b^n + c_1 b^{n-1} + \cdots + c_n \pmod{m}$, by Theorem 2.1c.

The reader is, of course, well aware of the property of real numbers that if $ax = ay$ and $a \neq 0$ then $x = y$. More care must be used in dividing a congruence through by a.

Theorem 2.3

(a) $ax \equiv ay \pmod{m}$ *if and only if* $x \equiv y \left(\bmod \dfrac{m}{(a, m)} \right)$.

(b) *If $ax \equiv ay \pmod{m}$ and $(a, m) = 1$, then $x \equiv y \pmod{m}$.*

(c) $x \equiv y \pmod{m_i}$ *for $i = 1, 2, \cdots, r$ if and only if $x \equiv y$* *(mod $[m_1, m_2, \cdots, m_r]$).*

Proof. (a) If $ax \equiv ay \pmod{m}$ then $ay - ax = mz$ for some integer z. Hence we have

$$\frac{a}{(a, m)} (y - x) = \frac{m}{(a, m)} z$$

and thus

$$\frac{m}{(a, m)} \,\bigg|\, \frac{a}{(a, m)} (y - x).$$

But $(a/(a, m), m/(a, m)) = 1$ by Theorem 1.7 and therefore $\{m/(a, m)\}|(y - x)$ by Theorem 1.10. This implies

$$x \equiv y \pmod{m/(a, m)}.$$

If $x \equiv y \pmod{m/(a, m)}$ then $\{m/(a, m)\}|(y - x)$ and hence $m|(a, m)(y - x)$. Using Theorem 1.1 we get $m|a(y - x)$, and then $ax \equiv ay \pmod{m}$ follows.

(*b*) This is a special case of part (*a*). It is listed separately because we will use it very often.

(*c*) If $x \equiv y \pmod{m_i}$ for $i = 1, 2, \cdots, r$, then $m_i | (y - x)$ for $i = 1, 2, \cdots, r$. That is, $y - x$ is a common multiple of $m_1, m_2, \cdots, m_r$, and therefore (see Theorem 1.12) $[m_1, m_2, \cdots, m_r] | (y - x)$. This implies $x \equiv y \pmod{[m_1, m_2, \cdots, m_r]}$.

If $x \equiv y \pmod{[m_1, m_2, \cdots, m_r]}$ then $x \equiv y \pmod{m_i}$ by Theorem 2.1e, since $m_i | [m_1, m_2, \cdots, m_r]$.

In dealing with integers modulo m we are essentially performing the ordinary operations of arithmetic but are disregarding multiples of m. In a sense we are not distinguishing between a and $a + mx$, where x is any integer. Given any integer a, let q and r be the quotient and remainder upon division by m; thus $a = qm + r$ by Theorem 1.2. Now $a \equiv r \pmod{m}$ and, since r satisfies the inequalities $0 \leqq r < m$, we see that every integer is congruent modulo m to one of the values 0, 1, 2, $\cdots$, $m - 1$. Also it is clear that no two of these m integers are congruent modulo m. These m values constitute a complete residue system modulo m, and we now give a general definition of this term.

Definition 2.2 *If* $x \equiv y \pmod{m}$ *then* y *is called a residue of* x *modulo* m. *A set* $x_1, x_2, \cdots, x_m$ *is called a complete residue system modulo* m *if for every integer* y *there is one and only one* x_j *such that* $y \equiv x_j \pmod{m}$.

It is obvious that there are infinitely many complete residue systems modulo m, the set 1, 2, $\cdots$, $m - 1$, m being another example.

A set of m integers forms a complete residue system modulo m if and only if no two integers in the set are congruent modulo m.

Theorem 2.4 *If* $x \equiv y \pmod{m}$ *then* $(x, m) = (y, m)$.

Proof. We have $y - x = mz$ for some integer z. Since $(x, m) | x$ and $(x, m) | m$, we have $(x, m) | y$ and hence $(x, m) | (y, m)$. In the same way we find $(y, m) | (x, m)$ and then have $(x, m) = (y, m)$ by Theorem 1.1 since (x, m) and (y, m) are positive.

Definition 2.3 *A reduced residue system modulo* m *is a set of integers* r_i *such that* $(r_i, m) = 1$, $r_i \not\equiv r_j \pmod{m}$ *if* $i \neq j$, *and such that every* x *prime to* m, *is congruent modulo* m *to some member* r_i *of the set.*

In view of Theorem 2.4 it is clear that a reduced residue system modulo m can be obtained by deleting from a complete residue system modulo m those members that are not relatively prime to m. Furthermore, all reduced residue systems modulo m will contain the same number of members, a number that is denoted by $\phi(m)$. This function is called Euler's ϕ-function, sometimes the totient. By applying this definition of $\phi(m)$ to the complete residue system $1, 2, \cdots, m$ mentioned in the paragraph following Definition 2.2, we can get what amounts to an alternative definition of $\phi(m)$, as given in the following theorem.

Theorem 2.5 *The number $\phi(m)$ is the number of positive integers less than or equal to m that are relatively prime to m.*

Theorem 2.6 *Let $(a, m) = 1$. Let $r_1, r_2, \cdots, r_n$ be a complete, or a reduced, residue system modulo m. Then $ar_1, ar_2, \cdots, ar_n$ is a complete, or a reduced, residue system, respectively, modulo m.*

Proof. If $(r_i, m) = 1$ then $(ar_i, m) = 1$ by Theorem 1.8.

There are the same number of $ar_1, ar_2, \cdots, ar_n$ as of $r_1, r_2, \cdots, r_n$. Therefore we need only show that $ar_i \not\equiv ar_j \pmod{m}$ if $i \neq j$. But Theorem 2.3b shows that $ar_i \equiv ar_j \pmod{m}$ implies $r_i \equiv r_j \pmod{m}$ and hence $i = j$.

Theorem 2.7 *Fermat's theorem. Let p denote a prime. If $p \nmid a$ then $a^{p-1} \equiv 1 \pmod{p}$. For every integer a, $a^p \equiv a \pmod{p}$.*

We will postpone the proof of this theorem and will obtain it as a corollary to Theorem 2.8.

Theorem 2.8 *Euler's generalization of Fermat's theorem. If $(a, m) = 1$ then*

$$a^{\phi(m)} \equiv 1 \pmod{m}.$$

Proof. Let $r_1, r_2, \cdots, r_{\phi(m)}$ be a reduced residue system modulo m. Then by Theorem 2.6, $ar_1, ar_2, \cdots, ar_{\phi(m)}$ is also a reduced residue system modulo m. Hence corresponding to each r_i there is one and only one ar_j such that $r_i \equiv ar_j \pmod{m}$. Furthermore, different r_i will have different corresponding ar_j. This means that the numbers $ar_1, ar_2, \cdots, ar_{\phi(m)}$ are just the residues modulo m of $r_1, r_2, \cdots, r_{\phi(m)}$, but not necessarily in the same order. Multiplying and using Theorem 2.1d we obtain

$$\prod_{j=1}^{\phi(m)} (ar_j) \equiv \prod_{i=1}^{\phi(m)} r_i \pmod{m}$$

and hence

$$a^{\phi(m)} \prod_{j=1}^{\phi(m)} r_j \equiv \prod_{j=1}^{\phi(m)} r_j \pmod{m}.$$

Now $(r_j, m) = 1$ so we can use Theorem 2.3b to cancel the r_j and we obtain $a^{\phi(m)} \equiv 1 \pmod{m}$.

Corollary. *Proof of Theorem 2.7* If $p \nmid a$ then $(a, p) = 1$ and $a^{\phi(p)} \equiv 1 \pmod{p}$. To find $\phi(p)$ we refer to Theorem 2.5. All the integers 1, 2, $\cdots$, $p - 1$, p with the exception of p are relatively prime to p. Thus we have $\phi(p) = p - 1$, and the first part of Fermat's theorem follows. The second part is now obvious.

Corollary 2.9 *If $(a, m) = 1$ then $ax \equiv b \pmod{m}$ has a solution $x = x_1$. All solutions are given by $x = x_1 + jm$ where $j = 0$, ± 1, ± 2, $\cdots$.*

Proof. Since $(1, m) = 1$ and $1 \leq m$, we see that $\phi(m) \geq 1$. Then we need merely set $x_1 = a^{\phi(m)-1}b$.

If x is any solution then $ax - ax_1 \equiv b - b \equiv 0 \pmod{m}$ and hence $a(x - x_1) \equiv 0 \pmod{m}$. Using Theorem 2.3b we get $x - x_1 \equiv 0 \pmod{m}$ which implies $x = x_1 + jm$. The fact that all these actually are solutions follows from Theorem 2.2.

Euler's function $\phi(m)$ is of considerable interest. We will consider it further in section 2.4 and section 4.2.

Theorem 2.10 *Wilson's theorem. If p is a prime then $(p - 1)! \equiv -1 \pmod{p}$.*

Proof. If $p = 2$ or $p = 3$ the congruence is easily verified.

Now we can suppose $p \geq 5$. The idea behind the proof is quite simple, but we must use a little care. We consider the integers whose product is $(p - 1)!$ and try to pair them off in such a way that the product of the two members of each pair is congruent to 1 modulo p.

Given an integer j satisfying $1 \leq j \leq p - 1$, then $(j, p) = 1$ and we see by Corollary 2.9 that there is exactly one integer i such that $ji \equiv 1 \pmod{p}$ and $0 \leq i \leq p - 1$. Obviously $i = 0$ is impossible so we have $1 \leq i \leq p - 1$. With each j we will associate the corresponding integer i. Since $ij \equiv ji \equiv 1 \pmod{p}$ we see that j is the integer associated with i. The integer 1 is associated with itself, and so is $p - 1$. Omitting these values for a moment we consider $2 \leq j \leq p - 2$. For these j we have $(j - 1, p) = (j + 1, p) = 1$ and hence $j^2 - 1 = (j - 1)(j + 1) \not\equiv 0 \pmod{p}$ by Theorem 1.8. Hence each of these j is associated with an $i \neq j$, $2 \leq i \leq p - 2$, and the associate of i is j itself. Thus the integers $2, 3, \cdots, p - 2$ can be paired off, j and its associate i, and $ji \equiv 1 \pmod{p}$. Multiplying all these pairs together we get $2 \cdot 3 \cdots (p - 2) \equiv 1 \pmod{p}$, and Wilson's theorem follows because $1 \cdot (p - 1) \equiv -1 \pmod{p}$.

Wilson's theorem and Fermat's theorem can be used to determine those primes p for which $x^2 \equiv -1 \pmod{p}$ has a solution. This is a special case of some results that we will take up later (see Chapter 3). However, it is interesting to see that this special case can be handled by fairly simple means.

Theorem 2.11 *Let p denote a prime. Then $x^2 \equiv -1 \pmod{p}$ has solutions if and only if $p = 2$ or $p \equiv 1 \pmod{4}$.*

Proof. If $p = 2$ we have the solution $x = 1$.

For any odd prime p we can write Wilson's theorem in the form

$$\left(1 \cdot 2 \cdots j \cdots \frac{p - 1}{2}\right)\left(\frac{p + 1}{2} \cdots (p - j) \cdots (p - 2)(p - 1)\right)$$
$$\equiv -1 \pmod{p}.$$

The product on the left has been divided into two parts, each with the same number of factors. Pairing off j in the first half with $p - j$ in the second half, we can rewrite the congruence in the form

$$\prod_{j=1}^{(p-1)/2} j(p - j) \equiv -1 \pmod{p}.$$

But $j(p - j) \equiv -j^2 \pmod{p}$, and so we have, if $p \equiv 1 \pmod{4}$,

$$\prod_{j=1}^{(p-1)/2} j(p - j) \equiv \prod_{j=1}^{(p-1)/2} (-j^2) \equiv (-1)^{(p-1)/2}\left(\prod_{j=1}^{(p-1)/2} j\right)^2$$
$$\equiv \left(\prod_{j=1}^{(p-1)/2} j\right)^2 \pmod{p}$$

and so we have a solution, $\displaystyle\prod_{j=1}^{(p-1)/2} j$, of $x^2 \equiv -1 \pmod{p}$.

If $p \neq 2$ and $p \not\equiv 1 \pmod 4$, then $p \equiv 3 \pmod 4$. In this case, if for some integer x, $x^2 \equiv -1 \pmod p$, then we have $x^{p-1} \equiv (x^2)^{(p-1)/2} \equiv (-1)^{(p-1)/2} \equiv -1 \pmod p$ since $(p-1)/2 \equiv 1 \pmod 2$. But clearly $p \nmid x$, so we have $x^{p-1} \equiv 1 \pmod p$ by Theorem 2.7. This contradiction shows that $x^2 \equiv -1 \pmod p$ has no solution in this case.

Problems

1. List all integers x in the range $1 \leq x \leq 100$ that satisfy $x \equiv 7 \pmod{17}$.
2. Exhibit a complete residue system modulo 17 composed entirely of multiples of 3.
3. Exhibit a reduced residue system for the modulus 12; for 30.
4. If an integer x is even, observe that it must satisfy the congruence $x \equiv 0 \pmod 2$. If an integer y is odd, what congruence does it satisfy? What congruence does an integer z of the form $6k + 1$ satisfy?
5. Write a single congruence that is equivalent to the pair of congruences $x \equiv 1 \pmod 4$, $x \equiv 2 \pmod 3$.
6. Prove that if p is a prime and $a^2 \equiv b^2 \pmod p$, then $p|(a + b)$ or $p|(a - b)$.
7. Show that if $f(x)$ is a polynomial with integral coefficients and if $f(a) \equiv k \pmod m$, then $f(a + tm) \equiv k \pmod m$ for every integer t.
8. Prove that any number which is a square must have one of the following for its units digit: 0, 1, 4, 5, 6, 9.
9. Prove that any fourth power must have one of 0, 1, 5, 6 for its units digit.
10. Evaluate $\phi(m)$ for $m = 1, 2, 3, \cdots, 12$.
11. Find the least positive integer x such that $13|(x^2 + 1)$.
12. Prove that 19 is not a divisor of $4n^2 + 4$ for any integer n.
13. Exhibit a reduced residue system modulo 7 composed entirely of powers of 3.
14. Solve $3x \equiv 5 \pmod{11}$ by the method of Corollary 2.9.
15. Illustrate the proof of Theorem 2.10 for $p = 11$ and $p = 13$ by actually determining the pairs of associated integers.
16. The integers 12, 23, 34, 45, 56 are congruent to 1 modulo 11. To solve $5x \equiv 1 \pmod{11}$ we merely note that $45 = 5 \cdot 9$ and hence that $x = 9$ is a solution. Solve $ax \equiv 1 \pmod{11}$ for $a = 2, 3, \cdots, 10$.
17. Prove that $n^6 - 1$ is divisible by 7 if $(n, 7) = 1$.
18. Prove that $n^7 - n$ is divisible by 42, for any integer n.
19. Prove that $n^{12} - 1$ is divisible by 7 if $(n, 7) = 1$.
20. Prove that $n^{6k} - 1$ is divisible by 7 if $(n, 7) = 1$, k being any positive integer.

21. Prove that $n^{13} - n$ is divisible by 2, 3, 5, 7, and 13 for any integer n.
22. Prove that $n^{12} - a^{12}$ is divisible by 13 if n and a are prime to 13.
23. Prove that $n^{12} - a^{12}$ is divisible by 91 if n and a are prime to 91.
24. Prove that $\frac{1}{5}n^5 + \frac{1}{3}n^3 + \frac{7}{15}n$ is an integer for every integer n.
25. What is the last digit in the ordinary decimal representation of 3^{400}? *Suggestion:* $3^4 \equiv 1 \pmod 5$ by Fermat's theorem, and this with $3^4 \equiv 1 \pmod 2$ implies that $3^4 \equiv 1 \pmod{10}$. Hence $3^{4n} \equiv 1 \pmod{10}$ for any $n \geq 1$.
26. What is the last digit in the ordinary decimal representation of 2^{400}?
27. What are the last two digits in the ordinary decimal representation of 3^{400}? *Suggestion:* use Theorem 2.8 to establish that $3^{20} \equiv 1 \pmod{25}$. In addition, $3^2 \equiv 1 \pmod 4$ so that $3^{20} \equiv 1 \pmod 4$, whence $3^{20} \equiv 1 \pmod{100}$.
28. Show that $-(m-1)/2, -(m-3)/2, \cdots, (m-3)/2, (m-1)/2$ is a complete residue system modulo m if m is odd, and that $-(m-2)/2, -(m-4)/2, \cdots, (m-2)/2, m/2$ is a complete residue system modulo m if m is even.
29. Show that $2, 4, 6, \cdots, 2m$ is a complete residue system modulo m if m is odd.
30. Show that $1^2, 2^2, \cdots, m^2$ is not a complete residue system modulo m if $m > 2$.
31. If n is composite, $n > 4$, prove that $(n-1)! \equiv 0 \pmod n$.
32. Show that an integer $m > 1$ is a prime if and only if m divides $(m-1)! + 1$.
33. For positive integers a, m, n with $m \neq n$, prove that

$$(a^{2^m} + 1, a^{2^n} + 1) = \begin{cases} 1, & \text{if } a \text{ is even,} \\ 2, & \text{if } a \text{ is odd.} \end{cases}$$

Suggestion: if p is a common divisor, $a^{2^m} \equiv -1 \pmod p$. Raise this to the power 2^{n-m}, presuming $m < n$.
34. For m odd, prove that the sum of the elements of any complete residue system modulo m is congruent to zero modulo m; prove the analogous result for any reduced residue system for $m > 2$.
35. Find all sets of positive integers a, b, c satisfying all three congruences $a \equiv b \pmod c$, $b \equiv c \pmod a$, $c \equiv a \pmod b$. *Suggestion:* if a, b, c is such a set, so also is ka, kb, kc for any positive integer k. Hence it suffices to determine all "primitive" sets with the property $(a, b, c) = 1$. Also there is no loss in generality in assuming that $a \leq b \leq c$.
36. Find all triples a, b, c of non-zero integers such that $a \equiv b \pmod{|c|}$ $b \equiv c \pmod{|a|}$, $c \equiv a \pmod{|b|}$.

37. If p is an odd prime, prove that:

$$1^2 \cdot 3^2 \cdot 5^2 \cdots (p-2)^2 \equiv (-1)^{(p+1)/2} \pmod{p},$$

and $\quad 2^2 \cdot 4^2 \cdot 6^2 \cdots (p-1)^2 \equiv (-1)^{(p+1)/2} \pmod{p}.$

38. Prove that $(a+b)^p \equiv a^p + b^p \pmod{p}.$

39. If $r_1, r_2, \cdots, r_{p-1}$ is any reduced residue system modulo a prime p, prove that

$$\prod_{j=1}^{p-1} r_j \equiv -1 \pmod{p}.$$

40. If $r_1, r_2, \cdots, r_p$ and $r'_1, r'_2, \cdots, r'_p$ are any two complete residue systems modulo a prime $p > 2$, prove that the set $r_1 r'_1, r_2 r'_2, \cdots, r_p r'_p$ cannot be a complete residue system modulo p.

41. If p is any prime other than 2 or 5, prove that p divides infinitely many of the integers $9, 99, 999, 9999, \cdots$. If p is any prime other than 2 or 5, prove that p divides infinitely many of the integers $1, 11, 111, 1111, \cdots$.

42. If p is a prime, and if $h + k = p - 1$ with $h \geq 0$ and $k \geq 0$, prove that $h! k! + (-1)^h \equiv 0 \pmod{p}.$

43. For any prime p, if $a^p \equiv b^p \pmod{p}$, prove that $a^p \equiv b^p \pmod{p^2}.$

44. Given an integer n, prove that there is an integer m which to base ten contains only the digits 0 and 1 such that $n \mid m$. Prove that the same holds for digits 0 and 2, or 0 and 3, $\cdots$, or 0 and 9, but for no other pair of digits.

45. If n is composite, prove that $(n-1)! + 1$ is not a power of n.

46. If $1 \leq k < n - 1$ prove that $(n-1)^2 \nmid (n^k - 1).$

47. If p is a prime, prove that $(p-1)! + 1$ is a power of p if and only if $p = 2, 3$ or 5. *Suggestion:* if $p > 5$, $(p-1)!$ has factors 2, $p - 1$, and $(p-1)/2$, and so $(p-1)!$ is divisible by $(p-1)^2$.

48. Prove
$$\prod_{\substack{1 \leq x \leq n \\ (x,n) = (x+1,n) = 1}} x \equiv 1 \pmod{n} \qquad \text{if } n > 2.$$

The symbol on the left denotes the product of all the positive integers x less than or equal to n such that both x and $x + 1$ are relatively prime to n.

49. Prove that there are infinitely many primes of the form $4n + 1$.

50. Prove that $(p-1)! \equiv p - 1 \pmod{1 + 2 + \cdots + (p-1)}$ if p is a prime.

51. For positive integers n let $\tau(n)$ denote the number of positive divisors of n, including n itself. For d such that $d \mid n$, $1 \leq d \leq \sqrt{n}$, pair d with n/d to prove that $\tau(n) < 2\sqrt{n}$.

2.2   Solutions of Congruences

In analogy with the solution of algebraic equations it is natural to consider the problem of solving a congruence. In the rest of this chapter we will let $f(x)$ denote a polynomial with integral coefficients, and we will write $f(x) = a_0 x^n + a_1 x^{n-1} + \cdots + a_n$. If u is an integer such that $f(u) \equiv 0 \pmod{m}$ then we say that u is a solution of the congruence $f(x) \equiv 0 \pmod{m}$. Whether or not an integer is a solution of a congruence depends on the modulus m as well as on the polynomial $f(x)$. If the integer u is a solution of $f(x) \equiv 0 \pmod{m}$, and if $v \equiv u \pmod{m}$, Theorem 2.2 shows that v is also a solution. Because of this we will say that $x \equiv u \pmod{m}$ is a solution of $f(x) \equiv 0 \pmod{m}$, meaning that every integer congruent to u modulo m satisfies $f(x) \equiv 0 \pmod{m}$. For example, the congruence $x^2 - x + 4 \equiv 0 \pmod{10}$ has the solution 3. It also has the solution 8. We can say $x \equiv 3 \pmod{10}$ and $x \equiv 8 \pmod{10}$ are solutions. In this case, since $8 \equiv 3 \pmod{5}$, we can even say that $x \equiv 3 \pmod{5}$ is a solution. In the general case, if $f(x) \equiv 0 \pmod{m}$ has a solution u, it has infinitely many solutions— all integers v such that $v \equiv u \pmod{m}$. It is more reasonable to count the solutions in a different way. We will not count v as distinct from u if $v \equiv u \pmod{m}$. In the example 3 and 13 are not counted separately. However, 3 and 8 are both counted since $3 \not\equiv 8 \pmod{10}$.

Definition 2.4 *Let* r_1, r_2, $\cdots$, r_m *denote a complete residue system modulo m. The number of solutions of* $f(x) \equiv 0 \pmod{m}$ *is the number of the* r_i *such that* $f(r_i) \equiv 0 \pmod{m}$.

It is clear from Theorem 2.2 that the number of solutions is independent of the choice of the complete residue system. Furthermore, the number of solutions cannot exceed the modulus m. If m is small it is a simple matter to just compute $f(r_i)$ for each of the r_i and thus to determine the number of solutions. In the above example the congruence has just two solutions. Some other examples are

$$x^2 + 1 \equiv 0 \pmod{7} \text{ has no solutions,}$$

$$x^2 + 1 \equiv 0 \pmod{5} \text{ has two solutions,}$$

$$x^2 - 1 \equiv 0 \pmod{8} \text{ has four solutions.}$$

Definition 2.5 Let $f(x) = a_0 x^n + a_1 x^{n-1} + \cdots + a_n$. If $a_0 \not\equiv 0$ (mod m) the degree of the congruence $f(x) \equiv 0$ (mod m) is n. If $a_0 \equiv 0$ (mod m), let j be the smallest positive integer such that $a_j \not\equiv 0$ (mod m); then the degree of the congruence is $n - j$. If there is no such integer j, that is, if all the coefficients of $f(x)$ are multiples of m, no degree is assigned to the congruence.

It should be noted that the degree of the congruence $f(x) \equiv 0$ (mod m) is not the same thing as the degree of the polynomial $f(x)$. The degree of the congruence depends on the modulus; the degree of the polynomial does not. Thus if $g(x) = 6x^3 + 3x^2 + 1$, then $g(x) \equiv 0$ (mod 5) is of degree 3, and $g(x) \equiv 0$ (mod 2) is of degree 2, whereas $g(x)$ is of degree 3.

Theorem 2.12 If $d \mid m$, $d > 0$, and if u is a solution of $f(x) \equiv 0$ (mod m), then u is a solution of $f(x) \equiv 0$ (mod d).

Proof. This follows directly from Theorem 2.1e.

Problems

1. If $f(x) \equiv 0$ (mod p) has exactly j solutions, and $g(x) \equiv 0$ (mod p) has no solutions, prove that $f(x)g(x) \equiv 0$ (mod p) has exactly j solutions.
2. Denoting the number of solutions of $f(x) \equiv k$ (mod m) by $N(k)$, prove that
$$\sum_{k=1}^{m} N(k) = m.$$
3. If a congruence $f(x) \equiv 0$ (mod m) has m solutions, prove that any integer whatsoever is a solution. (In such a case the congruence is sometimes called an identical congruence.)
4. The fact that the product of any three consecutive integers is divisible by 3 leads to the identical congruence $x(x + 1)(x + 2) \equiv 0$ (mod 3). Generalize this, and write an identical congruence modulo m.

2.3   Congruences of Degree 1

Any congruence of degree 1 can be put in the form $ax \equiv b$ (mod m), $a \not\equiv 0$ (mod m). From Corollary 2.9 we see that if $(a, m) = 1$, then $ax \equiv b$ (mod m) has exactly one solution, $x \equiv x_1$ (mod m).

Let g denote (a, m). If $ax \equiv b$ (mod m) has a solution u, then $b \equiv au$ (mod m) and hence $b \equiv au \equiv 0$ (mod g). Therefore, $ax \equiv b$ (mod m)

has no solution if $g \nmid b$. However, if $g \mid b$ then, for u an integer, $au \equiv b \pmod m$ holds if and only if $(a/g)u \equiv (b/g) \pmod{m/g}$ by Theorem 2.3a. Now $(a/g, m/g) = 1$ and the congruence $(a/g)x \equiv (b/g) \pmod{m/g}$ has just one solution $x \equiv x_1 \pmod{m/g}$. In other words the solutions of $ax \equiv b \pmod m$ are the integers u such that $u \equiv x_1 \pmod{m/g}$, that is $u = x_1 + t(m/g)$, $t = 0, \pm 1, \pm 2, \cdots$. If t is given the values $0, 1, \cdots, g-1$, then u takes on g values no two of which are congruent modulo m. If t is given any other value, the corresponding u will be congruent modulo m to one of these g values. Thus the solutions of $ax \equiv b \pmod m$ are $x \equiv x_1 + t(m/g) \pmod m$, $0 \le t \le g - 1$.

Theorem 2.13 *Let g denote (a, m). Then $ax \equiv b \pmod m$ has no solutions if $g \nmid b$. If $g \mid b$ it has g solutions $x \equiv (b/g)x_0 + t(m/g) \pmod m$, $t = 0, 1, \cdots, g-1$ where x_0 is any solution of $(a/g)x \equiv 1 \pmod{m/g}$.*

Proof. This theorem follows from what has already been proved since $(a/g)x \equiv 1 \pmod{m/g}$ has a solution x_0 and then $x_1 = (b/g)x_0$ is a solution of $(a/g)x \equiv (b/g) \pmod{m/g}$.

For reasonably small numbers the solution of a congruence can often be obtained by inspection or by trying all integers of a complete residue system modulo m. However, if the numbers are large the actual numerical solution of a congruence of the form $ax \equiv b \pmod m$ can be rather lengthy. The hardest part is solving congruences $ax \equiv 1 \pmod m$ with $(a, m) = 1$. The solution as given in the proof of Corollary 2.9 is not usually very practical. A number of special methods of solution have been developed, but perhaps the best general method is to use Euclid's algorithm. Using Theorem 1.11 we determine $g = (a, m)$ and at the same time obtain integers u and v such that $au + mv = g$. Then we can take u for the x_0 in Theorem 2.13, and the rest is easy.

Another way to go about solving a congruence of degree 1 is to factor the modulus $m = \prod_{i=1}^{k} p_i^{e_i}$. Writing $m_i = p_i^{e_i}$ we note that the m_i are relatively prime in pairs and that $[m_1, m_2, \cdots, m_k] = m$. From Theorem 2.3c we see that the problem of solving $ax \equiv b \pmod m$ is equivalent to solving the set of congruences $ax \equiv b \pmod{m_i}$, $i = 1, 2, \cdots, k$, simultaneously. The individual congruences $ax \equiv b \pmod{m_i}$ may be easier to solve since their moduli m_i are smaller than

m. Suppose the congruences $ax \equiv b \pmod{m_i}$ have the solutions $x \equiv u_i \pmod{m_i}$. There still remains the problem of finding the simultaneous solution x of the set of congruences. The proof of the next theorem will show how this can be done.

Theorem 2.14 *Chinese remainder theorem. Let $m_1, m_2, \cdots, m_r$ denote r positive integers that are relatively prime in pairs, and let $a_1, a_2, \cdots, a_r$ denote any r integers. Then the congruences $x \equiv a_i \pmod{m_i}$, $i = 1, 2, \cdots, r$, have common solutions. Any two solutions are congruent modulo $m_1 m_2 \cdots m_r$.*

Remark. If the moduli $m_1, m_2, \cdots, m_r$ are not relatively prime in pairs, there may not be any solution of the congruences. Necessary and sufficient conditions are given in Problem 14(c) in the next problem set.

Proof. Writing $m = m_1 m_2 \cdots m_r$ we see that m/m_j is an integer and that $(m/m_j, m_j) = 1$. Therefore, by Corollary 2.9, there are integers b_j such that $(m/m_j)b_j \equiv 1 \pmod{m_j}$. Clearly $(m/m_j)b_j \equiv 0 \pmod{m_i}$ if $i \neq j$. Now if we define x_0 as

$$(2.1) \qquad x_0 = \sum_{j=1}^{r} \frac{m}{m_j} b_j a_j$$

we have

$$x_0 \equiv \sum_{j=1}^{r} \frac{m}{m_j} b_j a_j \equiv \frac{m}{m_i} b_i a_i \equiv a_i \pmod{m_i}$$

so that x_0 is a common solution of the original congruences.

If x_0 and x_1 are both common solutions of $x \equiv a_i \pmod{m_i}$, $i = 1, 2, \cdots, r$, then $x_0 \equiv x_1 \pmod{m_i}$ for $i = 1, 2, \cdots, r$ and hence $x_0 \equiv x_1 \pmod{m}$ by Theorem 2.3c. This completes the proof.

The proof of this theorem provides us with an efficient method for solving a certain kind of problem. As an example let us find all integers that have remainders 1 or 2 when they are divided by each of 3, 4, and 5. In other words we are to find the common solutions of $x \equiv 1$ or 2 $\pmod 3$, $x \equiv 1$ or 2 $\pmod 4$, $x \equiv 1$ or 2 $\pmod 5$. We have $m_1 = 3$, $m_2 = 4$, $m_3 = 5$, $m = 60$, and each a_i is 1 or 2. To find b_1 we solve $(60/3)b_1 \equiv 1 \pmod 3$; that is $20b_1 \equiv 1 \pmod 3$, which is the same as $-b_1 \equiv 1 \pmod 3$. We can take $b_1 = -1$ and then have $(m/m_1)b_1 = -20$. Similarly we obtain $b_2 = -1$ and $(m/m_2)b_2 = -15$. For b_3 we have $12b_3 \equiv 1 \pmod 5$, $2b_3 \equiv 1$, $4b_3 \equiv 2$, $-b_3 \equiv 2$, and can take $b_3 = -2$, $(m/m_3)b_3 = -24$. Using (2.1) we have merely to insert the values of the a_i in $x \equiv -20a_1 - 15a_2 - 24a_3 \pmod{60}$. Doing this we obtain the values given in the following table.

a_1	a_2	a_3	$x \pmod{60}$
1	1	1	$-20 - 15 - 24 \equiv \ -59 \equiv \quad 1$
1	1	2	$-20 - 15 - 48 \equiv \ -83 \equiv -23$
1	2	1	$-20 - 30 - 24 \equiv \ -74 \equiv -14$
2	1	1	$-40 - 15 - 24 \equiv \ -79 \equiv -19$
2	2	1	$-40 - 30 - 24 \equiv \ -94 \equiv \ \ 26$
2	1	2	$-40 - 15 - 48 \equiv -103 \equiv \ \ 17$
1	2	2	$-20 - 30 - 48 \equiv \ -98 \equiv \ \ 22$
2	2	2	$-40 - 30 - 48 \equiv -118 \equiv \ \ \ 2$

The integers having remainders 1 or 2 when divided by 3, 4, 5 are given by $x \equiv 1, 2, 17, 22, 26, -14, -19, -23 \pmod{60}$.

Problems

1. Find all solutions of the congruences
    (a) $20x \equiv 4 \pmod{30}$;
    (b) $20x \equiv 30 \pmod 4$;
    (c) $353x \equiv 254 \pmod{400}$.
2. How many solutions are there to each of the following congruences:
    (a) $15x \equiv 25 \pmod{35}$;
    (b) $15x \equiv 24 \pmod{35}$;
    (c) $15x \equiv 0 \pmod{35}$?
3. Find the smallest positive integer (except $x = 1$) that satisfies the following congruences simultaneously: $x \equiv 1 \pmod 3$, $x \equiv 1 \pmod 5$, $x \equiv 1 \pmod 7$.
4. Find all integers that satisfy simultaneously: $x \equiv 2 \pmod 3$, $x \equiv 3 \pmod 5$, $x \equiv 5 \pmod 2$.
5. Solve the set of congruences: $x \equiv 1 \pmod 4$, $x \equiv 0 \pmod 3$, $x \equiv 5 \pmod 7$.
6. Find all integers that give the remainders 1, 2, 3 when divided by 3, 4, 5 respectively.
7. If a is selected at random from 1, 2, 3, $\cdots$, 14, and b is selected at random from 1, 2, 3, $\cdots$, 15, what is the probability that $ax \equiv b \pmod{15}$ has at least one solution? Exactly one solution?

8. Given any positive integer k, prove that there are k consecutive integers each divisible by a square > 1.

9. If x_2 is a solution of the congruence $ax \equiv b$ (mod m) (obtained perhaps by application of Euclid's algorithm to a and m), prove that $x \equiv x_2 + t(m/g)$ (mod m) gives all solutions as t runs through $0, 1, \cdots, g - 1$, where g is defined as $g = (a, m)$.

10. Suppose $(a, m) = 1$, and let x_1 denote a solution of $ax \equiv 1$ (mod m). For $s = 1, 2, \cdots$, let $x_s = 1/a - (1/a)(1 - ax_1)^s$. Prove that x_s is an integer and that it is a solution of $ax \equiv 1$ (mod m^s).

11. Suppose that $(a, m) = 1$. If $a = \pm 1$, the solution of $ax \equiv 1$ (mod m^s) is obviously $x \equiv a$ (mod m^s). If $a = \pm 2$, then m is odd and $x \equiv \frac{1}{2}(1 - m^s)\frac{1}{2}a$ (mod m^s) is the solution of $ax \equiv 1$ (mod m^s). For all other a use problem 11 to show that the solution of $ax \equiv 1$ (mod m^s) is $x \equiv k$ (mod m^s) where k is the nearest integer to $-(1/a)(1 - ax_1)^s$.

12. Solve $3x \equiv 1$ (mod 125) by Problem 12, taking $x_1 = 2$.

13. Let $m_1, m_2, \cdots, m_r$ be relatively prime in pairs. Assuming that each of the congruences $b_i x \equiv a_i$ (mod m_i), $i = 1, 2, \cdots, r$, is solvable, prove that the congruences have a simultaneous solution.

14. (a) Consider the set of congruences $x \equiv a_i$ (mod p^{e_i}), $i = 1, 2, \cdots, r$, with $e_1 \geq e_2 \geq \cdots \geq e_r$. Prove that $x = a_1$ is a simultaneous solution of these congruences if $p^{e_i}|(a_1 - a_i)$ for $i = 2, 3, \cdots, r$.
    (b) Let the canonical factoring of m be $p_1^{e_1} p_2^{e_2} \cdots p_k^{e_k}$. Prove that any simultaneous solution of the set of congruences $x \equiv a$ (mod $p_i^{e_i}$), $i = 1, 2, \cdots, k$, is a solution of $x \equiv a$ (mod m).
    (c) Prove that the set of congruences $x \equiv a_i$ (mod m_i), $i = 1, 2, \cdots, n$, has a simultaneous solution if, and only if, $(m_i, m_j)|(a_i - a_j)$ holds for every pair of moduli, that is for every pair of subscripts i, j such that $1 \leq i < j \leq n$. Any two solutions are congruent modulo $[m_1, m_2, \cdots, m_n]$.

15. Let $(a, b) = 1$ and $c > 0$. Prove that there is an integer x such that $(a + bx, c) = 1$.

16. Consider a square divided up into n^2 equal squares. Number the columns of small squares $1, 2, \cdots, n$ from left to right. Similarly number the rows $1, 2, \cdots, n$ and let $\{c, r\}$ denote the small square in the cth column and rth row.

    Let $a_0, b_0, a, b, \alpha, \beta$ be positive integers less than or equal to n and such that $(a, n) = (b, n) = (\alpha, n) = (\beta, n) = 1$. Write 1 in square $\{a_0, b_0\}$. Then count a columns to the right and b rows up from this square. If this takes you outside of the large square, count as if the large square were bent into a cylinder. Thus you will arrive at $\{a_0 + a, b_0 + b\}$ or $\{a_0 + a - n, b_0 + b\}$ or $\{a_0 + a, b_0 + b - n\}$ or $\{a_0 + a - n, b_0 + b - n\}$, whichever is actually one of the small squares. Write 2 in this square. Count a to the right and b up from 2 and insert 3 in the square. Continue until you have written in 1, 2, 3, $\cdot \cdot \cdot$, n. Prove that m will have been written in $\{x_m, y_m\}$ where x_m and y_m are uniquely determined by

$$x_m \equiv a_0 + a(m - 1) \pmod{n}, \qquad 1 \leqq x_m \leqq n$$

$$y_m \equiv b_0 + b(m - 1) \pmod{n}, \qquad 1 \leqq y_m \leqq n, \, 1 \leqq m \leqq n.$$

Also show that all these squares $\{x_m, y_m\}$ are different but that continuing the process one more step would put $n + 1$ in $\{a_0, b_0\}$ which is already occupied by 1.

Now having reached $\{a_0, b_0\}$ again, count α to the right and β up and write $n + 1$ in this square which may or may not already be occupied. Then revert to the original process with step a, b to insert $n + 2$, $n + 3$, $\cdot \cdot \cdot$, $2n$. Continue in this manner, using the extra step α, β just for $n + 1$, $2n + 1$, $\cdot \cdot \cdot$, $(n - 1)n + 1$, and stopping when n^2 has been inserted.

For $1 \leqq m \leqq n^2$ prove that m is in $\{x_m, y_m\}$ where

$$x_m \equiv a_0 + a(m - 1) + \alpha \left[\frac{m - 1}{n} \right] \pmod{n}, \qquad 1 \leqq x_m \leqq n,$$

$$y_m \equiv b_0 + b(m - 1) + \beta \left[\frac{m - 1}{n} \right] \pmod{n}, \qquad 1 \leqq y_m \leqq n,$$

and $\left[\dfrac{m - 1}{n} \right]$ is the quotient when n is divided into $m - 1$.

Also prove that if $(a\beta - b\alpha, n) = 1$ then each square contains one and only one integer m, $1 \leqq m \leqq n^2$.

From now on assume $(a\beta - b\alpha, n) = 1$. Writing $m - 1 = qn + s$, $0 \leqq s \leqq n - 1$, show that the entries in the cth column are just the $m = qn + s + 1$ for which $0 \leqq q \leqq n - 1$, $0 \leqq s \leqq n - 1$, and $as \equiv c - a_0 - \alpha q \pmod{n}$. Prove that there is one and only one s for each q and that each s is distinct from all the others. Then show:

$$\text{Sum of } m \text{ in } c\text{th column} = \sum_{q=0}^{n-1} qn + \sum_{s=0}^{n-1} s + n = \frac{n(n^2 + 1)}{2}.$$

Prove the same for the sum in a row. Since $n(n^2 + 1)/2$ is independent of c, the sums in each row and in each column are the same, and the square array of integers is a so-called magic square.

Note that the initial square $\{a_0, b_0\}$ is subject to no conditions. The only essential conditions are that a, b, α, β, $a\beta - b\alpha$ are relatively prime to n. Show that these conditions cannot be fulfilled if n is even. However, for odd n the values $a = b = \alpha = 1$, $\beta = 2$ always give a magic square.

2.4   The Function $\phi(n)$

We will return to the discussion of the solution of congruences in the next section. In this section we will use the Chinese remainder theorem to obtain an important property of the function $\phi(n)$ of Definition 2.3.

Theorem 2.15 *Let m and n denote any two positive, relatively prime integers. Then $\phi(nm) = \phi(n)\phi(m)$.*

Proof. Denote $\phi(m)$ by j and let $r_1, r_2, \cdots, r_j$ be a reduced residue system modulo m. Similarly write k for $\phi(n)$ and let $s_1, s_2, \cdots, s_k$ be a reduced residue system modulo n. If x is in a reduced residue system modulo mn, then $(x, m) = (x, n) = 1$, and hence $x \equiv r_h \pmod{m}$ and $x \equiv s_i \pmod{n}$ for some h and i. Conversely, if $x \equiv r_h \pmod{m}$ and $x \equiv s_i \pmod{n}$, then $(x, mn) = 1$. Thus a reduced residue system modulo mn can be obtained by determining all x such that $x \equiv r_h \pmod{m}$ and $x \equiv s_i \pmod{n}$ for some h and i. According to the Chinese remainder theorem, each pair h, i determines a single x modulo mn. Clearly, different pairs h, i yield different x modulo mn. There are jk of these pairs. Therefore a reduced residue system modulo mn contains $jk = \phi(m)\phi(n)$ numbers, and we have $\phi(mn) = \phi(m)\phi(n)$.

It is essential that m and n be relatively prime. In fact $\phi(2) = 1$ and $\phi(2^2) = 2 \neq \phi(2)\phi(2)$.

Theorem 2.16 *If $n > 1$ then $\phi(n) = n \prod_{p|n} (1 - 1/p)$. Also $\phi(1) = 1$.*

Remark. The symbol $\prod_{p|n}$ means the product over all primes that divide n. Thus if $n = p_1^{e_1} p_2^{e_2} \cdots p_r^{e_r}$ in canonical form, then $\prod_{p|n} (1 - 1/p)$ means $\prod_{j=1}^{r} (1 - 1/p_j)$. We will often use this notation as well as an analogous notation regarding sums. We will also write $\sum_{d|n}$ to mean the sum over all the positive divisors of n, prime or not. Furthermore we will sometimes use the convention that an empty sum is 0, an empty product is 1. Had we done so here we would not have had to treat $n = 1$ as a special case in the statement of the theorem.

Proof. It is obvious that $\phi(1) = 1$.

If $n > 1$ we can write $n = p_1^{e_1} p_2^{e_2} \cdots p_r^{e_r}$ in canonical form. Now $(p_j^{e_j}, p_{j+1}^{e_{j+1}} p_{j+2}^{e_{j+2}} \cdots p_r^{e_r}) = 1$ for $j = 1, 2, \cdots, r - 1$. Applying Theorem 2.15 repeatedly we obtain

$$\phi(n) = \prod_{j=1}^{r} \phi(p_j^{e_j}).$$

In order to compute $\phi(p^e)$, p a prime, we recall that $\phi(p^e)$ is the number of integers x such that $1 \leq x \leq p^e$, $(x, p^e) = 1$. There are p^e integers x between 1 and p^e, and we must count all of them except p, $2p$, $3p$, $\cdots$, $p^{e-1}p$. Therefore

$$\phi(p^e) = p^e - p^{e-1} = p^e \left(1 - \frac{1}{p}\right),$$

and hence

$$\phi(n) = \prod_{j=1}^{r} p_j^{e_j} \left(1 - \frac{1}{p_j}\right) = n \prod_{j=1}^{r} \left(1 - \frac{1}{p_j}\right) = n \prod_{p|n} \left(1 - \frac{1}{p}\right).$$

Theorem 2.17 *For $n \geq 1$ we have* $\sum_{d|n} \phi(d) = n$.

Proof. If $n = p^e$, p a prime, then

$$\sum_{d|n} \phi(d) = \phi(1) + \phi(p) + \phi(p^2) + \cdots + \phi(p^e)$$

$$= 1 + (p - 1) + p(p - 1) + \cdots + p^{e-1}(p - 1)$$

$$= p^e = n.$$

Therefore the theorem is true if n is a power of a prime. Now we proceed by induction. We suppose the theorem holds for integers with k or fewer distinct prime factors and consider any integer N with $k + 1$ distinct prime factors. Let p denote one of the prime factors of N, and let p^e be the highest power of p that divides N. Then $N = p^e n$, n has k distinct prime factors, and $(p, n) = 1$. Now as d ranges over the divisors of n, the set $d, pd, p^2d, \cdots, p^e d$ ranges over the divisors of N. Hence we have

$$\sum_{d|N} \phi(d) = \sum_{d|n} \phi(d) + \sum_{d|n} \phi(pd) + \sum_{d|n} \phi(p^2 d) + \cdots + \sum_{d|n} \phi(p^e d)$$

$$= \sum_{d|n} \phi(d)\{1 + \phi(p) + \phi(p^2) + \cdots + \phi(p^e)\}$$

$$= \sum_{d|n} \phi(d) \sum_{\delta|p^e} \phi(\delta) = np^e = N.$$

In Chapter 4 we will obtain a different proof of this theorem. It will be independent of the results of this section, and we will find that the order can be reversed, that we can begin by proving Theorem 2.17 and obtain Theorem 2.16 from it. It is then an easy matter to obtain Theorem 2.15 from Theorem 2.16.

Problems

1. For what values of n is $\phi(n)$ odd?
2. Find the number of positive integers ≤ 3600 that are prime to 3600.
3. Find the number of positive integers ≤ 3600 that have a factor in common with 3600.
4. Find the number of positive integers ≤ 7200 that are prime to 3600.
5. Find the number of positive integers ≤ 25200 that are prime to 3600. (Observe that $25200 = 7 \times 3600$.)
6. If m and k are positive integers, prove that the number of positive integers $\leq mk$ that are prime to m is $k\phi(m)$.
7. Show that $\phi(nm) = n\phi(m)$ if every prime that divides n also divides m.
8. If P denotes the product of the primes common to m and n, prove that $\phi(mn) = P\phi(m)\phi(n)/\phi(P)$. Hence if $(m, n) > 1$, prove $\phi(mn) > \phi(m)\phi(n)$.
9. If $\phi(m) = \phi(mn)$ and $n > 1$, prove that $n = 2$ and m is odd.
10. Characterize the set of positive integers n satisfying $\phi(2n) = \phi(n)$.
11. Characterize the set of positive integers satisfying $\phi(2n) > \phi(n)$.
12. Prove that there are infinitely many integers n so that $3 \nmid \phi(n)$.
13. Find all solutions x of $\phi(x) = 24$.
14. Prove that for a fixed integer n the equation $\phi(x) = n$ has only a finite number of solutions.
15. Find the smallest positive integer n so that $\phi(x) = n$ has no solution; exactly two solutions; exactly three solutions; exactly four solutions. (It

has been conjectured that there is no integer n such that $\phi(x) = n$ has exactly one solution, but this is an unsolved problem.)

16. Prove that there is no solution of the equation $\phi(x) = 14$, and that 14 is the least positive even integer with this property. Apart from 14, what is the next smallest positive even integer n such that $\phi(x) = n$ has no solution?

17. Prove that for $n \geq 2$ the sum of all positive integers less than n and prime to n is $n\phi(n)/2$.

18. If n has k distinct odd prime factors, prove that $2^k|\phi(n)$.

19. Define $f(n)$ as the sum of the positive integers less than n and prime to n. Prove that $f(m) = f(n)$ implies that $m = n$.

20. Let $\phi'(n)$ denote the number of integers x such that $1 \leq x \leq n$ and $(x, n) = (x + 1, n) = 1$. Prove

$$\phi'(n) = n \prod_{p|n} \left(1 - \frac{2}{p}\right).$$

21. (a) Let the canonical factorization of n be $n = \prod_{i=1}^{k} p_i^{\alpha_i}$. For every positive integer j, define

$$e_j(p_i) = \begin{cases} 1 \text{ if } p_i|j \\ 0 \text{ otherwise.} \end{cases}$$

Prove that $\sum_{j=1}^{n} e_j(p_1) = n/p_1$, and more generally

$$\sum_{j=1}^{n} e_j(p_1)e_j(p_2) \cdots e_j(p_r) = \frac{n}{p_1 p_2 \cdots p_r} \qquad \text{for } 1 \leq r \leq k.$$

(b) Prove that

$$\prod_{i=1}^{k} \{1 - e_j(p_i)\} = \begin{cases} 1 \text{ if } (j, n) = 1 \\ 0 \text{ otherwise,} \end{cases}$$

and hence that $\phi(n) = \sum_{j=1}^{n} \prod_{i=1}^{k} \{1 - e_j(p_i)\}$.

(c) Deduce that

$$\phi(n) = \sum_{j=1}^{n} \{1 - e_j(p_1) - e_j(p_2) - \cdots - e_j(p_k) + e_j(p_1)e_j(p_2)$$

$$+ e_j(p_1)e_j(p_3) + \cdots + e_j(p_{k-1})e_j(p_k) - e_j(p_1)e_j(p_2)e_j(p_3) - \text{etc.}\},$$

and so obtain an independent proof of Theorem 2.16.

22. If $d|n$ and $0 < d < n$, prove that $n - \phi(n) > d - \phi(d)$.

23. Prove the following generalization of Euler's theorem:

$$a^m \equiv a^{m-\phi(m)} \pmod{m}$$

for any integer a.

2.5 Congruences of Higher Degree

There is no general method for solving congruences. However, certain reductions can be made so that the problem finally becomes that of solving congruences with prime moduli. We can use the method of the Chinese remainder theorem in the first step of this reduction.

If $m = p_1^{e_1} p_2^{e_2} \cdots p_r^{e_r}$ then the congruence $f(x) \equiv 0 \pmod{m}$ is equivalent to the set of congruences $f(x) \equiv 0 \pmod{p_i^{e_i}}$, $i = 1, 2, \cdots, r$, in the sense that solutions of one are solutions of the other. If for some j, $1 \leq j \leq r$, the congruence $f(x) \equiv 0 \pmod{p_j^{e_j}}$ has no solution, then $f(x) \equiv 0 \pmod{m}$ has no solution. On the other hand, if all the congruences $f(x) \equiv 0 \pmod{p_i^{e_i}}$ have solutions, we can suppose that the ith congruence has exactly k_i solutions, say $a_i^{(1)}$, $a_i^{(2)}$, $\cdots$, $a_i^{(k_i)}$. No two of these are congruent modulo $p_i^{e_i}$, by Definition 2.4, and every solution of $f(x) \equiv 0 \pmod{p_i^{e_i}}$ is congruent to some $a_i^{(j)}$ modulo p_i.

Now an integer u is a root of $f(x) \equiv 0 \pmod{m}$ if and only if for each i there is a j_i such that $u \equiv a_i^{(j_i)} \pmod{p_i^{e_i}}$. Since the moduli $p_i^{e_i}$ are relatively prime in pairs, the Chinese remainder theorem is applicable. We determine integers b_i such that $mp_i^{-e_i}b_i \equiv 1 \pmod{p_i^{e_i}}$ and can then find u by means of (2.1);

$$(2.2) \qquad u \equiv \sum_{i=1}^{r} \frac{m}{p_i^{e_i}} b_i a_i^{(j_i)} \pmod{m}.$$

When actually solving a problem it is usually best to compute the coefficients $mp_i^{-e_i}b_i$ first since they are independent of the choice of the j_i. It is then easy to insert the various values of the $a_i^{(j_i)}$ in (2.2), and the problem is solved.

There will be a different u modulo m for each choice of the integers $j_1, j_2, \cdots, j_r$, and each j_i can take on any of k_i values. Therefore the congruence $f(x) \equiv 0 \pmod{m}$ has $k_1 k_2 \cdots k_r$ solutions. Since k_i is the number of solutions of $f(x) \equiv 0 \pmod{p_i^{e_i}}$, we have the following theorem.

Theorem 2.18 *Let $N(m)$ denote the number of solutions of the congruence $f(x) \equiv 0 \pmod{m}$. Then $N(m) = \prod\limits_{i=1}^{r} N(p_i^{e_i})$ if $m = p_1^{e_1} p_2^{e_2} \cdots p_r^{e_r}$ is the canonical factorization of m.*

Perhaps it should be remarked that the case in which $N(p_j^{e_j}) = 0$ for some j is not ruled out in Theorem 2.18.

Example. Solve $x^2 + x + 7 \equiv 0 \pmod{15}$.

Trying the values $x = 0, \pm1, \pm2$, we find that $x^2 + x + 7 \equiv 0 \pmod 5$ has no solution. Since $15 = 3 \cdot 5$, the original congruence has no solution.

Example. Solve $x^2 + x + 7 \equiv 0 \pmod{189}$, given that $x \equiv 4,\ 13,\ -5 \pmod{27}$ are the solutions of $x^2 + x + 7 \equiv 0 \pmod{27}$ and that $x \equiv 0,\ -1 \pmod 7$ are the solutions of $x^2 + x + 7 \equiv 0 \pmod 7$.

In this example we have $m = 189 = 27 \cdot 7 = 3^3 \cdot 7$, $p_1^{e_1} = 27$, $p_2^{e_2} = 7$, $a_1^{(1)} = 4$, $a_1^{(2)} = 13$, $a_1^{(3)} = -5$, $a_2^{(1)} = 0$, $a_2^{(2)} = -1$. To find b_1 we multiply the congruence $7b_1 \equiv 1 \pmod{27}$ by 4 and obtain $b_1 \equiv 28b_1 \equiv 4 \pmod{27}$. For b_2 we have $27b_2 \equiv 1 \pmod 7$ which gives us $b_2 \equiv -1 \pmod 7$. We can now write (2.2) as

$$u \equiv 7 \cdot 4a_1^{(j_1)} + 27(-1)a_2^{(j_2)} \equiv 28a_1^{(j_1)} - 27a_2^{(j_2)} \pmod{189}$$

for the required roots u. Using the known values of the $a_i^{(j)}$ we quickly find $u \equiv -77, -14, -140, -50, 13, -113 \pmod{189}$.

If the numbers had been larger we might have had more trouble finding b_1 and b_2. In any case the methods mentioned in section 2.3 can be used.

Problems

1. Solve the congruences:
$$x^3 + 2x - 3 \equiv 0 \pmod 9;$$
$$x^3 + 2x - 3 \equiv 0 \pmod 5;$$
$$x^3 + 2x - 3 \equiv 0 \pmod{45}.$$

2. Solve the congruence $x^3 + 4x + 8 \equiv 0 \pmod{15}$.

3. Solve the congruence $x^3 - 9x^2 + 23x - 15 \equiv 0 \pmod{503}$ by observing that 503 is a prime and that the polynomial factors into $(x-1)(x-3)(x-5)$.

4. Solve the congruence $x^3 - 9x^2 + 23x - 15 \equiv 0 \pmod{143}$.

2.6 Prime Power Moduli

The problem of solving a congruence has now been reduced to that of solving a congruence whose modulus is a power of a single prime.

If r is a solution of $f(x) \equiv 0 \pmod{p^s}$, then $f(r) \equiv 0 \pmod{p^t}$ for $t = 1, 2, \cdots, s$. Let $x_s^{(1)}, x_s^{(2)}, \cdots, x_s^{(h_s)}$ be the solutions of $f(x) \equiv 0 \pmod{p^s}$. There may be no such solutions, or there may be many. Consider $s \geq 2$. If there is a solution $x_s^{(i)}$ then there is a solution $x_{s-1}^{(j_i)}$ of $f(x) \equiv 0 \pmod{p^{s-1}}$ such that $x_s^{(i)} \equiv x_{s-1}^{(j_i)} \pmod{p^{s-1}}$. Therefore $x_s^{(i)} \equiv x_{s-1}^{(j_i)} + v_{s-1}p^{s-1} \pmod{p^s}$ for some integer v_{s-1}.

Remembering that $f(x)$ is a polynomial of degree n with integral coefficients, we see that $\dfrac{1}{1!} f'(x)$, $\dfrac{1}{2!} f''(x)$, $\cdots$ are polynomials with integral coefficients and that $f^{(t)}(x)$ is identically zero for $t > n$. Thus the Taylor's expansion of $f(x)$ is finite and we have

$$f(x + h) = f(x) + f'(x)h + \frac{1}{2} f''(x)h^2 + \cdots + \frac{1}{n!} f^{(n)}(x)h^n,$$

and then

$$0 = f(x_s^{(i)}) \equiv f(x_{s-1}^{(j_i)} + v_{s-1}p^{s-1})$$
$$\equiv f(x_{s-1}^{(j_i)}) + f'(x_{s-1}^{(j_i)})v_{s-1}p^{s-1} \pmod{p^s}.$$

But $f(x_{s-1}^{(j_i)}) \equiv 0 \pmod{p^{s-1}}$ so we have

$$(2.3) \qquad f'(x_{s-1}^{(j_i)})v_{s-1} \equiv -\frac{1}{p^{s-1}} f(x_{s-1}^{(j_i)}) \pmod{p}.$$

Conversely, if

$$(2.4) \qquad f'(x_{s-1}^{(j)})v \equiv -\frac{1}{p^{s-1}} f(x_{s-1}^{(j)}) \pmod{p},$$

then $f(x_{s-1}^{(j)} + vp^{s-1}) \equiv 0 \pmod{p^s}$. This shows us how to find all the solutions of $f(x) \equiv 0 \pmod{p^s}$, $s \geq 2$, if we know those of $f(x) \equiv 0 \pmod{p^{s-1}}$. For each root $x_{s-1}^{(j)}$ we find all the solutions v of (2.4), and then the integers $x_{s-1}^{(j)} + vp^{s-1}$ will be solutions of $f(x) \equiv 0 \pmod{p^s}$. It can, of course, happen that there are no v corresponding to some x_{s-1}^{j}. In this case we have no solutions of $f(x) \equiv 0 \pmod{p^s}$ arising from this particular $x_{s-1}^{(j)}$.

We can say a little more about the solutions. In solving $f(x) \equiv$

$0 \pmod{p^s}$, $s \geq 2$, we start with the solutions $x_1^{(j)}$ of $f(x) \equiv 0 \pmod{p}$. Fixing upon a particular $x_1^{(j_i)}$ we must first solve (2.3), with $s = 2$, for v_1. For each v_1 we have a root $x_2^{(k)} \equiv x_1^{(j_i)} + v_1 p \pmod{p^2}$ of $f(x) \equiv 0 \pmod{p^2}$. Using each one of these $x_2^{(k)}$ we must then solve (2.3) with $s = 3$, $j_i = k$, in order to find solutions of $f(x) \equiv 0 \pmod{p^3}$. But the congruence for v_2 has modulus p and $x_2^{(k)} \equiv x_1^{(j_i)} \pmod{p}$, and hence we can write it as

$$f'(x_1^{(j_i)})v_2 \equiv -\frac{1}{p^2} f(x_2^{(k)}) \pmod{p}.$$

This happens at each stage, and hence we may determine v_{s-1} from

$$(2.5) \qquad f'(x_1^{(j_i)})v_{s-1} \equiv -\frac{1}{p^{s-1}} f(x_{s-1}^{(k)}) \pmod{p}$$

for all the $x_{s-1}^{(k)}$ that ultimately arose from the solution $x_1^{(j_i)}$ of $f(x) \equiv 0 \pmod{p}$.

The congruence (2.5) is a linear congruence. If $f'(x_1^{(j_i)}) \not\equiv 0 \pmod{p}$, then there will be exactly one v_{s-1} for each of the $x_{s-1}^{(k)}$ arising ultimately from $x_1^{(j_i)}$. If $f'(x_1^{(j_i)}) \equiv 0 \pmod{p}$, then there will be p or no v_{s-1} according as $f'(x_{s-1}^{(k)})/p^{s-1}$ is or is not congruent to 0 modulo p.

Example. Solve $x^2 + x + 7 \equiv 0 \pmod{27}$.

By trial we find that $x \equiv 1 \pmod{3}$ is the only solution of $f(x) \equiv 0 \pmod{3}$ for the present $f(x)$. Then $f'(x) = 2x + 1$ and $f'(1) \equiv 0 \pmod{3}$. There is only one x_1, and (2.5) reduces to

$$0 \equiv -\frac{1}{3^{s-1}} f(x_{s-1}^{(k)}) \pmod{3},$$

which means that there are no v_{s-1} if $f(x_{s-1}^{(k)}) \not\equiv 0 \pmod{3^s}$ and that $v_{s-1} \equiv 0$, 1, $-1 \pmod{3}$ if $f(x_{s-1}^{(k)}) \equiv 0 \pmod{3^s}$. We now find

$$x_1^{(1)} \equiv 1 \pmod{3}, f(x_1^{(1)}) = 9, \qquad v_1 \equiv 0, 1, -1 \pmod{3}$$

$$x_2^{(1)} \equiv 1 \pmod{3^2}, f(x_2^{(1)}) = 9, \qquad \text{no } v_2$$

$$x_2^{(2)} \equiv 4 \pmod{3^2}, f(x_2^{(2)}) = 27, \qquad v_2 \equiv 0, 1, -1 \pmod{3}$$

$$x_2^{(3)} \equiv -2 \pmod{3^2}, f(x_2^{(3)}) = 9, \qquad \text{no } v_2$$

$$x_3^{(1)} \equiv 4 \pmod{3^3}$$

$$x_3^{(2)} \equiv 13 \pmod{3^3}$$

$$x_3^{(3)} \equiv -5 \pmod{3^3}.$$

Example. Solve $x^2 + x + 7 \equiv 0 \pmod{3^4}$.
Continuing from the previous example, we find

$$f(x_3^{(1)}) = 27, \quad f(x_3^{(2)}) = 189, \quad f(x_3^{(3)}) = 27.$$

The congruence has no solution since $27 \not\equiv 0$, $189 \not\equiv 0 \pmod{3^4}$.

Example. Solve $x^2 + x + 7 \equiv 0 \pmod{7^3}$.
The solutions of $f(x) \equiv 0 \pmod 7$ are $x \equiv 0, -1 \pmod 7$. Furthermore, $f'(0) = 1, f'(-1) = -1$. There will be just one $x_s^{(1)}$ corresponding to $x_1^{(1)} = 0$ and one $x_s^{(2)}$ corresponding to $x_1^{(2)} = -1$. Now (2.5) becomes

$$v_{s-1} \equiv -\frac{1}{7^{s-1}} f(x_{s-1}^{(1)}) \pmod 7 \qquad \text{corresponding to } x_1^{(1)} = 0$$

$$v_{s-1} \equiv \frac{1}{7^{s-1}} f(x_{s-1}^{(2)}) \pmod 7 \qquad \text{corresponding to } x_1^{(2)} = -1.$$

Then we find

$$x_1^{(1)} = 0, \quad f(x_1^{(1)}) = 7, \quad v_1 = -1, \quad x_2^{(1)} = -7, \quad f(x_2^{(1)}) = 49,$$
$$v_2 = -1, \quad x_3^{(1)} = -56,$$
$$x_1^{(2)} = -1, \quad f(x_1^{(2)}) = 7, \quad v_1 = 1, \quad x_2^{(2)} = 6, \quad f(x_2^{(2)}) = 49,$$
$$v_2 = 1, \quad x_3^{(2)} = 55.$$

The solutions of $x^2 + x + 7 \equiv 0 \pmod{7^3}$ are $x \equiv -56 \pmod{7^3}$ and $x \equiv 55 \pmod{7^3}$.

When solving numerical problems one often must determine whether or not one integer k divides another integer n. If $(k, 10) = 1$ and k is not too large, there is a rather simple way to do this. As a first example consider $k = 31$, $n = 23754$. Then $n - 4k = 23754 - 4 \cdot 30 - 4 = 10(2375 - 4 \cdot 3) = 10 \cdot 2363$. Since $(31, 10) = 1$ we see that $31 | 23754$ if and only if $31 | 2363$. We can repeat the argument to reduce 2363 still further. The entire process can be put in a more convenient form.

$$
\begin{array}{r}
23754 \\
\underline{12} \\
2363 \\
\underline{9} \\
227 \\
\underline{21} \\
1
\end{array}
\qquad 31 \nmid 23754.
$$

This process can be used for any k whose last digit is 1. We can write $k = 10j + 1$ and $n = 10a + b$. Then $n - bk = 10a + b - 10bj - b = 10(a - bj)$, and $k|n$ if and only if $k|(a - bj)$.

If the last digit of k is 9, we can write $k = 10j - 1$ and $n = 10a + b$, and we have $n + bk = 10a + b + 10bj - b = 10(a + bj)$. Then $k|n$ if and only if $k|(a + bj)$. If the last digit of k is 3, we can write $3k = 10j - 1$ and find $n + 3bk = 10(a + bj)$, and hence $k|n$ if and only if $k|(a + bj)$. Similarly, if the last digit of k is 7, we write $3k = 10j + 1$ and obtain $k|n$ if and only if $k|(a - bj)$.

Example.

$19 = 10 \cdot 2 - 1$	$3 \cdot 7 = 10 \cdot 2 + 1$
20513	8638
6	16
2057	847
14	14
219	70
18	
39	
$19 \nmid 20513$	$7|8638$

Problems

1. The foregoing method determines whether k divides n, but in general the number we finally reach is not congruent to n modulo k. Consider the following scheme, exemplified for $n = 1234$.

$$
\begin{array}{l}
1\,2\,3\,4 \\
3\,6\,9 \\
1\,0\,8 \\
3\,0 \\
9
\end{array}
$$

Here we have written down 1234, then $3 \cdot 123$, $3 \cdot 36$, $3 \cdot 10$, $3 \cdot 3$, in turn. We drop off the right digit at each step and multiply what is left by 3. Now we have $n = 1234 \equiv 4 + 9 + 8 + 0 + 9 \equiv 30 \equiv 2 \pmod 7$ and also $n = 1234 \equiv 4 - 9 + 8 - 0 + 9 \equiv 12 \pmod{13}$. Show why this works for all positive integers n. What multiplier should be used instead of 3 if the modulus k is 9 or 11; if $k = 17$; if $k = 19$? For $k = 17$ and 19 the procedure is likely to be too long to be of any practical value. Find more satisfactory variations of the method. For example:

$$1\ 7\ 3\ 4\ 5\ 6\ 2$$
$$8\ 6\ 7\ 2\ 5$$
$$4\ 3\ 3\ 5$$
$$2\ 1\ 5$$
$$1\ 0$$

$1734562 \equiv 62 + 25 + 35 + 15 + 10 \equiv 147 \equiv 47 + 5 \equiv 52 \equiv 14 \pmod{19}$.

2. Show that for $k = 9$ the method in the text and the method of problem 1 are essentially the same and that they amount to the familiar process of "casting out nines."

3. Using the fact that $1001 = 7 \cdot 11 \cdot 13$, and assuming that you can recognize all multiples of 7 or 11 or 13 having no more than three digits, work out a scheme for testing for divisibility by 7 or 11 or 13 simultaneously.

4. Prove $(y + vp^{s-1})^j \equiv y^j + jy^{j-1}vp^{s-1} \pmod{p^s}$ if $s \geq 2$.
   Prove

$$f(y + vp^{s-1}) - f(y) \equiv \sum_{i=0}^{n-1} (n - i)a_i y^{n-i-1} vp^{s-1} \pmod{p^s} \text{ if } s \geq 2$$

and $f(x) = \sum_{i=0}^{n} a_i x^{n-i}$.

This can be used to replace the use of Taylor's expansion at the beginning of this section.

5. Apply the method of this section to solve $ax - 1 \equiv 0 \pmod{p^s}$, $(a, p) = 1$. How are these solutions related to those given by Problem 11 of section 2.3 with m replaced by p^s?

6. Solve $x^5 + x^4 + 1 \equiv 0 \pmod{3^4}$.

7. Solve $x^3 + x + 57 \equiv 0 \pmod{5^3}$.

8. Solve $x^2 + 5x + 24 \equiv 0 \pmod{36}$.

9. Solve $x^3 + 10x^2 + x + 3 \equiv 0 \pmod{3^3}$.

10. Solve $x^3 + x^2 - 4 \equiv 0 \pmod{7^3}$.

11. Solve $x^3 + x^2 - 5 \equiv 0 \pmod{7^3}$.

2.7 Prime Modulus

We have now reduced the problem of solving $f(x) \equiv 0 \pmod{m}$ to its last stage, congruences with prime moduli. It is here that we will not be able to find a general method. However, there are some general facts concerning the solutions, and we will find that we are led to some new and interesting matters.

As before, we write $f(x) = a_0 x^n + a_1 x^{n-1} + \cdots + a_n$ and we assume that p is a prime and $a_0 \not\equiv 0 \pmod p$.

Theorem 2.19 *If the degree n of $f(x) \equiv 0 \pmod p$ is greater than or equal to p, then either every integer is a solution of $f(x) \equiv 0 \pmod p$ or there is a polynomial $g(x)$ having integral coefficients, with leading coefficient 1, and such that $g(x) \equiv 0 \pmod p$ is of degree less than p and the solutions of $g(x) \equiv 0 \pmod p$ are precisely those of $f(x) \equiv 0 \pmod p$.*

Proof. Dividing $f(x)$ by $x^p - x$ we obtain $f(x) = q(x)(x^p - x) + r(x)$ where $q(x)$ is a polynomial with integral coefficients and $r(x)$ is either zero or a polynomial with integral coefficients and degree less than p. Fermat's theorem shows that $u^p - u \equiv 0 \pmod p$, and hence $f(u) \equiv r(u) \pmod p$ for every integer u. Therefore if $r(x)$ is zero, or if every coefficient in $r(x)$ is divisible by p, then every integer is a solution of $f(x) \equiv 0 \pmod p$. The only other possibility is $r(x) = b_0 x^m + b_1 x^{m-1} + \cdots + b_m$, $m < p$, $(b_0, p) = 1$. In this case there is an integer b such that $bb_0 \equiv 1 \pmod p$, and clearly $r(x) \equiv 0 \pmod p$ and $br(x) \equiv 0 \pmod p$ have the same solutions. We need only take $g(x) = br(x)$.

In the statement of Theorem 2.19, $g(x)$ is described as having the property that $g(x) \equiv 0 \pmod p$ and $f(x) \equiv 0 \pmod p$ have the same solutions. From the proof of the theorem we see that $g(u) \equiv bf(u) \pmod p$ for every integer u. However, we do not say that the polynomials $g(x)$ and $bf(x)$ are congruent modulo p; we will use this last statement to mean that each coefficient in $g(x)$ is congruent modulo p to the corresponding coefficient in $bf(x)$.

Theorem 2.20 *The congruence $f(x) \equiv 0 \pmod p$ of degree n has at most n solutions.*

Proof. The proof is by induction on the degree of $f(x) \equiv 0 \pmod p$. If $n = 0$, the polynomial $f(x)$ is just a_0 with $a_0 \not\equiv 0 \pmod p$, and hence the congruence has no solution. If $n = 1$, the congruence has exactly one solution by Theorem 2.13. Assuming the truth of the theorem for all congruences of degree $<n$, suppose that there are more than n solutions of the congruence $f(x) \equiv 0 \pmod p$ of degree n. Let the leading term of $f(x)$ be $a_0 x^n$ and let $u_1, u_2, \cdots, u_n, u_{n+1}$ be solutions of the congruence, with $u_i \not\equiv u_j \pmod p$ for $i \neq j$. We define $g(x)$ by

the equation

$$g(x) = f(x) - a_0(x - u_1)(x - u_2) \cdots (x - u_n),$$

noting the cancellation of $a_0 x^n$ on the right. Then either $g(x)$ is identically zero, or it is a polynomial of degree k, $0 \le k < n$.

We wish to prove that $g(x)$ is either identically zero or is a polynomial having all its coefficients divisible by p. If this were not so the congruence $g(x) \equiv 0 \pmod{p}$ would have a degree, say k, and we see that $k < n$. But $g(x) \equiv 0 \pmod{p}$ has n solutions $u_1, u_2, \cdots, u_n$, and this is impossible by our induction hypothesis.

Now what we have proved about $g(x)$ shows that $g(u) \equiv 0 \pmod{p}$ for all integers u and hence that $f(u) \equiv a_0(u - u_1)(u - u_2) \cdots (u - u_n) \pmod{p}$ for all integers u. In particular,

$$a_0(u_{n+1} - u_1)(u_{n+1} - u_2) \cdots (u_{n+1} - u_n) \equiv f(u_{n+1}) \equiv 0 \pmod{p}.$$

But this contradicts Theorem 1.15, and hence the assumption that $f(x) \equiv 0 \pmod{p}$ has more than n solutions is false.

Corollary 2.21 *If $b_0 x^n + b_1 x^{n-1} + \cdots + b_n \equiv 0 \pmod{p}$ has more than n solutions then all the coefficients b_j are divisible by p.*

Theorem 2.22 *The congruence $f(x) \equiv 0 \pmod{p}$ of degree n, with leading coefficient $a_0 = 1$, has n solutions if and only if $f(x)$ is a factor of $x^p - x$ modulo p, that is, if and only if $x^p - x = f(x)q(x) + ps(x)$ where $q(x)$ and $s(x)$ have integral coefficients, and where either $s(x)$ is a polynomial of degree less than n or $s(x)$ is zero.*

Proof. If $f(x) \equiv 0 \pmod{p}$ has n solutions, then $n \le p$. Dividing $x^p - x$ by $f(x)$, we find $x^p - x = f(x)q(x) + r(x)$ where $r(x)$ is zero or $r(x)$ has degree less than n. For every solution u of $f(x) \equiv 0 \pmod{p}$ we have $u^p - u \equiv 0 \pmod{p}$, and hence $r(u) \equiv 0 \pmod{p}$. Therefore if $r(x)$ is not zero, it is a polynomial of degree less than n having n solutions. According to Corollary 2.21 all the coefficients of $r(x)$ are divisible by p, and we can write $r(x) = ps(x)$.

Conversely, if $x^p - x = f(x)q(x) + ps(x)$, then $f(u)q(u) \equiv u^p - u - ps(u) \equiv 0 \pmod{p}$ for every integer u. Therefore $f(x)q(x) \equiv 0 \pmod{p}$ has p solutions. But $q(x)$ is of degree $p - n$, and hence has at most $p - n$ solutions, $v_1, v_2, \cdots, v_k$, say, with $k \le p - n$. If u is any of the other $p - k$ residues modulo p, then $(q(u), p) = 1$

and $f(u)q(u) \equiv 0 \pmod{p}$, and we have $f(u) \equiv 0 \pmod{p}$ by Theorem 1.9. Hence $f(x) \equiv 0 \pmod{p}$ has at least $p - k \geq p - (p - n) = n$ solutions. This, with Theorem 2.20, shows that $f(x) \equiv 0 \pmod{p}$ has exactly n solutions.

The restriction $a_0 = 1$ in this theorem is needed so that we may divide $x^p - x$ by $f(x)$ and obtain a polynomial $q(x)$ with integral coefficients. However, it is not very much of a restriction. We can always find an integer a such that $aa_0 \equiv 1 \pmod{p}$. Then $af(x) - (aa_0 - 1)x^n \equiv 0 \pmod{p}$ has the same solutions as $f(x) \equiv 0 \pmod{p}$, and $af(x) - (aa_0 - 1)x^n$ has its leading coefficient 1.

Problems

1. Reduce the following congruences to equivalent congruences of degree ≤ 6:
   (a) $x^{11} + x^8 + 5 \equiv 0 \pmod{7}$;
   (b) $x^{20} + x^{13} + x^7 + x \equiv 2 \pmod{7}$;
   (c) $x^{15} - x^{10} + 4x - 3 \equiv 0 \pmod{7}$.
2. Prove that $2x^3 + 5x^2 + 6x + 1 \equiv 0 \pmod{7}$ has three solutions by use of Theorem 2.22.
3. Prove that $x^{14} + 12x^2 \equiv 0 \pmod{13}$ has thirteen solutions and so it is an identical congruence.
4. Prove that if $f(x) \equiv 0 \pmod{p}$ has j solutions $x \equiv a_1, x \equiv a_2, \cdots, x \equiv a_j \pmod{p}$, there is a polynomial $q(x)$ such that $f(x) \equiv (x - a_1)(x - a_2) \cdots (x - a_j)q(x) \pmod{p}$. *Suggestion:* begin by showing that there is a $q_1(x)$ such that $f(x) \equiv (x - a_1)q_1(x) \pmod{p}$ and that $q_1(x) \equiv 0 \pmod{p}$ has solutions $x \equiv a_2, x \equiv a_3, \cdots, x \equiv a_j \pmod{p}$. Then use induction.
5. With the assumptions and notation of the previous problem, prove that if the degree of $f(x)$ is j, then $q(x)$ is a constant and can be taken as the leading coefficient of $f(x)$.
6. Prove that Fermat's theorem implies that

$$x^{p-1} - 1 \equiv (x - 1)(x - 2) \cdots (x - p + 1) \pmod{p}$$

and $\quad x^p - x \equiv x(x - 1)(x - 2) \cdots (x - p + 1) \pmod{p}$.

7. By comparing coefficients of x in the previous problem, give another proof of Wilson's theorem.
8. Let m be composite. Prove that Theorem 2.20 is false if "mod p" is replaced by "mod m".

2.8 Congruences of Degree Two, Prime Modulus

If $f(x) \equiv 0 \pmod{p}$ is of degree two, then $f(x) = ax^2 + bx + c$, and a is relatively prime to p. We will suppose $p > 2$ since the case $p = 2$ offers no difficulties. Then p is odd, and $4af(x) = (2ax + b)^2 + 4ac - b^2$. Hence u is a solution of $f(x) \equiv 0 \pmod{p}$ if and only if $2au + b \equiv v \pmod{p}$, where v is a solution of $v^2 \equiv b^2 - 4ac \pmod{p}$. Furthermore, since $(2a, p) = 1$, for each solution v there is one, and only one, u modulo p such that $2au + b \equiv v \pmod{p}$. Clearly different v modulo p yield different u modulo p. Thus the problem of solving the congruence of degree two is reduced to that of solving a congruence of the form $x^2 \equiv a \pmod{p}$.

In Chapter 3 we will consider the congruence $x^2 \equiv a \pmod{p}$ in detail. For the present we will merely obtain some general results concerning the more general congruence $x^n \equiv a \pmod{p}$ and certain related concepts.

Problem

1. Reduce the following congruences to the form $x^2 \equiv a \pmod{p}$:
   (a) $4x^2 + 2x + 1 \equiv 0 \pmod{5}$;   (b) $3x^2 - x + 5 \equiv 0 \pmod{7}$;
   (c) $2x^2 + 7x - 10 \equiv 0 \pmod{11}$;   (d) $x^2 + x - 1 \equiv 0 \pmod{13}$.

2.9 Power Residues

Definition 2.6 *If $x^n \equiv a \pmod{p}$ has a solution, then a is called an nth power residue modulo p.*

Definition 2.7 *Let m denote a positive integer and a any integer such that $(a, m) = 1$. Let h denote the smallest positive integer such that $a^h \equiv 1 \pmod{m}$. We say that a belongs to the exponent h modulo m.*

Since $a^{\phi(m)} \equiv 1 \pmod{m}$ by Euler's theorem, we see that every a relatively prime to m, belongs to some exponent $h \leq \phi(m)$ modulo m. Dividing $\phi(m)$ by h we obtain $\phi(m) = qh + r$, $0 \leq r < h$. But then $a^r \equiv a^{r+qh} \equiv a^{\phi(m)} \equiv 1 \pmod{m}$. Since h is the least positive integer such that $a^h \equiv 1 \pmod{m}$, and since $0 \leq r < h$, we see that r cannot be positive. Therefore $r = 0$, and we have the first assertion in the following theorem.

Theorem 2.23 *If a belongs to the exponent h modulo m then $h \mid \phi(m)$. Furthermore $a^j \equiv a^k \pmod{m}$ if and only if $h \mid (j - k)$.*

Proof. There is no loss in generality in assuming $j > k$, and since $(a, m) = 1$, the congruence $a^j \equiv a^k \pmod{m}$ is equivalent to $a^{j-k} \equiv 1 \pmod{m}$. Thus the second assertion in the theorem follows as in the proof of the first assertion.

Theorem 2.24 *If a belongs to the exponent h modulo m then a^k belongs to the exponent $h/(h, k)$ modulo m.*

Proof. According to Theorem 2.23, $(a^k)^j \equiv 1 \pmod{m}$ if and only if $h \mid kj$. But $h \mid kj$ if and only if $\{h/(h, k)\} \mid \{k/(h, k)\} j$ and hence if and only if $\{h/(h, k)\} \mid j$. Therefore the least positive integer j such that $(a^k)^j \equiv 1 \pmod{m}$ is $j = h/(h, k)$.

Definition 2.8 *If a belongs to the exponent $\phi(m)$ modulo m, then a is called a primitive root modulo m.*

Theorem 2.25 *If p is a prime, then there exist $\phi(p - 1)$ primitive roots modulo p. The only integers having primitive roots are p^e, $2p^e$, 2 and 4, with p an odd prime.*

Proof. Each integer a, $1 \leq a \leq p - 1$, belongs to some exponent h modulo p with $h \mid (p - 1)$. If a belongs to the exponent h, then $(a^k)^h \equiv 1 \pmod{p}$ for all k, and $1, a, a^2, \cdots , a^{h-1}$ are distinct modulo p. Therefore, from Theorem 2.20, these h numbers are all the solutions of $x^h \equiv 1 \pmod{p}$. By Theorem 2.24 just $\phi(h)$ of these numbers belong to the exponent h modulo p. The others belong to smaller exponents. Also, any integer a that belongs to the exponent h modulo p is a solution of $x^h \equiv 1 \pmod{p}$. Therefore for each h that divides $p - 1$ there will be either $\phi(h)$ or no integers a, $1 \leq a \leq p - 1$, such that a belongs to the exponent h modulo p. Let $\psi(h)$ denote the number of the integers a that belong to the exponent h modulo p. Then $\psi(h) \leq \phi(h)$ for each h that divides $p - 1$ and $\sum_{h \mid p-1} \psi(h) = p - 1$. But $\sum_{h \mid p-1} \phi(h) = p - 1$ according to Theorem 2.17, so we have $\sum_{h \mid p-1} (\psi(h) - \phi(h)) = 0$ and $\psi(h) - \phi(h) \leq 0$. This implies $\psi(h) = \phi(h)$ for all h that divide $p - 1$, and in particular $\psi(p - 1) = \phi(p - 1) > 0$. This proves the first part of the theorem.

It is easily seen that $\phi(n)$ is even for $n > 2$. Let $m = 2^f \prod_{i=1}^{k} p_i^{e_i}$ where the p_i are distinct odd primes, $f \geq 0$, $e_i > 0$, and $k \geq 1$. If $(a, m) = 1$ we have $a^{\phi(p_i^{e_i})} \equiv 1 \pmod{p_1^{e_1}}$ and $a^{\phi(m/p_1^{e_1})} \equiv 1 \pmod{m/p_1^{e_1}}$. Suppose that $k \geq 2$ or $f \geq 2$. Then both $\phi(p_1^{e_1})$ and $\phi(m/p_1^{e_1})$ are even, and therefore $a^{\frac{1}{2}\phi(p_1^{e_1})\phi(m/p_1^{e_1})}$ is congruent to 1 modulo $p_1^{e_1}$ and modulo $m/p_1^{e_1}$, hence modulo m. This shows that the only m that can possibly have primitive roots are p^e, $2p^e$, 2 and 4, with p an odd prime.

Consider $m = p^e$ and let a be a primitive root modulo p. Let $b = a + pt$. Then by the binomial theorem,

$$b^{p-1} \equiv a^{p-1} + (p - 1)a^{p-2}pt \pmod{p^2}$$

and we can choose t to make $b^{p-1} = 1 + n_1 p$ with $n_1 \not\equiv 0 \pmod{p}$. Noting that $(1 + np^{j-1})^p \equiv 1 + np^j \pmod{p^{2j-1}}$ we use induction to see that $b^{p^{j-1}(p-1)} = 1 + n_j p^j$ with $n_j \equiv n_{j-1} \pmod{p^{j-1}}$. Then $n_j \equiv n_1 \not\equiv 0 \pmod{p}$. For $e \geq 2$ let b belong to the exponent h modulo p^e. Then $h | p^{e-1}(p - 1)$ and hence $h = p^s d$, $s \leq e - 1$, which implies $b^{p^s(p-1)} \equiv 1 \pmod{p^e}$, $1 + n_{s+1} p^{s+1} \equiv 1 \pmod{p^e}$, and therefore $s \geq e - 1$, $s = e - 1$. We also have $b^d \equiv b^{p^s d} \equiv 1 \pmod{p}$, which implies that $(p - 1) | d$ by Theorem 2.23 since $b \equiv a \pmod{p}$ and a belongs to the exponent $p - 1$. Then we have $h = \phi(p^e)$ and b is a primitive root modulo p^e. Notice that b is independent of e.

Now consider $m = 2p^e$ and let a be a primitive root modulo p^e. Let $b = a$ or $a + p^e$, whichever is odd. Then $b^h \equiv 1 \pmod 2$ for all h, and $b^h \equiv a^h \equiv 1 \pmod{p^e}$ if and only if $p^{e-1}(p - 1) | h$. This implies that b is a primitive root modulo $2p^e$.

Finally, we note that 3 is a primitive root modulo 4.

Theorem 2.26 *Suppose that m has a primitive root g. Then $g^j \equiv g^k \pmod{m}$ if and only if $j \equiv k \pmod{\phi(m)}$; in particular, $g^j \equiv 1 \pmod{m}$ if and only if $\phi(m) | j$. The set $g, g^2, \cdots, g^{\phi(m)}$ forms a reduced residue system modulo m, so that if a is any integer satisfying $(a, m) = 1$, there is one and only one g^j in the set such that $g^j \equiv a \pmod{m}$.*

Proof. The first part of the theorem is a special case of Theorem 2.23. It follows that $g, g^2, \cdots, g^{\phi(m)}$ are incongruent in pairs modulo m, and so this set forms a reduced residue system modulo m.

The exponent j such that $g^j \equiv a \pmod{m}$ is called the *index* of a. The index depends on m and g as well as on a. Indices behave very much like logarithms, and they are sometimes useful as an aid to computation as well as being of theoretical interest.

Theorem 2.27 *If p is a prime and $(a, p) = 1$, then the congruence* $x^n \equiv a \pmod{p}$ *has $(n, p - 1)$ solutions or no solutions according as*

$$a^{(p-1)/(n,p-1)} \equiv 1 \pmod{p} \quad \text{or} \quad a^{(p-1)/(n,p-1)} \not\equiv 1 \pmod{p}.$$

Proof. Let b denote $(n, p - 1)$. If $x^n \equiv a \pmod{p}$ has a solution u, then

$$a^{(p-1)/b} \equiv u^{n(p-1)/b} \equiv u^{(p-1)(n/b)} \equiv 1 \pmod{p}.$$

Therefore $x^n \equiv a \pmod{p}$ has no solution if $a^{(p-1)/b} \not\equiv 1 \pmod{p}$.

Conversely, suppose that $a^{(p-1)/b} \equiv 1 \pmod{p}$. By Theorems 2.25 and 2.26, there is a primitive root g modulo p and an exponent j such that $g^j \equiv a \pmod{p}$. Thus we have

$$g^{j(p-1)/b} \equiv a^{(p-1)/b} \equiv 1 \pmod{p}$$

and this implies that $j(p - 1)/b \equiv 0 \pmod{p - 1}$ by Theorem 2.26, so that $b \mid j$. Now any solution of $x^n \equiv a \pmod{p}$, if any exist, can also be written as a power of g, say g^y, modulo p. Hence the solutions in x, if any, of $x^n \equiv a \pmod{p}$ correspond to the solutions in y of $g^{yn} \equiv g^j \pmod{p}$. This congruence, by Theorem 2.23, has solutions if and only if $yn \equiv j \pmod{p - 1}$ has solutions, which it does by Theorem 2.13 since $b \mid j$. Moreover there are $(n, p - 1)$ solutions by Theorem 2.13, and thus we have $(n, p - 1)$ solutions of $x^n \equiv a \pmod{p}$.

Corollary 2.28 *If p is an odd prime and $(a, p) = 1$ then* $x^2 \equiv a \pmod{p}$ *has two or no solutions according as $a^{(p-1)/2} \equiv 1$ or $-1 \pmod{p}$.*

Proof. From Fermat's theorem we have

$$(a^{(p-1)/2} - 1)(a^{(p-1)/2} + 1) \equiv a^{p-1} - 1 \equiv 0 \pmod{p},$$

and hence $a^{(p-1)/2} \equiv \pm 1 \pmod{p}$.

Problems

1. Find a primitive root of the prime 3; the prime 5; the prime 7; the prime 11; the prime 13.

2. Find a primitive root of 23.

3. How many primitive roots does the prime 13 have?

4. To what exponents do each of 1, 2, 3, 4, 5, 6 belong modulo 7?
   To what exponents do they belong modulo 11?

5. Let p be an odd prime. Prove that a belongs to the exponent 2 modulo p if and only if $a \equiv -1 \pmod{p}$.

6. If a belongs to the exponent h modulo m, prove that no two of a, a^2, a^3, $\cdots$, a^h are congruent modulo m.

7. If p is an odd prime, how many solutions are there to $x^{p-1} \equiv 1 \pmod{p}$; to $x^{p-1} \equiv 2 \pmod{p}$?

8. Prove that 3 is a primitive root of 17 by observing that the powers of 3 are congruent to 3, 9, 10, 13, 5, 15, 11, 16, 14, 8, 7, 4, 12, 2, 6, 1 modulo 17. Then use Theorem 2.27 to decide how many solutions each of the following congruences has:
   (a) $x^{12} \equiv 16 \pmod{17}$ (b) $x^{48} \equiv 9 \pmod{17}$
   (c) $x^{20} \equiv 13 \pmod{17}$ (d) $x^{11} \equiv 9 \pmod{17}$
   Suggestion: $16 \equiv 3^8$, $13 \equiv 3^4 \pmod{17}$.

9. Using the data of the previous problem, decide which of the congruences $x^2 \equiv 1$, $x^2 \equiv 2$, $x^2 \equiv 3$, $\cdots$, $x^2 \equiv 16 \pmod{17}$, have solutions.

10. Prove that if p is a prime and $(a, p) = 1$ and $(n, p - 1) = 1$, then $x^n \equiv a \pmod{p}$ has exactly one solution.

11. Prove that if g is a primitive root modulo p, and if $(k, p - 1) = 1$, then g^k is also a primitive root.

12. Prove that if a belongs to the exponent 3 modulo p, then $1 + a + a^2 \equiv 0 \pmod{p}$, and $1 + a$ belongs to the exponent 6.

13. Prove that if a belongs to the exponent h modulo a prime p, and if h is even, then $a^{h/2} \equiv -1 \pmod{p}$.

14. Prove that if a belongs to an exponent h, and b to an exponent k, modulo m, then ab belongs to an exponent which is a divisor of hk. Furthermore, if $(h, k) = 1$, then ab belongs to the exponent hk modulo m. *Suggestion:* if ab belongs to the exponent r, then

$$1 \equiv (ab)^r \equiv (ab)^{hr} \equiv (a^h)^r b^{hr} \equiv b^{hr} \pmod{m},$$

so that $k \mid hr$.

15. Given that $ab \equiv 1 \pmod{m}$, and that a belongs to the exponent h modulo m, prove that b belongs to the exponent h. Then prove that if $p > 3$, the product of all the primitive roots of p is congruent to 1 modulo p.

16. Let a and $n > 1$ be any integers such that

$$a^{n-1} \equiv 1 \pmod{n} \quad \text{but} \quad a^x \not\equiv 1 \pmod{n}$$

for every proper divisor x of $n - 1$. Prove that n is a prime.

17. For any prime p and any integer a such that $(a, p) = 1$, say that a is a cubic residue of p if $x^3 \equiv a$ (mod p) has at least one solution. Prove that if p is of the form $3k + 2$, then all integers in a reduced residue system modulo p are cubic residues, whereas if p is of the form $3k + 1$, only one-third of the members of a reduced residue system are cubic residues.

18. Prove Wilson's theorem using primitive roots.

19. Let p be an odd prime. Let $r_1, r_2, \cdots, r_{p-1}$ be the integers $1, 2, \cdots, p - 1$ in any order. Prove that at least two of the numbers $1 \cdot r_1, 2 \cdot r_2, \cdots, (p - 1)r_{p-1}$ are congruent modulo p.

The following problems form a related set:

20. Consider the infinite decimal expansion $\alpha = .\alpha_1\alpha_2\alpha_3 \cdots$ to base ten, where the succession of digits is neither all zeros beyond a certain point, nor all nines beyond a certain point. Similarly, let $\beta = .\beta_1\beta_2\beta_3 \cdots$. Prove that $\alpha = \beta$ if and only if $\alpha_j = \beta_j$ for all $j = 1, 2, 3, \cdots$.

21. The decimal expansion of α is said to be periodic if there is a positive integer k and a non-negative integer n_0 such that $\alpha_{n+k} = \alpha_n$ for all integers $n > n_0$. If the decimal expansion of α is periodic, the least integer k that will serve is called the period of α. If $n_0 = 0$ will serve, then the decimal expansion of α is said to be purely periodic. Prove that a real number is rational if and only if its decimal expansion is finite (terminating) or periodic.

22. Let a and b be positive integers with $a < b$ and $(a, b) = 1$. Prove that the decimal expansion of a/b is terminating or has an infinite succession of nines if and only if b is divisible by no primes other than 2 and 5. Prove that the decimal expansion of a/b is purely periodic if and only if b is divisible by neither 2 nor 5.

23. Assuming that $(b, 10) = 1$, let k be the power of 10 to which b belongs. Prove that k is the period of the decimal expansion of a/b. *Suggestion:* $(10^k - 1)a/b$ is an integer.

24. Assuming that $(b, 10) > 1$, write $b = 2^r5^sb_0$ where $(b_0, 10) = 1$. Assume that $b_0 > 1$, and let k_0 be the power of 10 to which k_0 belongs. Write $t = \max(r, s)$. Prove that the period of the decimal expansion of a/b is k_0, and that the length of the nonperiodic block of digits (i.e. the least value of n_0 that will serve in the definition above) is t.

2.10   Number Theory from an Algebraic Viewpoint

In this and the next section we discuss some of the forms in which the elementary concepts of number theory turn up in algebra. The theory of numbers provides a rich source of examples of the structures of abstract algebra. We shall treat briefly three of these structures: groups, rings, and fields.

Before giving the technical definition of a group, let us explain some of the language used. Operations like addition and multiplication are called "binary operations" because two elements are added, or multiplied, to produce a third element. The subtraction of pairs of elements, $a - b$, is likewise a binary operation. So also is exponentiation, a^b, in which the element a is raised to the bth power. Now, a group consists of a set of elements together with a binary operation on those elements, such that certain properties hold. The number theoretic groups with which we deal will have integers or sets of integers as elements, and the operation will be either addition or multiplication. However, a general group can have elements of any sort and any kind of binary operation, just so long as it satisfies the conditions that we shall impose shortly.

We begin with a general binary operation denoted by $\oplus$, and we shall presume that this binary operation is single-valued. This means that for each pair a, b of elements, $a \oplus b$ has a unique value or is not defined. A set of elements is said to be "closed" with respect to an operation $\oplus$, or closed "under" the operation, if $a \oplus b$ is defined and is an element of the set for every pair of elements a, b of the set. For example, the natural numbers 1, 2, 3, $\cdot$ $\cdot$ $\cdot$ are closed under addition but are not closed under subtraction. An element e is said to be an "identity element" of a set with respect to the operation $\oplus$ if the property

$$a \oplus e = e \oplus a = a$$

holds for every element a in the set. In case the elements of the set are numbers, then e is the zero element, $e = 0$, if $\oplus$ is ordinary addition, whereas e is the unity element, $e = 1$, if $\oplus$ is ordinary multiplication. Assuming the existence of an identity element e, an element a is said to have an "inverse," written a^{-1}, if the property

$$a \oplus a^{-1} = a^{-1} \oplus a = e$$

holds. If the elements are numbers and $\oplus$ is ordinary addition, we usually write $a + b$ for $a \oplus b$ and $-a$ for the inverse a^{-1} because the additive inverse is the negative of the number a. On the other hand, if the operation $\oplus$ is ordinary multiplication, we write $a \cdot b$ for $a \oplus b$. In this case the notation a^{-1} is the customary one in elementary algebra for the multiplicative inverse. Here, and throughout this section, the word "number" means any sort of number, integral, rational, real, or complex.

Definition 2.9 *A group G is a set of elements a, b, c, $\cdots$ together with a single-valued binary operation $\oplus$ such that*

(1) *the set is closed under the operation;*
(2) *the associative law holds, namely,*

$$a \oplus (b \oplus c) = (a \oplus b) \oplus c \text{ for all elements } a,\, b,\, c \text{ in } G;$$

(3) *the set has a unique identity element, e;*
(4) *each element in G has a unique inverse in G.*

A group G is called "abelian" or "commutative" if $a \oplus b = b \oplus a$ for every pair of elements a, b in G. A "finite group" is one with a finite number of elements; otherwise it is an "infinite group." If a group is finite, the number of its elements is called the "order" of the group.

Properties 1, 2, 3, and 4 are not the minimum possible postulates for a group. For example, in postulate 4 we could have required merely that each element a have a left inverse, that is an inverse a' such that $a' \oplus a = e$, and then we could prove the other half of postulate 4 as a consequence. However, to avoid too lengthy a discussion of group theory, we leave such refinements to the books on algebra.

The set of all integers 0, ± 1, ± 2, $\cdots$ is a group under addition; in fact it is an abelian group. But the integers are not a group under multiplication because of the absence of inverses for all elements except ± 1.

Another example of a group is obtained by considering congruences modulo m. In case $m = 6$, to give a concrete example, we are familiar with such simple congruences as

$$3 + 4 \equiv 1 \pmod 6, \qquad 5 + 5 \equiv 4 \pmod 6.$$

We get "the additive group modulo 6" by taking a complete residue system, say 0, 1, 2, 3, 4, 5, and replacing congruence modulo 6 by equality:

$$3 + 4 = 1, \qquad 5 + 5 = 4.$$

The complete addition table for this system is:

$\oplus$	0	1	2	3	4	5
0	0	1	2	3	4	5
1	1	2	3	4	5	0
2	2	3	4	5	0	1
3	3	4	5	0	1	2
4	4	5	0	1	2	3
5	5	0	1	2	3	4

Of course, any complete residue system modulo 6 would do just as well; thus 1, 2, 3, 4, 5, 6, or 7, -2, 17, 30, 8, 3, could serve as the elements, provided we perform additions modulo 6. If we were to use the system 7, -2, 17, 30, 8, 3, the addition table would look quite different. However, the two groups are essentially the same; we have just renamed the elements: 0 is now called 30, 1 is 7, and so on. We say that the two groups are "isomorphic," and we do not consider isomorphic groups as being different. Thus we speak of "the" additive group modulo 6, not "an" additive group modulo 6.

Definition 2.10 *Two groups, G with operation $\oplus$ and G′ with operation $\odot$, are said to be isomorphic if there is a one-to-one correspondence between the elements of G and those of G′, such that if a in G corresponds to a′ in G′, and b in G corresponds to b′ in G′, then a $\oplus$ b in G corresponds to a′ $\odot$ b′ in G′.*

Another way of thinking of the additive group modulo 6 is in terms of the so-called residue classes. Put two integers a and b into the same residue class modulo 6 if $a \equiv b \pmod 6$, and the result is to separate all integers into six residue classes:

$$C_0: \cdots, -18, -12, -6, 0, \quad 6, 12, 18, \cdots$$
$$C_1: \cdots, -17, -11, -5, 1, \quad 7, 13, 19, \cdots$$
$$C_2: \cdots, -16, -10, -4, 2, \quad 8, 14, 20, \cdots$$
$$C_3: \cdots, -15, \quad -9, -3, 3, \quad 9, 15, 21, \cdots$$
$$C_4: \cdots, -14, \quad -8, -2, 4, \quad 10, 16, 22, \cdots$$
$$C_5: \cdots, -13, \quad -7, -1, 5, \quad 11, 17, 23, \cdots$$

If any element in class C_2 is added to any element in class C_3, the sum is an element in class C_5, so it is reasonable to write $C_2 + C_3 = C_5$.

Similarly we observe that $C_3 + C_4 = C_1$, $C_5 + C_3 = C_2$, etc., and so we could make up an addition table for these classes. But the addition table so constructed would be simply a repetition of the addition table of the elements 0, 1, 2, 3, 4, 5 modulo 6. Thus the six classes C_0, C_1, C_2, C_3, C_4, C_5 form a group under this addition that is isomorphic to the additive group modulo 6. This residue class formulation of the additive group modulo 6 has the advantage that such a peculiar equation as $5 + 5 = 4$ (in which the symbols have a different meaning than in elementary arithmetic) is replaced by the more reasonable form $C_5 + C_5 = C_4$.

Theorem 2.29 *Any complete residue system modulo m forms a group under addition modulo m. Two complete residue systems modulo m constitute isomorphic groups under addition, and so we speak of "the" additive group modulo m.*

Proof. Let us begin with the complete residue system 0, 1, 2, $\cdots$, $m - 1$ modulo m. This system is closed under addition modulo m, and the associative property of addition is inherited from the corresponding property for all integers, that is $a + (b + c) = (a + b) + c$ implies $a + (b + c) \equiv (a + b) + c \pmod{m}$. The identity element is 0, and it is unique. Finally, the additive inverse of 0 is 0, and the additive inverse of any other element a is $m - a$. These inverses are unique.

Passing from the system 0, 1, $\cdots$, $m - 1$ to any complete residue system $r_0, r_1, \cdots , r_{m-1}$, we observe that all the above observations hold with a replaced by r_a, $a = 0, 1, \cdots , m - 1$, so that we have essentially the same group with new notation.

Problems

1. Which of the following are groups?
    (a) the even integers under addition;
    (b) the odd integers under addition;
    (c) the integers under subtraction;
    (d) the even integers under multiplication;
    (e) all integers which are multiples of 7, under addition;
    (f) all rational numbers under addition (recall that a rational number is one of the form a/b where a and b are integers, with $b \neq 0$);
    (g) the same set as in (f), but under multiplication;

(h) the set as in (f) with the zero element deleted, under multiplication;

(i) all rational numbers a/b having $b = 1$ or $b = 2$, under addition;

(j) all rational numbers a/b having $b = 1$, $b = 2$, or $b = 3$, under addition.

2. Let G have as elements the four pairs $(1, 1)$, $(1, -1)$, $(-1, 1)$, $(-1, -1)$, and let $(a, b) \oplus (c, d) = (ac, bd)$. Prove that G is a group.

3. Using the complete residue system 7, -2, 17, 30, 8, 3, write out the addition table for the additive group modulo 6. Rewrite this table replacing 7 by 1, 30 by 0, etc. Verify that this table gives the same values for $a \oplus b$ as the one in the text.

4. Prove that the set of elements e, a, b, c, with the following table for the binary operation,

$\oplus$	e	a	b	c
e	e	a	b	c
a	a	e	c	b
b	b	c	a	e
c	c	b	e	a

is a group. Prove that this group is isomorphic to the additive group modulo 4.

5. Prove that the set of elements e, u, v, w, with the following table for tne binary operation,

$\oplus$	e	u	v	w
e	e	u	v	w
u	u	e	w	v
v	v	w	e	u
w	w	v	u	e

is a group. Prove that this group is not isomorphic to the additive group modulo 4, but that it is isomorphic to the group described in Problem 2.

6. Prove that the set of elements 1, 2, 3, 4, under the operation of multiplication modulo 5, is a group which is isomorphic to the group in Problem 4.

7. Prove that the set of complex numbers $+1$, -1, $+i$, $-i$, where $i^2 = -1$, is a group under multiplication and that it is isomorphic to the group in Problem 4.

8. Prove that the isomorphism property is "transitive," that is, if a group G_1 is isomorphic to G_2, and if G_2 is isomorphic to G_3, then G_1 is isomorphic to G_3.

9. Prove that the elements 1, 3, 5, 7 under multiplication modulo 8 form a group which is isomorphic to the group in Problem 5.

10. Prove that there are essentially only two groups of order 4, that is that any group of order 4 is isomorphic to one of the groups in Problems 4 and 5.

11. For any positive integer $m > 1$, separate all integers into classes C_0, C_1, $\cdots$, C_{m-1}, putting integers r and s into the same class if $r \equiv s$ (mod m), thus

$$C_0: \cdots, \ -2m, \ -m, \ 0, \ m, \ 2m, \ \cdots$$
$$C_1: \cdots, \ -2m + 1, \ -m + 1, \ 1, \ m + 1, \ 2m + 1, \ \cdots$$
etc.

Prove that if any two integers, one from class C_a and one from class C_b, are added, the sum is always an integer in a unique class, namely, either C_{a+b} or C_{a+b-m} according as $a + b < m$ or $a + b \geq m$. Define the sum $C_a + C_b = C_{a+b}$ or $C_a + C_b = C_{a+b-m}$ accordingly, and prove that these classes form a group under this addition. Prove that this group is isomorphic to the additive group modulo m.

2.11   Multiplicative Groups, Rings, and Fields

Theorem 2.30 *Let $m > 1$ be a positive integer. Any reduced residue system modulo m is a group under multiplication modulo m. The group is of order $\phi(m)$. Any two such groups are isomorphic, and so we speak of "the multiplicative group modulo m".*

Proof. Let us consider any reduced residue system $r_1, r_2, \cdots, r_n$ where $n = \phi(m)$. This set is closed under multiplication modulo m by Theorem 1.8. The associative property of multiplication is inherited from the corresponding property for integers, because $a(bc) = (ab)c$ implies that $a(bc) \equiv (ab)c$ (mod m). The reduced residue system contains one element, say r_j, such that $r_j \equiv 1$ (mod m), and this is clearly the unique identity element of the group. Finally, for each r_j, the congruence $xr_i \equiv r_j$ (mod m) has a solution by Theorem 2.13, and this solution is unique within the reduced residue system $r_1, r_2, \cdots, r_n$. Two different reduced residue systems modulo m are congruent, element by element, modulo m, and so we have an isomorphism between the two groups.

Notation. We have been using the symbol $\oplus$ for the binary operation of the group, and we have found that in particular groups $\oplus$ may represent addition or multiplication or some other operation. In dealing with general groups it is convenient to drop the symbol $\oplus$, just as the dot representing ordinary multiplication is usually omitted in algebra. We will write ab for $a \oplus b$, abc for $a \oplus (b \oplus c) = (a \oplus b) \oplus c$, a^2 for $a \oplus a$, a^3 for $a \oplus (a \oplus a)$, etc. Also, $abcd$ can be written for $(a \oplus b \oplus c) \oplus d = (a \oplus b) \oplus (c \oplus d)$ etc., as can be seen by applying induction to the associative law. We will even use the word multiplication for the operation $\oplus$, but it must be remembered that we do not mean the ordinary multiplication of arithmetic. In fact we are dealing with general groups so that a is not a number, it is just an abstract element of a group. It is convenient to write a^0 for e, a^{-2} for $(a^{-1})^2$, a^{-3} for $(a^{-1})^3$, etc. It is not difficult to show that the usual laws of exponents are valid under this definition.

Theorem 2.31 *In any group G, $ab = ac$ implies $b = c$. If a is any element of a finite group G with identity element e, then there is a (unique) smallest positive integer r such that $a^r = e$.*

Proof. The first part of the theorem is established by multiplying $ab = ac$ on the left by a^{-1}, thus $a^{-1}(ab) = a^{-1}(ac)$, $(a^{-1}a)b = (a^{-1}a)c$, $eb = ec$, $b = c$. To prove the second part, consider the series of elements obtained by repeated multiplication by a,

$$e, a, a^2, a^3, a^4, \cdots .$$

Since the group is finite, and since the members of this series are elements of the group, there must occur a repetition of the form $a^s = a^t$ with, say, $s < t$. But this equation can be written in the form $a^s e = a^s a^{t-s}$, whence $a^{t-s} = e$. Thus there is some positive integer, $t - s$, such that $a^{t-s} = e$ and the smallest positive exponent with this property is the value of r in the theorem.

Definition 2.11 *Let G be any group, finite or infinite, and a an element of G. If $a^s = e$ for some positive integer s, then a is said to be of finite order. If a is of finite order, the order of a is the smallest positive integer r such that $a^r = e$. If there is no positive integer s such that $a^s = e$, then a is said to be of infinite order. A group G is said to be cyclic if it contains an element a such that the powers of a*

$$\cdots , a^{-3}, a^{-2}, a^{-1}, a^0 = e, a, a^2, a^3, \cdots$$

comprise the whole group; such an element a is said to generate the group and is called a generator.

Theorem 2.31 shows that all the elements of a finite group are of finite order. Every group, finite or infinite, contains at least the single element e that is of finite order. There are infinite groups consisting entirely of elements of finite order.

If a cyclic group is finite, and has generator a, then the group consists of $e, a, a^2, a^3, \cdots, a^{r-1}$, where r is the order of the element a. All other powers of a are superfluous because they merely repeat these.

Theorem 2.32 *The order of an element of a finite group G is a divisor of the order of the group. If the order of the group is denoted by n, then $a^n = e$.*

Proof. Let the element a have order r. It is easily seen that

(A) $\qquad\qquad\qquad e, a, a^2, a^3, \cdots, a^{r-1}$

are r distinct elements of G. If these r elements do not exhaust the group, there is some other element, say b_2. Then we can prove that

(B) $\qquad\qquad\qquad b_2, b_2a, b_2a^2, b_2a^3, \cdots, b_2a^{r-1}$

are r distinct elements, all different from the r elements of A. For in the first place if $b_2a^s = b_2a^t$, then $a^s = a^t$ by Theorem 2.31. And on the other hand, if $b_2a^s = a^t$, then $b_2 = a^{t-s}$, so that b_2 would be among the powers of a.

If G is not exhausted by the sets A and B, then there is another element b_3 which gives rise to r new elements

$$b_3, b_3a, b_3a^2, b_3a^3, \cdots, b_3a^{r-1},$$

all different from the elements in A and B, by a similar argument. This process of obtaining new elements $b_2, b_3, \cdots$ must terminate since G is finite. So if the last batch of new elements is, say

$$b_k, b_ka, b_ka^2, b_ka^3, \cdots, b_ka^{r-1},$$

then the order of the group G is kr, and the first part of the theorem is proved. To prove the second part, we observe that $n = kr$ and $a^r = e$ by Theorem 2.31, whence $a^n = e$.

It can be noted that Theorem 2.32 implies the theorems of Fermat and Euler, where the set of integers relatively prime to the modulus m is taken as the group. In making this implication, the reader will see the necessity of "translating" the language and notation of group theory into that of number theory. In the same way we note that the language of Definition 2.7, that "a belongs to the exponent h modulo m", is translated into group theoretic language as "the element a of the multiplicative group modulo m has order h". Also the "primitive root modulo m" of Definition 2.8 is called a "generator" of the multiplicative group modulo m in group theory.

Definition 2.12 *A ring is a set of at least two elements with two binary operations, $\oplus$ and $\odot$, such that it is a commutative group under $\oplus$, is closed under $\odot$, and such that $\odot$ is associative and distributive with respect to $\oplus$. The identity element with respect to $\oplus$ is called the "zero" of the ring. If all the elements of a ring, other than the zero, form a commutative group under $\odot$, then it is called a field.*

It is customary to call $\oplus$ addition and $\odot$ multiplication and to write $a + b$ for $a \oplus b$, ab for $a \odot b$. The conditions on $\odot$ for a ring are then $a(bc) = (ab)c$, $a(b + c) = ab + ac$, $(b + c)a = ba + ca$. In general, the elements a, b, c, $\cdots$ are not numbers, and the operations of addition and multiplication are not the ordinary ones of arithmetic. However, the only rings and fields that will be considered here will have numbers for elements, and the operations will either be ordinary addition and multiplication, or addition and multiplication modulo m.

Theorem 2.33 *The set I_m of elements $0, 1, 2, \cdots, m - 1$, with addition and multiplication defined modulo m, is a ring for any integer $m > 1$. Such a ring is a field if and only if m is a prime.*

Proof. We have already seen in Theorem 2.29 that any complete residue system modulo m is a group under addition modulo m. This group is commutative, and the associative and distributive properties of multiplication modulo m are inherited from the corresponding properties for ordinary multiplication. Therefore I_m is a ring.

Next, by Theorem 2.30 any reduced residue system modulo m is a group under multiplication modulo m. If m is a prime p, the reduced residue system of I_p is $1, 2, \cdots, p - 1$, that is, all the elements of I_p other than 0. Since 0 is the zero of the ring, I_p is a field. On the other hand if m is not a prime, then m is of the form ab with $1 < a \leqq b < m$. Then the elements of I_m other than 0 do not form a group under multiplication modulo m because there is no inverse for the element a, no solution of $ax \equiv 1 \pmod{m}$. Thus I_m is not a field.

Problems

1. Prove that the multiplicative group modulo 9 is isomorphic to the additive group modulo 6.
2. Prove that the additive group modulo m is cyclic with 1 as generator. Prove that any one of $\phi(m)$ elements could serve as generator.
3. Prove that any two cyclic groups of order m are isomorphic.
4. Prove that the group of all integers under addition is an infinite cyclic group.
5. If a is an element of order r of a group G, prove that $a^k = e$ if and only if $r|k$.
6. What is the smallest positive integer m such that the multiplicative group modulo m is not cyclic?
7. A subgroup S of a group G is a subset of elements of G which form a group under the same binary operation. If G is finite, prove that the order of a subgroup S is a divisor of the order of G.
8. Prove Theorem 2.32 in a manner analogous to the proof of Theorem 2.8.
9. Prove Theorem 2.8 by the method used in the proof of Theorem 2.32.
10. Let G consist of all possible sequences $(a_1, a_2, a_1, \cdot \cdot \cdot)$ with each $a_i = 1$ or -1. Let $(a_1, a_2, a_3, \cdot \cdot \cdot) \oplus (b_1, b_2, b_3, \cdot \cdot \cdot) = (a_1b_1, a_2b_2, a_3b_3, \cdot \cdot \cdot)$. Show that G is an infinite group all of whose elements are of finite order.
11. Let G consist of a, b, c, d, e, f and let $\oplus$ be defined by the following table.

$\oplus$	e	a	b	c	d	f
e	e	a	b	c	d	f
a	a	e	d	f	b	c
b	b	f	e	d	c	a
c	c	d	f	e	a	b
d	d	c	a	b	f	e
f	f	b	c	a	e	d

Show that G is a noncommutative group.
12. Prove that the multiplicative group modulo p is cyclic if p is a prime.
13. Exhibit the addition and multiplication tables for the elements of the field of residues modulo 7.
14. Prove that the set of all integers under ordinary addition and multiplication is a ring but not a field.
15. Prove that the set of all even integers under ordinary addition and multiplication is a ring.

16. Prove that the set 0, 3, 6, 9 is a ring under addition and multiplication modulo 12.

17. Prove that in any field $a0 = 0a = 0$ for every element a.

18. Let a be a divisor of m, say $m = aq$ with $1 < a < m$. Prove that the set of elements 0, a, $2a$, $3a$, $\cdots$, $(q - 1)a$, with addition and multiplication modulo m, forms a ring. Under what circumstances is it a field?

19. Prove that the set of all rational numbers forms a field.

20. Prove that the set of all rational functions $f(x)/g(x)$, where $f(x)$ and $g(x)$ are polynomials with integral coefficients, and $g(x) \not\equiv 0$, forms a field.

21. If x, y, z, are any numbers, real or complex, the cancellation law states that $xy = xz$ implies $y = z$ if $x \neq 0$. There is a "weak" cancellation law that states that $x^2 y = x^2 z$ implies $xy = xz$ whether x is zero or not. Consider the set of all integers modulo m with multiplication modulo m, $m > 1$. Show that the cancellation law holds if and only if m is a prime, and that the "weak" law holds if and only if m is a square-free, that is m is a product of distinct primes.

22. Consider the system of all integers modulo m under multiplication modulo m, $m > 1$. Show that:
    (a) It is not a group.
    (b) It is associative.
    (c) It is commutative.
    (d) It is closed.
    (e) It has a unique unity—an element u such that $ux = x$ for all x.
    (f) It has a unique zero—an element z such that $zx = z$ for all x.

23. For $m = 30$ find all idempotent elements (x such that $x^2 = x$). Also find the elements w such that $wx = z$, the zero element, for some $x \neq z$.

24. An integral domain is a ring with the following additional properties: (i) there is a unique identity element with respect to multiplication; (ii) multiplication is commutative; (iii) if $ab = ac$ and $a \neq 0$, then $b = c$. Prove that any field is an integral domain. Which of the following are integral domains?
    (a) the set of all integers;
    (b) the set I_m of Theorem 2.33;
    (c) the set $F[x]$ of all polynomials in a variable or indeterminate x, with coefficients in a field F.

25. Let m be a positive integer and consider the set of all the divisors of m. For numbers in this set define two operations $\odot$ and $\oplus$ as $a \odot b = (a, b)$, $a \oplus b = [a, b]$, g.c.d. and l.c.m. Prove that $\odot$ and $\oplus$ are associative and commutative. Prove the distributive law $a \odot (b \oplus c) = (a \odot b) \oplus (a \odot c)$

and its dual $a \oplus (b \odot c) = (a \oplus b) \odot (a \oplus c)$. Show that $a \odot a = a \oplus a = a$. Also prove $1 \odot a = 1$ and $1 \oplus a = a$, so that 1 behaves like an ordinary zero, and $m \odot a = a$, and $m \oplus a = m$. Define a relation $\oslash$ as $a \oslash b$ if $a \odot b = a$. Prove $a \oslash a$, that $\oslash$ is transitive, and that $a \oslash b$ if and only if $a \oplus b = b$.

Prove that if m is not divisible by any square other than 1, then corresponding to each divisor a there is a divisor a' such that $a \odot a' = 1$, $a \oplus a' = m$. (These algebras with square-free m are examples of Boolean algebras.)

Chapter 3

Quadratic Reciprocity

3.1 Quadratic Residues

Definition 3.1 *For all a such that $(a, m) = 1$, a is called a quadratic residue modulo m if the congruence $x^2 \equiv a \pmod{m}$ has a solution. If it has no solution, then a is called a quadratic nonresidue modulo m.*

Since $a + m$ is a quadratic residue or nonresidue modulo m according as a is or is not, we consider as distinct residues or nonresidues only those that are distinct modulo m. The quadratic residues modulo 5 are 1 and 4, whereas 2 and 3 are the nonresidues.

Definition 3.2 *If p denotes an odd prime and $(a, p) = 1$, the Legendre symbol $\left(\dfrac{a}{p}\right)$ is defined to be 1 if a is a quadratic residue, -1 if a is a quadratic nonresidue modulo p.*

Theorem 3.1 *Let p be an odd prime and let a and b denote integers relatively prime to p. Then*

(a) $\left(\dfrac{a}{p}\right) \equiv a^{(p-1)/2} \pmod{p}$,

(b) $\left(\dfrac{a}{p}\right)\left(\dfrac{b}{p}\right) = \left(\dfrac{ab}{p}\right)$,

(c) $a \equiv b \pmod{p}$ *implies that* $\left(\dfrac{a}{p}\right) = \left(\dfrac{b}{p}\right)$,

(d) $\left(\dfrac{a^2}{p}\right) = 1$, $\left(\dfrac{1}{p}\right) = 1$, $\left(\dfrac{-1}{p}\right) = (-1)^{(p-1)/2}$.

69

Proof. Part (*a*) of the theorem follows from Corollary 2.28. The remaining parts are all simple consequences of part (*a*). Part (*a*) can also be proved without the use of Corollary 2.28. If $\left(\dfrac{a}{p}\right) = 1$, then $x^2 \equiv a \pmod{p}$ has a solution, say x_0. Then, by Theorem 2.7,

$$a^{(p-1)/2} \equiv x_0^{p-1} \equiv 1 \equiv \left(\frac{a}{p}\right) \pmod{p}.$$

On the other hand, if $\left(\dfrac{a}{p}\right) \equiv -1$, then $x^2 \equiv a \pmod{p}$ has no solution, and we proceed as in the proof of Theorem 2.10. To each j satisfying $1 \leq j \leq p - 1$ we associate the unique integer i such that $ji \equiv a \pmod{p}$, $0 \leq i \leq p - 1$. We see that $i = 0$ is impossible and that the associate of i is j. Since $x^2 \equiv a \pmod{p}$ has no solution, no integer j is associated with itself. Thus the integers $1, 2, \cdots, p - 1$, can be paired off, j and its associate i, and $ji \equiv a \pmod{p}$. There are $(p - 1)/2$ pairs. Multiplying all these pairs together we get $(p - 1)! \equiv a^{(p-1)/2} \pmod{p}$. Using Theorem 2.10 we obtain $a^{(p-1)/2} \equiv -1 \equiv \left(\dfrac{a}{p}\right) \pmod{p}$.

Theorem 3.2 *Lemma of Gauss. Let p be an odd prime and let $(a, p) = 1$. Consider the integers $a, 2a, 3a, \cdots, \{(p - 1)/2\}a$ and their least nonnegative residues modulo p. If n denotes the number of these residues that exceed $\dfrac{p}{2}$, then $\left(\dfrac{a}{p}\right) = (-1)^n$.*

Proof. Let $r_1, r_2, \cdots, r_n$ denote the residues that exceed $p/2$, and let $s_1, s_2, \cdots, s_k$ denote the remaining residues. The r_i and s_i are all distinct, and none is zero. Furthermore $n + k = (p - 1)/2$. Now $0 < p - r_i < p/2$, $i = 1, 2, \cdots, n$, and the numbers $p - r_i$ are distinct. Also no $p - r_i$ is an s_j for if $p - r_i = s_j$ then $r_i \equiv \rho a$, $s_j \equiv \sigma a$, for some ρ, σ, $1 \leq \rho \leq (p - 1)/2$, $1 \leq \sigma \leq (p - 1)/2$, and $p - \rho a \equiv \sigma a \pmod{p}$. Since $(a, p) = 1$ this implies $a(\rho + \sigma) \equiv 0$, $\rho + \sigma \equiv 0 \pmod{p}$, which is impossible. Thus $p - r_1, p - r_2, \cdots, p - r_n$, $s_1, s_2, \cdots, s_k$ are all distinct, are all at least 1 and less than $p/2$, and they are $n + k = (p - 1)/2$ in number. That is, they are just the integers $1, 2, \cdots, (p - 1)/2$ in some order. Multiplying them together we have

$$(p - r_1)(p - r_2) \cdots (p - r_n)s_1 s_2 \cdots s_k = 1 \cdot 2 \cdots \frac{p - 1}{2}$$

and then

$$(-r_1)(-r_2) \cdots (-r_n)s_1 s_2 \cdots s_k \equiv 1 \cdot 2 \cdots \frac{p - 1}{2} \pmod{p},$$

$$(-1)^n r_1 r_2 \cdots r_n s_1 s_2 \cdots s_k \equiv 1 \cdot 2 \cdots \frac{p - 1}{2} \pmod{p},$$

$$(-1)^n a \cdot 2a \cdot 3a \cdots \frac{p - 1}{2} a \equiv 1 \cdot 2 \cdots \frac{p - 1}{2} \pmod{p}.$$

We can cancel the factors $2, 3, \cdots, (p - 1)/2$ to obtain $(-1)^n a^{(p-1)/2} \equiv 1 \pmod{p}$ which gives us $(-1)^n \equiv a^{(p-1)/2} \equiv \left(\dfrac{a}{p} \right) \pmod{p}$ by Theorem 3.1a.

Definition 3.3 *For real x, the symbol $[x]$ denotes the greatest integer less than or equal to x.*

For example, $[15/2] = 7$, $[-15/2] = -8$, $[-15] = -15$.

Theorem 3.3 *If p is an odd prime and $(a, 2p) = 1$, then*

$$\left(\frac{a}{p} \right) = (-1)^t \quad where \quad t = \sum_{j=1}^{(p-1)/2} \left[\frac{ja}{p} \right], \quad and \quad \left(\frac{2}{p} \right) = (-1)^{(p^2-1)/8}.$$

Proof. We use the same notation as in the proof of Theorem 3.2. The r_i and s_i are just the least positive remainders obtained on dividing the integers ja by p, $j = 1, 2, \cdots, (p - 1)/2$. The quotient in this division is easily seen to be $q = [ja/p]$. Then for $(a, p) = 1$, whether a is odd or even, we have

$$\sum_{j=1}^{(p-1)/2} ja = \sum_{j=1}^{(p-1)/2} p \left[\frac{ja}{p} \right] + \sum_{j=1}^{n} r_j + \sum_{j=1}^{k} s_j$$

and

$$\sum_{j=1}^{(p-1)/2} j = \sum_{j=1}^{n} (p - r_j) + \sum_{j=1}^{k} s_j = np - \sum_{j=1}^{n} r_j + \sum_{j=1}^{k} s_j$$

and hence by subtraction,

$$(a - 1) \sum_{j=1}^{(p-1)/2} j = p\left(\sum_{j=1}^{(p-1)/2} \left[\frac{ja}{p}\right] - n \right) + 2 \sum_{j=1}^{n} r_j.$$

But

$$\sum_{j=1}^{(p-1)/2} j = \frac{p^2 - 1}{8}$$

so we have

$$(a - 1) \frac{p^2 - 1}{8} \equiv \sum_{j=1}^{(p-1)/2} \left[\frac{ja}{p}\right] - n \pmod 2.$$

If a is odd, this implies $n \equiv \sum_{j=1}^{(p-1)/2} \left[\frac{ja}{p}\right] \pmod 2$. If $a = 2$ it implies $n \equiv (p^2 - 1)/8 \pmod 2$ since $[2j/p] = 0$ for $1 \le j \le (p - 1)/2$. Our theorem now follows by Theorem 3.2.

Problems

1. Find $[3/2]$, $[-3/2]$, $[\pi]$, $[-7]$, $[x]$ for $0 \le x < 1$.
2. With reference to the notation of Theorem 1.2 prove that $q = [b/a]$.
3. Prove that 3 is a quadratic residue of 13, but a quadratic nonresidue of 7.
4. Find the values of $\left(\dfrac{a}{p}\right)$ in each of the 12 cases, $a = -1$, 2, -2, 3 and $p = 11$, 13, 17.
5. Prove that the quadratic residues of 11 are 1, 3, 4, 5, 9, and list all solutions of each of the ten congruences $x^2 \equiv a \pmod{11}$ and $x^2 \equiv a \pmod{11^2}$ where $a = 1$, 3, 4, 5, 9.
6. List the quadratic residues of each of the primes 7, 13, 17, 29, 37.
7. Which of the following congruences have solutions? How many?
    (a) $x^2 \equiv 2 \pmod{61}$ (b) $x^2 \equiv 2 \pmod{59}$
    (c) $x^2 \equiv -2 \pmod{61}$ (d) $x^2 \equiv -2 \pmod{59}$
    (e) $x^2 \equiv 2 \pmod{122}$ (f) $x^2 \equiv 2 \pmod{118}$
    (g) $x^2 \equiv -2 \pmod{122}$ (h) $x^2 \equiv -2 \pmod{118}$.

8. How many solutions are there to each of the congruences:

   (a) $x^2 \equiv -1 \pmod{61}$ (b) $x^2 \equiv -1 \pmod{59}$

   (c) $x^2 \equiv -1 \pmod{365}$ (d) $x^2 \equiv -1 \pmod{3599}$

   (e) $x^2 \equiv -1 \pmod{122}$ (f) $x^2 \equiv -1 \pmod{244}$.

9. Let p be a prime, and let $(a, p) = (b, p) = 1$. Prove that if $x^2 \equiv a \pmod{p}$ and $x^2 \equiv b \pmod{p}$ are not solvable, then $x^2 \equiv ab \pmod{p}$ is solvable.

10. Prove that if p is an odd prime then $x^2 \equiv 2 \pmod{p}$ has solutions if and only if $p \equiv 1$ or $7 \pmod 8$.

11. Denote quadratic residues by r, nonresidues by n. Prove that $r_1 r_2$ and $n_1 n_2$ are residues and that rn is a nonresidue for a prime p. Show that there are $(p - 1)/2$ quadratic residues and $(p - 1)/2$ nonresidues for an odd prime p.

12. Let g be a primitive root of an odd prime p. Prove that the quadratic residues modulo p are congruent to $g^2, g^4, g^6, \cdots, g^{p-1}$, and the non-residues are congruent to $g, g^3, g^5, g^7, \cdots, g^{p-2}$.

13. Prove that if r is a quadratic residue modulo m, then $r^{\phi(m)/2} \equiv 1 \pmod m$. *Suggestion:* use the fact that there is some integer a such that $r \equiv a^2 \pmod m$.

14. Show that if a is a quadratic residue modulo m, and $ab \equiv 1 \pmod m$, then b is also a quadratic residue. Then prove that the product of the quadratic residues modulo p is congruent to $+1$ or -1 according as the prime p is of the form $4k + 3$ or $4k + 1$.

15. Prove that if p is a prime having the form $4k + 3$, and if m is the number of quadratic residues less than $p/2$, then $1 \cdot 3 \cdot 5 \cdots (p - 2) \equiv (-1)^{m+k+1} \pmod p$, and $2 \cdot 4 \cdot 6 \cdots (p - 1) \equiv (-1)^{m+k} \pmod p$.

16. Prove that the quadratic residues modulo p are congruent to $1^2, 2^2, 3^2,$ $\cdots, \{(p - 1)/2\}^2$. Hence prove that if $p > 3$, the sum of the quadratic residues is divisible by p.

17. For all primes p prove that $x^8 \equiv 16 \pmod p$ is solvable. *Suggestion:* use Theorem 2.27.

18. Let p be an odd prime. Prove that if there is an integer x such that

$$\begin{aligned}
p\,|\,(x^2 + 1) \quad &\text{then} \quad p \equiv 1 \pmod 4; \\
p\,|\,(x^2 - 2) \quad &\text{then} \quad p \equiv 1 \text{ or } 7 \pmod 8; \\
p\,|\,(x^2 + 2) \quad &\text{then} \quad p \equiv 1 \text{ or } 3 \pmod 8; \\
p\,|\,(x^4 + 1) \quad &\text{then} \quad p \equiv 1 \pmod 8.
\end{aligned}$$

Show that there are infinitely many primes of each of the forms $8n + 1$, $8n + 3$, $8n + 5$, $8n + 7$. *Suggestion:* use Theorem 2.27 for the case $p\,|\,(x^4 + 1)$.

3.2 Quadratic Reciprocity

Theorem 3.4 *The Gaussian reciprocity law. If p and q are distinct odd primes, then*

$$\left(\frac{p}{q}\right)\left(\frac{q}{p}\right) = (-1)^{\frac{(p-1)}{2}\frac{(q-1)}{2}}.$$

Proof. Let S be the set of all pairs of integers (x, y) satisfying $1 \leq x \leq (p-1)/2, 1 \leq y \leq (q-1)/2$. The set S has $(p-1)(q-1)/4$ members. Separate this set into two mutually exclusive subsets S_1 and S_2 according as $qx > py$ or $qx < py$. Note that there are no pairs (x, y) in S such that $qx = py$. The set S_1 can be described as the set of all pairs (x, y) such that $1 \leq x \leq (p-1)/2, 1 \leq y < qx/p$. The number of pairs in S_1 is then seen to be $\sum_{x=1}^{(p-1)/2} [qx/p]$. Similarly S_2 consists of the pairs (x, y) such that $1 \leq y \leq (q-1)/2, 1 \leq x < py/q$, and the number of pairs in S_2 is $\sum_{y=1}^{(q-1)/2} [py/q]$. Thus we have

$$\sum_{j=1}^{(p-1)/2} \left[\frac{qj}{p}\right] + \sum_{j=1}^{(q-1)/2} \left[\frac{pj}{q}\right] = \frac{p-1}{2}\frac{q-1}{2}$$

and hence

$$\left(\frac{p}{q}\right)\left(\frac{q}{p}\right) = (-1)^{\{(p-1)/2\}\{(q-1)/2\}}$$

by Theorem 3.3.

This theorem, together with Theorem 3.1 and the second part of Theorem 3.3, makes the computation of $\left(\frac{a}{p}\right)$ fairly simple. For example, we have

$$\left(\frac{-42}{61}\right) = \left(\frac{-1}{61}\right)\left(\frac{2}{61}\right)\left(\frac{3}{61}\right)\left(\frac{7}{61}\right),$$

$$\left(\frac{-1}{61}\right) = (-1)^{60/2} = 1,$$

$$\left(\frac{2}{61}\right) = (-1)^{(61^2-1)/8} = -1,$$

$$\left(\frac{3}{61}\right) = \left(\frac{61}{3}\right)(-1)^{(2/2)(60/2)} = \left(\frac{1}{3}\right) = 1,$$

$$\left(\frac{7}{61}\right) = \left(\frac{61}{7}\right)(-1)^{(6/2)(60/2)} = \left(\frac{5}{7}\right) = \left(\frac{7}{5}\right)(-1)^{(4/2)(6/2)} = \left(\frac{2}{5}\right)$$

$$= (-1)^{24/8} = -1$$

Hence $\left(\dfrac{-42}{61}\right) = 1$. This computation demonstrates a number of differ-

ent sorts of steps; it was chosen for this purpose and is not the shortest possible. A shorter way is

$$\left(\frac{-42}{61}\right) = \left(\frac{19}{61}\right) = \left(\frac{61}{19}\right) \cdot 1 = \left(\frac{4}{19}\right) = 1.$$

One could also obtain the value of $\left(\dfrac{-42}{61}\right)$ by use of Theorem 3.2

or the first part of Theorem 3.3, but the computation would be con-siderably longer.

There is another kind of problem that is of some importance. As an example, let us find all odd primes p such that 3 is a quadratic residue modulo p. We have

$$\left(\frac{3}{p}\right) = \left(\frac{p}{3}\right)(-1)^{(p-1)/2},$$

$$\left(\frac{p}{3}\right) = \begin{cases} \left(\dfrac{1}{3}\right) = 1 \text{ if } p \equiv 1 \pmod 3 \\ \left(\dfrac{2}{3}\right) = -1 \text{ if } p \equiv 2 \pmod 3, \end{cases}$$

and

$$(-1)^{(p-1)/2} = \begin{cases} 1 \text{ if } p \equiv 1 \pmod 4 \\ -1 \text{ if } p \equiv 3 \pmod 4. \end{cases}$$

Thus $\left(\dfrac{3}{p}\right) = 1$ if and only if $p \equiv 1 \pmod 3$, $p \equiv 1 \pmod 4$, or $p \equiv 2 \pmod 3$, $p \equiv 3 \pmod 4$; that is $p \equiv 1$ or $11 \pmod{12}$.

Results of this type are sometimes useful if one is trying to determine whether or not a certain number is a prime. Consider the number 9997. We might notice that $9997 = 100^2 - 3$, so that $3 \equiv 100^2 \pmod{p}$ if $p | 9997$. That is, either $p = 3$ or $\left(\dfrac{3}{p}\right) = 1$. Since $3 \nmid 9997$ we have $\left(\dfrac{3}{p}\right) = 1$, and hence $p \equiv 1$ or $11 \pmod{12}$. We need test only p such that $p \le \sqrt{9997}$. If we list the numbers 1, 13, 25, $\cdots$, 97, and 11, 23, 35, $\cdots$, 95, we can delete 1 and all composite numbers, and we find just eleven primes that must be tested. It will be found that 13 divides 9997 and that $9997 = 13 \cdot 769$. Is 769 a prime? If $p | 769$ then $p | 9997$ and it will be in our list. The only p in our list such that $p \le \sqrt{769}$ are 13, 11, and 23. None of these divides 769, and hence 769 is a prime.

Problems

1. In the preceding example why was it unnecessary to test any primes $p > \sqrt{9997}$?
2. Prove that if p and q are primes of the form $4k + 3$, and if $x^2 \equiv p \pmod{q}$ has no solutions, then $x^2 \equiv q \pmod{p}$ has two solutions.
3. Prove that if a prime p is a quadratic residue of an odd prime q, and p is of the form $4k + 1$, then q is a quadratic residue of p.
4. Which of the following congruences are solvable?
    (a) $x^2 \equiv 5 \pmod{227}$ 　　　(b) $x^2 \equiv 5 \pmod{229}$
    (c) $x^2 \equiv -5 \pmod{227}$ 　　(d) $x^2 \equiv -5 \pmod{229}$
    (e) $x^2 \equiv 7 \pmod{1009}$ 　　(f) $x^2 \equiv -7 \pmod{1009}$
    (Note that 227, 229, and 1009 are primes.)
5. Find the values of $\left(\dfrac{p}{q}\right)$ in the nine cases obtained from all combinations of $p = 7, 11, 13$ and $q = 227, 229, 1009$.
6. Decide whether $x^2 \equiv 150 \pmod{1009}$ is solvable or not.
7. Find all primes p such that $x^2 \equiv 11 \pmod{p}$ has a solution.
8. Find all primes p such that $\left(\dfrac{10}{p}\right) = 1$.
9. Find all primes p such that $\left(\dfrac{5}{p}\right) = -1$.

10. Of which primes is -2 a quadratic residue?

11. If a is a quadratic nonresidue of each of the odd primes p and q, is $x^2 \equiv a \pmod{pq}$ solvable?

12. In the proof of Theorem 3.4 consider the pairs (x, y) as points in a plane. Let O, A, B, C denote the points $(0, 0)$, $(p/2, 0)$ $(p/2, q/2)$, $(0, q/2)$, respectively, and draw the lines OA, OB, OC, AB, and BC. Repeat the proof of Theorem 3.4 using geometrical language—pairs of points, etc.

13. Prove that there are infinitely many primes of each of the forms $3n + 1$ and $3n - 1$. *Suggestion:* first determine the primes p such that $\left(\dfrac{-3}{p}\right) = 1$.

3.3 The Jacobi Symbol

Definition 3.4 *Let* $(P, Q) = 1, Q > 0, Q$ *odd, so that* $Q = q_1 q_2 \cdots q_s$ *where the* q_i *are odd primes, not necessarily distinct. Then the Jacobi symbol* $\left(\dfrac{P}{Q}\right)$ *is defined by*

$$\left(\frac{P}{Q}\right) = \prod_{j=1}^{s} \left(\frac{P}{q_j}\right)$$

where $\left(\dfrac{P}{q_j}\right)$ *is the Legendre symbol.*

If Q is an odd prime, the Jacobi symbol and Legendre symbol are indistinguishable. However, this can cause no confusion since their values are the same in this case. Clearly $\left(\dfrac{P}{Q}\right) = \pm 1$ but it is not true that $\left(\dfrac{P}{Q}\right) = 1$ implies that P is a quadratic residue modulo Q. For example, $\left(\dfrac{2}{9}\right) = 1$ but $x^2 \equiv 2 \pmod 9$ has no solution. A number a is a quadratic residue modulo Q only if $(a, Q) = 1$ and a is a quadratic residue modulo all primes p that divide Q. If $\left(\dfrac{a}{Q}\right) = -1$, then a is not a quadratic residue.

Theorem 3.5 *Suppose that* Q *and* Q' *are odd and positive and that* $(PP', QQ') = 1.$ *Then*

(a) $\left(\dfrac{P}{Q}\right)\left(\dfrac{P}{Q'}\right) = \left(\dfrac{P}{QQ'}\right),$

(b) $\left(\dfrac{P}{Q}\right)\left(\dfrac{P'}{Q}\right) = \left(\dfrac{PP'}{Q}\right),$

(c) $\left(\dfrac{P^2}{Q}\right) = \left(\dfrac{P}{Q^2}\right) = 1,$

(d) $\left(\dfrac{P'P^2}{Q'Q^2}\right) = \left(\dfrac{P'}{Q'}\right),$

(e) $P' \equiv P \pmod{Q}$ *implies* $\left(\dfrac{P'}{Q}\right) = \left(\dfrac{P}{Q}\right).$

Proof. First (a) is obvious from the definition of $\left(\dfrac{P}{Q}\right)$ and (b) follows from the definition and Theorem 3.1b. Then (c) follows from (b) and (a) and so also does (d). To prove (e) we write $Q = q_1 q_2 \cdots q_s$. Then $P' \equiv P \pmod{q_j}$ so that $\left(\dfrac{P'}{q_j}\right) = \left(\dfrac{P}{q_j}\right)$ by Theorem 3.1c, and then we have (e) from Definition 3.4.

Theorem 3.6 *If* Q *is odd and* $Q > 0$, *then*

$$\left(\frac{-1}{Q}\right) = (-1)^{(Q-1)/2} \quad \text{and} \quad \left(\frac{2}{Q}\right) = (-1)^{(Q^2-1)/8}$$

Proof. We have

$$\left(\frac{-1}{Q}\right) = \prod_{j=1}^{s}\left(\frac{-1}{q_j}\right) = \prod_{j=1}^{s}(-1)^{(q_j-1)/2} = (-1)^{\sum_{j=1}^{s}(q_j-1)/2}$$

If a and b are odd, then

$$\frac{ab-1}{2} - \left(\frac{a-1}{2} + \frac{b-1}{2}\right) = \frac{(a-1)(b-1)}{2} \equiv 0 \pmod{2}$$

and hence

$$\frac{a-1}{2} + \frac{b-1}{2} \equiv \frac{ab-1}{2} \pmod{2}.$$

Applying this repeatedly we obtain

$$(3.1) \qquad \sum_{j=1}^{s} \frac{q_j - 1}{2} \equiv \frac{1}{2}\left(\prod_{j=1}^{s} q_j - 1\right) \equiv \frac{Q-1}{2} \pmod 2,$$

and thus $\left(\dfrac{-1}{Q}\right) = (-1)^{(Q-1)/2}$.

Similarly, if a and b are odd, then

$$\frac{a^2 b^2 - 1}{8} - \left(\frac{a^2-1}{8} + \frac{b^2-1}{8}\right) = \frac{(a^2-1)(b^2-1)}{8} \equiv 0 \pmod 8,$$

so we have

$$\frac{a^2-1}{8} + \frac{b^2-1}{8} \equiv \frac{a^2 b^2 - 1}{8} \pmod 2,$$

$$\sum_{j=1}^{s} \frac{q_j^2 - 1}{8} \equiv \frac{Q^2-1}{8} \pmod 2,$$

and hence,

$$\left(\frac{2}{Q}\right) = \prod_{j=1}^{s} \left(\frac{2}{q_j}\right) = (-1)^{\sum_{j=1}^{s} (q_j{}^2 - 1)/8} = (-1)^{(Q^2-1)/8}.$$

Theorem 3.7 *If P and Q are odd and positive and if $(P, Q) = 1$, then*

$$\left(\frac{P}{Q}\right)\left(\frac{Q}{P}\right) = (-1)^{\{(P-1)/2\}\{(Q-1)/2\}}.$$

Proof. Writing $P = \prod_{i=1}^{r} p_i$ as well as $Q = \prod_{j=1}^{s} q_j$, we have

$$\left(\frac{P}{Q}\right) = \prod_{j=1}^{s}\left(\frac{P}{q_j}\right) = \prod_{j=1}^{s}\prod_{i=1}^{r}\left(\frac{p_i}{q_j}\right) = \prod_{j=1}^{s}\prod_{i=1}^{r}\left(\frac{q_j}{p_i}\right)(-1)^{\{(p_i-1)/2\}\{(q_j-1)/2\}}$$

$$= \left(\frac{Q}{P}\right)(-1)^{\sum_{j=1}^{s}\sum_{i=1}^{r}\{(p_i-1)/2\}\{(q_j-1)/2\}}$$

where we have used Theorem 3.4. But

$$\sum_{j=1}^{s} \sum_{i=1}^{r} \frac{p_i - 1}{2} \frac{q_j - 1}{2} = \sum_{i=1}^{r} \frac{p_i - 1}{2} \sum_{j=1}^{s} \frac{q_j - 1}{2}$$

and

$$\sum_{i=1}^{r} \frac{p_i - 1}{2} \equiv \frac{P - 1}{2}, \qquad \sum_{j=1}^{s} \frac{q_j - 1}{2} \equiv \frac{Q - 1}{2} \pmod 2$$

as in (3.1) in the proof of Theorem 3.6. Therefore we have

$$\left(\frac{P}{Q}\right) = \left(\frac{Q}{P}\right) (-1)^{\{(P-1)/2\}\{(Q-1)/2\}}$$

which proves the theorem.

The theorem we have just proved shows that the Jacobi symbol obeys the law of reciprocity. It is worthwhile to consider what has been done. In this chapter we have been interested in quadratic residues. The definition of the Legendre symbol is a natural one to make. We then proved the useful and celebrated law of reciprocity for this symbol. The Jacobi symbol is an extension of the Legendre symbol, defining $\left(\frac{P}{Q}\right)$ for composite Q. However, at first it might have seemed more natural to define $\left(\frac{P}{Q}\right)$ to be 1 for quadratic residues P and -1 for nonresidues modulo Q. Had this been done, there would have been no reciprocity law ($P = 5$, $Q = 9$ is an example). What we have done is this: we have dropped the connection with quadratic residues in favor of the law of reciprocity. This does not mean that the Jacobi symbol cannot be used in computations like those in Section 3.2. In fact, the Jacobi symbol plays an important role in such calculations. In Section 3.2 we used the reciprocity law to invert the symbol $\left(\frac{p}{q}\right)$ to $\left(\frac{q}{p}\right)$, but we could do it only if q was a prime. In order to compute $\left(\frac{a}{p}\right)$ we had to factor a and consider a product of Legendre symbols. Now however, using Jacobi symbols we do not need to factor a if it is odd and positive. We compute $\left(\frac{a}{p}\right)$ as a Jacobi symbol and then know the quadratic character of a modulo p if p is a prime.

For example:

$$\left(\frac{105}{317}\right) = \left(\frac{317}{105}\right) = \left(\frac{2}{105}\right) = 1,$$

and hence 105 is a quadratic residue modulo the prime number 317.

Problems

1. Evaluate: $\left(\dfrac{-23}{83}\right); \left(\dfrac{51}{71}\right); \left(\dfrac{71}{73}\right); \left(\dfrac{-35}{97}\right).$

2. Which of the following congruences are solvable:
   (a) $x^2 \equiv 10 \pmod{127}$;
   (b) $x^2 \equiv 73 \pmod{173}$;
   (c) $x^2 \equiv 137 \pmod{401}$?

3. Which of the following congruences are solvable:
   (a) $x^2 \equiv 11 \pmod{61}$;   (b) $x^2 \equiv 42 \pmod{97}$;
   (c) $x^2 \equiv -43 \pmod{79}$;   (d) $x^2 - 31 \equiv 0 \pmod{103}$?

4. Show that if p and q are odd primes one of which is of the form $4k + 1$, then $\left(\dfrac{p}{q}\right) = \left(\dfrac{q}{p}\right).$

5. Prove that $\displaystyle\sum_{j=1}^{p-1} \left(\frac{j}{p}\right) = 0$, p an odd prime.

6. If p is an odd prime and $(a, p) = 1$, prove that $ax^2 + bx + c \equiv 0 \pmod{p}$ has two, one, or no solutions according as $b^2 - 4ac$ is a quadratic residue, is congruent to zero, or is a quadratic nonresidue modulo p.

7. Use Wilson's theorem to prove that if p is a prime of the form $4n + 3$, then

$$1 \cdot 2 \cdot 3 \cdots \frac{p-1}{2} \equiv (-1)^m \pmod{p}$$

where m is the number of quadratic nonresidues among the factors on the left side.

8. (a) Let p be an odd prime with a quadratic residue a. Prove that $x^2 \equiv a \pmod{p^2}$ has exactly two solutions, by writing $x = x_1 + py$, where x_1 is a solution of $x^2 \equiv a \pmod{p}$.
   (b) Generalize by the use of mathematical induction, and establish that $x^2 \equiv a \pmod{p^k}$ has exactly two solutions.

9. Let the prime divisors of the odd integer m be $p_1, p_2, \cdots, p_n$, and let $(a, m) = 1$. Prove that $x^2 \equiv a \pmod{m}$ has a solution if and only if $\left(\dfrac{a}{p_i}\right) = 1$ for $i = 1, 2, \cdots, n$.

10. For which primes p do there exist integers x and y with $(x, p) = 1$, $(y, p) = 1$, such that $x^2 + y^2 \equiv 0 \pmod{p}$?

11. For which prime powers p^a do there exist integers x and y with $(x, p) = 1$, $(y, p) = 1$, such that $x^2 + y^2 \equiv 0 \pmod{p^a}$?

12. For which positive integers n do there exist integers x and y with $(x, n) = 1$, $(y, n) = 1$, such that $x^2 + y^2 \equiv 0 \pmod{n}$?

13. Let the integers $1, 2, \cdots, p - 1$ modulo p, p an odd prime, be divided into two nonempty sets S_1 and S_2 so that the product of two elements in the same set is in S_1, whereas the product of an element of S_1 and an element of S_2 is in S_2. Prove that S_1 consists of the quadratic residues, S_2 of the nonresidues, modulo p. *Suggestion:* use a primitive root modulo p.

14. Let k be odd. Prove: if $a \geq n$, then $x^2 \equiv 2^a k \pmod{2^n}$ has at least one solution. If $a < n$, then the congruence has a solution if and only if a is even and $x^2 \equiv k \pmod{2^{n-a}}$ has a solution.

15. Let k be odd. Prove that $x^2 \equiv k \pmod{2}$ has exactly one solution. Furthermore, $x^2 \equiv k \pmod{2^2}$ is solvable if and only if $k \equiv 1 \pmod{4}$, in which case there are two solutions.

16. Let k be odd, and let $n \geq 3$. Prove that $x^2 \equiv k \pmod{2^n}$ is solvable if and only if $k \equiv 1 \pmod{8}$. *Suggestion:* use mathematical induction. Assuming that $x^2 \equiv k \pmod{2^n}$ has a solution u, show that an integer t can be found so that $(u + 2^{n-1}t)^2 \equiv k \pmod{2^{n+1}}$.

17. Assume that $n \geq 3$ and $k \equiv 1 \pmod{8}$. Prove that any solution u of $x^2 \equiv k \pmod{2^n}$ gives rise to three other solutions, $-u$, $u + 2^{n-1}$, and $-u + 2^{n-1}$. Prove that these four solutions are incongruent modulo 2^n.

18. Prove that if u and v are any odd numbers, then one of $u - v$ and $u + v$ is of the form $4m + 2$.

19. Let $n \geq 3$ and $k \equiv 1 \pmod{8}$. Prove that if u and v are two incongruent solutions of $x^2 \equiv k \pmod{2^n}$, then v has one of the three forms $-u$, $u + 2^{n-1}$, $-u + 2^{n-1}$ modulo 2^n. Hence the congruence has exactly four solutions. *Suggestion:* analyze $u^2 \equiv v^2 \pmod{2^n}$, and hence $(u - v)(u + v) \equiv 0 \pmod{2^n}$, in the light of the preceding problem.

20. Consider the congruence $x^2 \equiv a \pmod{p^s}$ with p a prime, $s \geq 1$, $a = p^t b$, $(b, p) = 1$. Prove: if $t \geq s$ the congruence is solvable. If $t < s$ the congruence is solvable if and only if t is even and $x^2 \equiv b \pmod{p^{s-t}}$ is solvable.

21. Consider the congruence $x^2 \equiv a \pmod{m}$. For each prime factor p of m, let p^{s_p} denote the highest power of p that divides m, and p^{t_p} the highest power that divides a, so that $s_p \geq 1$, $t_p \geq 0$. Write c_p for a/p^{t_p}. Prove that the congruence is solvable if and only if

    (1) for each odd prime factor p of m such that $t_p < s_p$, the integer t_p is even and $\left(\dfrac{c_p}{p}\right) = 1$;

(2) in case m is even and $t_2 < s_2$, then t_2 is even and $c_2 \equiv 1 \pmod{2^r}$ where $r = \min(3, s_2 - t_2)$.

22. Let p be any odd prime. Let $f(a)$ denote the number of solutions x, y of $x^2 - y^2 \equiv a \pmod{p}$, where two solutions x_1, y_1 and x_2, y_2 are counted separately unless $x_1 \equiv x_2$ and $y_1 \equiv y_2 \pmod{p}$. Prove that $f(a) = p - 1$ unless $p | a$, in which case the result is $f(a) = 2p - 1$.

For the next few problems we extend the range of meaning of the symbol $\left(\dfrac{a}{p}\right)$ by defining it to be 0 whenever $p | a$.

23. Prove that

$$\sum_{m=1}^{p} \left(\frac{am + b}{p}\right) = 0,$$

assuming $a \not\equiv 0 \pmod{p}$. Also prove that $\left(\dfrac{ab}{p}\right) = \left(\dfrac{a}{p}\right)\left(\dfrac{b}{p}\right)$, and that $\left(\dfrac{a}{p}\right) = \left(\dfrac{b}{p}\right)$ if $a \equiv b \pmod{p}$.

24. For any odd prime p consider the sequence $\left(\dfrac{1}{p}\right), \left(\dfrac{2}{p}\right), \cdots, \left(\dfrac{p-1}{p}\right)$.
Any consecutive pair of terms of the sequence is of one of the four types, 1, 1 or -1, -1 or 1, -1 or -1, 1. Denote the number of occurrences of each of these types by $N(1, 1)$, $N(-1, -1)$, $N(1, -1)$ and $N(-1, 1)$ respectively. Prove that

$$2N(1, 1) - 2N(-1, -1) = \sum_{x=1}^{p-2} \left\{ \left(\frac{x}{p}\right) + \left(\frac{x+1}{p}\right) \right\},$$

$$2N(1, -1) - 2N(-1, 1) = \sum_{x=1}^{p-2} \left\{ \left(\frac{x}{p}\right) - \left(\frac{x+1}{p}\right) \right\}.$$

25. Prove that $\displaystyle\sum_{x=1}^{p} \left(\frac{x}{p}\right)\left(\frac{x+1}{p}\right) = -1$ if p is any odd prime. *Suggestion:*
define $s(a, p) = \displaystyle\sum_{x=1}^{p} \left(\frac{x}{p}\right)\left(\frac{x+a}{p}\right)$ and prove that $s(a, p) = s(1, p)$ if $p \nmid a$. Then evaluate $\displaystyle\sum_{a=1}^{p-1} s(a, p)$.

26. Using the notation of the two preceding problems show that $-s(1, p)$ is the excess of the number of changes of sign in the sequence $\left(\dfrac{1}{p}\right), \left(\dfrac{2}{p}\right), \cdots,$

$\left(\dfrac{p-1}{p}\right)$ over the number of times that the sign does not change. Hence prove that

$$N(1, -1) + N(-1, 1) - N(1, 1) - N(-1, -1) = +1.$$

Then establish in case $p \equiv 1 \pmod 4$ that

$$N(1, 1) + 1 = N(1, -1) = N(-1, 1) = N(-1, -1) = (p - 1)/4,$$

and in case $p \equiv 3 \pmod 4$ that

$$N(1, -1) - 1 = N(1, 1) = N(-1, 1) = N(-1, -1) = (p - 3)/4.$$

27. Prove that if p is an odd prime then $\displaystyle\sum_{m=1}^{p} \left(\dfrac{m^2 - b}{p}\right) = -1$ unless $p | b$, in which case the sum has value $p - 1$.

Chapter 4

Some Functions of Number Theory

4.1 Greatest Integer Function

The function $[x]$ was introduced in Definition 3.3. It is defined for all real x and it assumes integral values only. Many of its properties are included in the following theorem.

Theorem 4.1 *Let x and y be real numbers. Then we have*

(a) $[x] \leq x < [x] + 1,\ x - 1 < [x] \leq x,\ 0 \leq x - [x] < 1.$

(b) $[x] = \sum\limits_{1 \leq i \leq x} 1$ *if* $x \geq 0.$

(c) $[x + m] = [x] + m$ *if m is an integer.*

(d) $[x] + [y] \leq [x + y] \leq [x] + [y] + 1.$

(e) $[x] + [-x] = \begin{cases} 0 & \text{if } x \text{ is an integer,} \\ -1 & \text{otherwise.} \end{cases}$

(f) $\left[\dfrac{[x]}{m}\right] = \left[\dfrac{x}{m}\right]$ *if m is a positive integer.*

(g) $x - [x]$ *is the fractional part of x.*

(h) $-[-x]$ *is the least integer $\geq x$.*

(i) $[x + \frac{1}{2}]$ *is the nearest integer to x. If two integers are equally near to x, it is the larger of the two.*

(j) $-[-x + \frac{1}{2}]$ *is the nearest integer to x. If two integers are equally near to x, it is the smaller of the two.*

85

Proof. The first part of (*a*) is just the definition of [*x*] in algebraic form. The two other parts are rearrangements of the first part.

In (*b*) the sum is vacuous if $x < 1$. We adopt the convention that a vacuous sum is zero. Then, for $x \geq 0$, the sum counts the number of positive integers i that are less than or equal to x. This number is evidently just [*x*].

Part (*c*) is obvious from the definition of [*x*].

To prove (*d*) we write $x = n + \nu$, $y = m + \mu$, where n and m are integers and $0 \leq \nu < 1, 0 \leq \mu < 1$. Then

$$[x] + [y] = n + m \leq [n + \nu + m + \mu]$$

$$= n + m + [\nu + \mu] \leq n + m + 1 = [x] + [y] + 1.$$

Again writing $x = n + \nu$, we also have $-x = -n - 1 + 1 - \nu$, $0 < 1 - \nu \leq 1$. Then

$$[x] + [-x] = n + [-n - 1 + 1 - \nu]$$

$$= n - n - 1 + [1 - \nu] = \begin{cases} 0 & \text{if } \nu = 0 \\ -1 & \text{if } \nu > 0, \end{cases}$$

and we have (*e*).

To prove (*f*) we write $x = n + \nu$, $n = qm + r$, $0 \leq \nu < 1, 0 \leq r \leq m - 1$, and have

$$\left[\frac{x}{m}\right] = \left[\frac{qm + r + \nu}{m}\right] = q + \left[\frac{r + \nu}{m}\right] = q,$$

since $0 \leq r + \nu < m$. Then (*f*) follows because

$$\left[\frac{[x]}{m}\right] = \left[\frac{n}{m}\right] = \left[q + \frac{r}{m}\right] = q.$$

Part (*g*) is nothing more than a definition of the words "fractional part of *x*."

Replacing x by $-x$ in (*a*) we get $-x - 1 < [-x] \leq -x$ and hence $x \leq -[-x] < x + 1$, which proves (*h*).

To prove (*i*) we let n be the nearest integer to x, taking the larger one if two are equally distant. Then $n = x + \theta$, $-\frac{1}{2} < \theta \leq \frac{1}{2}$, and $[x + \frac{1}{2}] = n + [-\theta + \frac{1}{2}] = n$, since $0 \leq -\theta + \frac{1}{2} < 1$.

The proof of (*j*) is similar to that of (*i*).

Theorem 4.2 *Let p denote a prime. Then the largest exponent e such that $p^e | n!$ is*

$$e = \sum_{i=1}^{\infty} \left[\frac{n}{p^i} \right].$$

Proof. If $p^i > n$, then $[n/p^i] = 0$. Therefore the sum terminates; it is not really an infinite series. The theorem is easily proved by mathematical induction. It is true for $1!$. Assume it is true for $(n-1)!$ and let j denote the largest integer such that $p^j | n$. Since $n! = n \cdot (n-1)!$, we must prove that $\sum [n/p^i] - \sum [(n-1)/p^i] = j$. But

$$\left[\frac{n}{p^i} \right] - \left[\frac{n-1}{p^i} \right] = \begin{cases} 1 \text{ if } p^i | n \\ 0 \text{ if } p^i \nmid n \end{cases}$$

and hence

$$\sum \left[\frac{n}{p^i} \right] - \sum \left[\frac{n-1}{p^i} \right] = j.$$

The preceding proof is short, but it is rather artificial. A different proof can be based on a simple, but interesting, observation. If a_1, a_2, $\cdots$, a_n are non-negative integers let $f(1)$ denote the number of them that are greater than or equal to 1, $f(2)$ the number greater than or equal to 2, etc. Then

$$a_1 + a_2 + \cdots + a_n = f(1) + f(2) + f(3) + \cdots .$$

Now, for $1 \le j \le n$, we let a_j be the largest integer such that $p^{a_j} | j$. Then $f(1)$ counts the number of integers $\le n$ that are divisible by p, $f(2)$ the number divisible by p^2, etc. Hence $f(k)$ counts the integers p^k, $2p^k$, $3p^k$, $\cdots$, $[n/p^k]p^k$, so that $f(k) = [n/p^k]$. Thus we see that

$$e = a_1 + a_2 + \cdots + a_n = \sum_{i=1}^{\infty} f(i) = \sum_{i=1}^{\infty} \left[\frac{n}{p^i} \right].$$

Formula (f) of Theorem 4.1 shortens the work of computing e in Theorem 4.2. For example, if we wish to find the highest power of 7 that divides $1000!$ we compute

$$[1000/7] = 142, \ [142/7] = 20, \ [20/7] = 2, \ [2/7] = 0.$$

Adding, we find that $7^{164} | 1000!$, $7^{165} \nmid 1000!$.

The applications of Theorem 4.2 are not restricted to numerical problems. As an example, let us prove that

$$\frac{n!}{a_1!a_2! \cdots a_r!}$$

is an integer if $a_i \geq 0$, $a_1 + a_2 + \cdots + a_r = n$. To do this we merely have to show that every prime divides the numerator to at least as high a power as it divides the denominator. Using Theorem 4.2 we need only prove

$$\sum \left[\frac{n}{p^i}\right] \geq \sum \left[\frac{a_1}{p^i}\right] + \sum \left[\frac{a_2}{p^i}\right] + \cdots + \sum \left[\frac{a_r}{p^i}\right].$$

But repeated use of Theorem 4.1d gives us

$$\left[\frac{a_1}{p^i}\right] + \left[\frac{a_2}{p^i}\right] + \cdots + \left[\frac{a_r}{p^i}\right] \leq \left[\frac{a_1 + a_2 + \cdots + a_r}{p^i}\right] = \left[\frac{n}{p^i}\right].$$

Summing this over i we have our desired result.

A slightly more complicated example is to prove that

$$\frac{(ab)!}{a!(b!)^a}$$

s an integer. We must show that

$$\sum \left[\frac{ab}{p^i}\right] - \sum \left[\frac{a}{p^i}\right] - a \sum \left[\frac{b}{p^i}\right] \geq 0$$

for every prime p. Let r and s denote the integers such that $p^r \leq a < p^{r+1}$ and $p^s \leq b < p^{s+1}$. Then

$$\sum \left[\frac{ab}{p^i}\right] - \sum \left[\frac{a}{p^i}\right] - a \sum \left[\frac{b}{p^i}\right]$$

$$= \sum_{i=1}^{s} \left[\frac{ab}{p^i}\right] + \sum_{i=s+1}^{r+s} \left[\frac{ab}{p^i}\right] + \sum_{i=r+s+1}^{\infty} \left[\frac{ab}{p^i}\right] - \sum_{i=1}^{r} \left[\frac{a}{p^i}\right] - \sum_{i=1}^{s} a \left[\frac{b}{p^i}\right]$$

$$= \sum_{i=1}^{s} \left(\left[\frac{ab}{p^i}\right] - a \left[\frac{b}{p^i}\right]\right) + \sum_{i=1}^{r} \left(\left[\frac{ab}{p^{s+i}}\right] - \left[\frac{a}{p^i}\right]\right) + \sum_{i=r+s+1}^{\infty} \left[\frac{ab}{p^i}\right]$$

$$\geq \sum_{i=1}^{s} \left(\left[\frac{ab}{p^i} \right] - a \left[\frac{b}{p^i} \right] \right) + \sum_{i=1}^{r} \left(\left[\frac{ap^s}{p^{s+i}} \right] - \left[\frac{a}{p^i} \right] \right)$$

$$= \sum_{i=1}^{s} \left(\left[\frac{ab}{p^i} \right] - a \left[\frac{b}{p^i} \right] \right) \geq 0$$

since $[ab/p^i] \geq a[b/p^i]$ by repeated use of Theorem 4.1d.

Problems

1. What is the highest power of 2 dividing 533!? The highest power of 3? The highest power of 6? The highest power of 12? The highest power of 70?

2. If 100! were written out in the ordinary decimal notation without the factorial sign, how many zeros would there be in a row at the right end?

3. For what real numbers x is it true that
   (a) $[x] + [x] = [2x]$;
   (b) $[x + 3] = 3 + [x]$;
   (c) $[x + 3] = 3 + x$;
   (d) $[x + \frac{1}{2}] + [x - \frac{1}{2}] = [2x]$;
   (e) $[9x] = 9$?

4. Given that $[x + y] = [x] + [y]$ and $[-x - y] = [-x] + [-y]$, prove that x or y is an integer.

5. Find formulas for the highest exponent e of the prime p such that p^e divides (a) the product $2 \cdot 4 \cdot 6 \cdots (2n)$ of the first n even numbers; (b) the product of the first n odd numbers.

6. For any real number x prove that $[x] + [x + \frac{1}{2}] = [2x]$.

7. For any positive real numbers x and y prove that $[x] \cdot [y] \leq [xy]$.

8. For any positive real numbers x and y prove that

$$[x - y] \leq [x] - [y] \leq [x - y] + 1.$$

9. Prove that $(2n)!/(n!)^2$ is even if n is a positive integer.

10. Let m be any real number not zero or a positive integer. Prove that an x exists so that the equation of Theorem 4.1f is false.

11. If p and q are distinct primes, prove that the divisors of p^2q^3 coincide with the terms of $(1 + p + p^2)(1 + q + q^2 + q^3)$ when the latter is multiplied out.

12. Prove that $\prod_{i=1}^{n} (a + i)$ is divisible by $n!$.

13. If a and b are integers such that $(a, b) = 1$, and ρ is a real number such that $a\rho$ and $b\rho$ are integers, then ρ is an integer. Hence prove that $\rho = n!/(a!b!)$ is an integer if $(a, b) = 1$ and $a + b = n + 1$. Generalize this to prove that

$$\rho = \frac{n!}{a_1!a_2! \cdots a_r!}$$

   is an integer if $(a_1, a_2, \cdots, a_r) = 1$ and $a_1 + a_2 + \cdots + a_r = n + 1$.

14. Consider an integer $n \geq 1$ and the integers i, $1 \leq i \leq n$. For each $k = 0$, $1, 2, \cdots$ find the number of i's that are divisible by 2^k but not by 2^{k+1}. Thus prove

$$\sum_{j=1}^{\infty} \left[\frac{n}{2^j} + \frac{1}{2} \right] = n,$$

   and hence that we get the correct value for the sum $n/2 + n/4 + n/8 + \cdots$ if we replace each term by its nearest integer, using the larger one if two exist.

15. If n is any positive integer and ξ any real number, prove that

$$[\xi] + \left[\xi + \frac{1}{n} \right] + \cdots + \left[\xi + \frac{n-1}{n} \right] = [n\xi].$$

16. Prove that a number α is rational if and only if there exists a positive integer k such that $[k\alpha] = k\alpha$. Prove that a number α is rational if and only if there exists a positive integer k such that $[(k!)\alpha] = (k!)\alpha$.

17. Recalling that the mathematical constant e has value $\sum_{j=0}^{\infty} 1/j!$, prove that

$$[(k!)e] = k! \sum_{j=0}^{k} 1/j! < (k!)e.$$

   Hence prove that e is irrational.

18. If $(m, n) = 1$, prove that

$$\sum_{x=1}^{n-1} \left[\frac{mx}{n} \right] = \frac{(m-1)(n-1)}{2}.$$

19. If $m \geq 1$, prove that $[(1 + \sqrt{3})^{2m+1}]$ is divisible by 2^{m+1} but not by 2^{m+2}.

20. Let θ be irrational, and $0 < \theta < 1$. Define

$$g_n = \begin{cases} 0 \text{ if } [n\theta] = [(n-1)\theta], \\ 1 \text{ otherwise.} \end{cases}$$

Prove that $\quad\displaystyle\lim_{n\to\infty} \frac{g_1 + g_2 + \cdots + g_n}{n} = \theta.$

21. Let n be an odd integer > 5. If n factors into the product of two integers, $n = uv$, with $u > v$ and $u - v \leq \sqrt[4]{64n}$, prove that the roots of $x^2 - 2[\sqrt{n} + 1]x + n = 0$ are integers. *Suggestion:* use the identity $\{(u+v)/2\}^2 - \{(u-v)/2\}^2 = uv$ to get bounds on the integer $(u+v)/2$.

22. Let α be a positive irrational number. Prove that the two sequences,

$$[1 + \alpha], [2 + 2\alpha], \cdots, [n + n\alpha], \cdots, \text{ and}$$
$$[1 + \alpha^{-1}], [2 + 2\alpha^{-1}], \cdots, [n + n\alpha^{-1}], \cdots,$$

together contain every positive integer exactly once. Prove that this is false if α is rational.

23. Let S be the set of integers given by $[\alpha x]$ and $[\beta x]$ for $x = 1, 2, \cdots$. Prove that S consists of every positive integer, each appearing exactly once, if and only if α and β are positive irrational numbers such that $\dfrac{1}{\alpha} + \dfrac{1}{\beta} = 1$.

24. For positive real numbers α, β, γ define $f(\alpha, \beta, \gamma)$ as the sum of all positive terms of the series

$$\left[\frac{\gamma - \alpha}{\beta}\right] + \left[\frac{\gamma - 2\alpha}{\beta}\right] + \left[\frac{\gamma - 3\alpha}{\beta}\right] + \left[\frac{\gamma - 4\alpha}{\beta}\right] + \cdots.$$

(If there are no positive terms, define $f(\alpha, \beta, \gamma) = 0$.) Prove that $f(\alpha, \beta, \gamma) = f(\beta, \alpha, \gamma)$. *Suggestion:* $f(\alpha, \beta, \gamma)$ is related to the number of solutions of $\alpha x + \beta y \leq \gamma$ in non-negative integer pairs x, y.

25. Prove that if p is a prime and $0 \leq n \leq p^k$ then

$$\binom{p^k}{n} \equiv \begin{cases} 1 \pmod{p} \text{ if } n = 0 \text{ or } p^k, \\ 0 \pmod{p} \text{ if } 1 \leq n \leq p^k - 1, \end{cases}$$

where $\dbinom{p^k}{n}$ is the binomial coefficient.

26. Prove that if p is a prime and $0 \leq n \leq p^k$ then

$$\binom{p^k}{n} \equiv \begin{cases} 1 \pmod{p^2} \text{ if } n = 0 \text{ or } p^k, \\ pa'(-1)^{a-1} \pmod{p^2} \text{ if } n = ap^{k-1}, 1 \leq a \leq p - 1, \\ \qquad\qquad\qquad\qquad\qquad\qquad aa' \equiv 1 \pmod{p}, \\ 0 \pmod{p^2} \text{ otherwise.} \end{cases}$$

27. Prove that if p is a prime and $m = \sum\limits_{j=0}^{r} a_j p^j$, $n = \sum\limits_{j=0}^{r} b_j p^j$,

$0 \leq a_j \leq p - 1$, $0 \leq b_j \leq p - 1$, then

$$\binom{m}{n} \equiv \binom{a_0}{b_0}\binom{a_1}{b_1}\binom{a_2}{b_2} \cdots \binom{a_r}{b_r} \pmod{p}.$$

Suggestion: consider $(1 + x)^m \pmod{p}$.

4.2   Numerical Functions

Functions, such as $\phi(m)$ of Theorem 2.5, that are defined for positive integral values of their argument, are called numerical functions.

Definition 4.1 *For positive integers n we make the following definitions.*
$\tau(n)$ *is the number of positive divisors of n.*
$\sigma(n)$ *is the sum of the positive divisors of n.*
$\sigma_k(n)$ *is the sum of the kth powers of the positive divisors of n.*

For example, $\tau(6) = 4$, $\sigma(6) = 12$, $\sigma_2(6) = 50$. These are all numerical functions. The value of k can be any real number, positive, negative, or zero. The functions $\tau(n)$ and $\sigma(n)$ are merely special cases of $\sigma_k(n)$, because $\tau(n) = \sigma_0(n)$, $\sigma(n) = \sigma_1(n)$. It is convenient to use the symbols $\sum\limits_{d|n} f(d)$ and $\prod\limits_{d|n} f(d)$ for the sum and product of $f(d)$ over all positive divisors d of n. Thus we write

$$\tau(n) = \sum_{d|n} 1, \quad \sigma(n) = \sum_{d|n} d, \quad \sigma_k(n) = \sum_{d|n} d^k.$$

Theorem 4.3 *If $n = p_1^{e_1} p_2^{e_2} \cdots p_r^{e_r}$ then*

$$\tau(n) = (e_1 + 1)(e_2 + 1) \cdots (e_r + 1). \quad Also \ \tau(1) = 1.$$

Proof. A positive integer d divides n if, and only if, $d = p_1^{f_1} p_2^{f_2} \cdots p_r^{f_r}$ with $0 \leq f_i \leq e_i$ for $i = 1, 2, \cdots, r$. Thus there are just $(e_1 + 1)(e_2 + 1) \cdots (e_r + 1)$ such d.

If $(m, n) = 1$ it follows from Theorem 4.3 that $\tau(mn) = \tau(m)\tau(n)$.

Definition 4.2 *If $f(n)$ is a numerical function such that $f(mn) = f(m)f(n)$ for every pair m, n satisfying $(m, n) = 1$, then $f(n)$ is said to be multiplicative. If $f(mn) = f(m)f(n)$ whether m and n are relatively prime or not, $f(n)$ is said to be totally multiplicative.*

Theorem 4.4 *Let* $f(n)$ *be a multiplicative function and let* $F(n) = \sum_{d \mid n} f(d)$. *Then* $F(n)$ *is multiplicative.*

Proof. Suppose $(m, n) = 1$. Then m and n have canonical representations

$$n = p_1^{\alpha_1} p_2^{\alpha_2} \cdots p_r^{\alpha_r}, \qquad m = q_1^{\beta_1} q_2^{\beta_2} \cdots q_s^{\beta_s},$$

with positive exponents α_i and β_i and where $p_1, p_2, \cdots, p_r, q_1, q_2, \cdots, q_s$ are distinct primes. The positive divisors d_1 of n are just the numbers $d_1 = p_1^{\gamma_1} p_2^{\gamma_2} \cdots p_r^{\gamma_r}$ for all possible choices of the γ's satisfying $0 \leq \gamma_i \leq \alpha_i$. Similarly the positive divisors d_2 of m are given by $d_2 = q_1^{\delta_1} q_2^{\delta_2} \cdots q_s^{\delta_s}, 0 \leq \delta_i \leq \beta_i$. Therefore as d_1 runs through all positive divisors of n, and d_2 runs through all positive divisors of m, their product $d_1 d_2$ runs through the values $d = d_1 d_2 = p_1^{\gamma_1} p_2^{\gamma_2} \cdots p_r^{\gamma_r} q_1^{\delta_1} q_2^{\delta_2} \cdots q_s^{\delta_s}, 0 \leq \gamma_i \leq \alpha_i, 0 \leq \delta_i \leq \beta_i$; but these are just all the positive divisors of $nm = p_1^{\alpha_1} p_2^{\alpha_2} \cdots p_r^{\alpha_r} q_1^{\beta_1} q_2^{\beta_2} \cdots q_s^{\beta_s}$. In other words

$$\sum_{d_1 \mid n} \sum_{d_2 \mid m} f(d_1 d_2) = \sum_{d \mid nm} f(d).$$

It is clear that $(d_1, d_2) = 1$, and hence we have

$$F(nm) = \sum_{d \mid nm} f(d) = \sum_{d_1 \mid n} \sum_{d_2 \mid m} f(d_1 d_2) = \sum_{d_1 \mid n} \sum_{d_2 \mid m} f(d_1) f(d_2)$$

$$= \sum_{d_1 \mid n} f(d_1) \sum_{d_2 \mid m} f(d_2) = F(n) F(m).$$

We could have used this theorem and Definition 4.1 to prove that $\tau(n)$ is multiplicative. Since $\tau(n) = \sum_{d \mid n} 1$ is of the form $\sum_{d \mid n} f(d)$, and since the function $f(n) = 1$ is multiplicative, Theorem 4.4 can be used, and we see that $\tau(n)$ is multiplicative. Then Theorem 4.3 would have been easy to prove. If p_i is a prime, then $\tau(p_i^{e_i}) = e_i + 1$, since $p_i^{e_i}$ has the $e_i + 1$ positive divisors $1, p_i, p_i^2, \cdots, p_i^{e_i}$ and no more. Then, since $\tau(n)$ is multiplicative, we have

$$\tau(p_1^{e_1} p_2^{e_2} \cdots p_r^{e_r}) = \tau(p_1^{e_1}) \tau(p_2^{e_2}) \cdots \tau(p_r^{e_r})$$
$$= (e_1 + 1)(e_2 + 1) \cdots (e_r + 1).$$

This exemplifies a useful method for handling certain numerical functions. We will use it to find a formula for $\sigma(n)$ in the following theorem. However, it should be pointed out that $\sigma(n)$ can also be found quite simply in the same manner as we first obtained the formula for $\tau(n)$.

Theorem 4.5 *If* $n = p_1^{e_1} p_2^{e_2} \cdots , p_r^{e_r}$, *then*

$$\sigma(n) = \prod_{i=1}^{r} \frac{p_i^{e_i+1} - 1}{p_i - 1}, \qquad \sigma(1) = 1.$$

Proof. By definition $\sigma(n) = \sum_{d|n} d$, so we can apply Theorem 4.4 with $f(n) = n$, $F(n) = \sigma(n)$. Thus $\sigma(n)$ is multiplicative and $\sigma(n) = \prod_{i=1}^{n} \sigma(p_i^{e_i})$. But the positive divisors of $p_i^{e_i}$ are just $1, p_i, p_i^2, \cdots ,$ $p_i^{e_i}$ whose sum is $(p_i^{e_i+1} - 1)/(p_i - 1)$.

Problems

1. Find the smallest integer x for which $\phi(x) = 6$.
2. Find the smallest integer x for which $\tau(x) = 6$.
3. Find the smallest positive integer n so that $\sigma(x) = n$ has no solutions; exactly one solution; exactly two solutions; exactly three solutions.
4. Find the smallest positive integer m for which there is another positive integer $n \neq m$ such that $\sigma(m) = \sigma(n)$.
5. Prove that $\prod_{d|n} d = n^{\tau(n)/2}$.
6. Prove that $\sum_{d|n} d = \sum_{d|n} n/d$, and more generally than $\sum_{d|n} f(d) = \sum_{d|n} f(n/d)$.
7. Prove that $\sigma_{-k}(n) = n^{-k}\sigma_k(n)$.
8. Find a formula for $\sigma_k(n)$.
9. If $f(n)$ and $g(n)$ are multiplicative functions, and $g(n) \neq 0$ for every n, show that the functions $F(n) = f(n)g(n)$ and $G(n) = f(n)/g(n)$ are also multiplicative.
10. Give an example to show that if $f(n)$ is totally multiplicative, $F(n)$ need not also be totally multiplicative, where $F(n)$ is defined as $\sum_{d|n} f(d)$.
11. Prove that the number of positive irreducible fractions ≤ 1 with denominator $\leq n$ is $\phi(1) + \phi(2) + \phi(3) + \cdots + \phi(n)$.
12. Prove that the number of divisors of n is odd if and only if n is a perfect square. If $k \geq 1$, prove that $\sigma_k(n)$ is odd if and only if n is a square or double a square.

13. Given any positive integer $n > 1$, prove that there are infinitely many integers x satisfying $\tau(x) = n$.

14. Given any positive integer n, prove that there is only a finite number of integers x satisfying $\phi(x) = n$; similarly for $\sigma(x) = n$.

15. Prove that if $(a, b) > 1$ then $\sigma_k(ab) < \sigma_k(a)\sigma_k(b)$ and $\tau(ab) < \tau(a)\tau(b)$.

16. We say (following Euclid) that m is a perfect number if $\sigma(m) = 2m$, that is, if m is the sum of all its positive divisors other than itself. If $2^n - 1$ is a prime p, prove that $2^{n-1}p$ is a perfect number. Use this result to find three perfect numbers.

17. Prove that an integer q is a prime if and only if $\sigma(q) = q + 1$.

18. Show that if $\sigma(q) = q + k$ where $k|q$ and $k < q$, then $k = 1$.

19. Prove that every even perfect number has the form given in Problem 16. *Suggestion:* assume that $2^{n-1}q$ is a perfect number, where $n > 1$ and q is odd. Write $\sigma(q) = q + k$ and so deduce from $\sigma(2^{n-1}q) = 2^n q$ that $q = k(2^n - 1)$. Thus $k|q$ and $k < q$.

20. For any integer $n \geq 2$ define $\nu(n)$ as $(-1)^j$, where j is the total number of prime factors of n. For example, if $n = 16$, then $j = 4$; if $n = 72$, $j = 5$. Also define $\nu(1) = 1$. Prove that $\nu(n)$ is a totally multiplicative function and that

$$\sum_{d|n} \nu(d) = \begin{cases} 1 \text{ if } n \text{ is a perfect square,} \\ 0 \text{ otherwise.} \end{cases}$$

21. If $d|n$ and $\delta|(n/d)$, then $d|(n/\delta)$. Prove that the set of ordered pairs (d, δ) where d ranges over all positive divisors of a fixed integer n and, for each value of d, δ ranges over all positive divisors of n/d, is a symmetric set in the sense that if (a, b) is in the set, so is (b, a).

22. Prove that the set of pairs in the preceding problem is the same as the set of pairs (d, δ) over all positive d and δ such that $d\delta|n$.

23. Consider the set of ordered pairs (d, γ) where d ranges over all positive divisors of a fixed integer n, and for each such d, γ ranges over all positive divisors of d. Prove that this is the same as the set of ordered pairs $(\beta\gamma, \gamma)$ where γ ranges over all divisors of n and, for each such γ, β runs through the positive divisors of n/γ.

4.3   The Moebius Inversion Formula

Definition 4.3 *The Moebius function $\mu(n)$ is defined by*

$$\mu(n) = \begin{cases} 1 & \text{if } n = 1 \\ 0 & \text{if } a^2|n \text{ for some } a > 1 \\ (-1)^r & \text{if } n = p_1 p_2 \cdots p_r, \, p_i \text{ distinct primes.} \end{cases}$$

Theorem 4.6 *The function $\mu(n)$ is multiplicative and*

$$\sum_{d|n} \mu(d) = \begin{cases} 1 \ \text{if } n = 1 \\ 0 \ \text{if } n > 1. \end{cases}$$

Proof. It is clear from the definition that $\mu(n)$ is multiplicative. If $F(n) = \sum_{d|n} \mu(d)$, then $F(n)$ is multiplicative by Theorem 4.4. Since

$$F(1) = \mu(1) = 1 \ \text{ and } \ F(p^e) = \sum_{f=0}^{e} \mu(p^f) = 1 + (-1) = 0, \ \text{ we have}$$

the desired result.

Theorem 4.7 *Moebius inversion formula. If $F(n) = \sum_{d|n} f(d)$ for every positive integer n, then $f(n) = \sum_{d|n} \mu(d)F(n/d)$.*

Proof. We have

$$\sum_{d|n} \mu(d)F\left(\frac{n}{d}\right) = \sum_{d|n} \mu(d) \sum_{\delta|(n/d)} f(\delta) = \sum_{\delta|n} \sum_{d|(n/\delta)} \mu(d)f(\delta)$$

$$= \sum_{\delta|n} f(\delta) \sum_{d|(n/\delta)} \mu(d) = f(n)$$

by Theorem 4.6.

Theorem 4.8 *If $f(n) = \sum_{d|n} \mu(d)F(n/d)$ for every positive integer n, then $F(n) = \sum_{d|n} f(d)$.*

Proof. Again by Theorem 4.6 we find

$$\sum_{d|n} f(d) = \sum_{d|n} \sum_{\delta|d} \mu(\delta)F\left(\frac{d}{\delta}\right) = \sum_{d|n} \sum_{\gamma|d} \mu\left(\frac{d}{\gamma}\right)F(\gamma)$$

$$= \sum_{\gamma|n} \sum_{\beta\gamma|n} \mu\left(\frac{\beta\gamma}{\gamma}\right)F(\gamma) = \sum_{\gamma|n} F(\gamma) \sum_{\beta|(n/\gamma)} \mu(\beta)$$

$$= F(n).$$

It should be noted that Theorem 4.7 and its converse, Theorem 4.8, do not require that $f(n)$ or $F(n)$ be multiplicative.

The last two theorems are often very useful. As an example we will obtain the results of Section 2.4 concerning Euler's ϕ-function in a different way. In Theorem 2.5 we saw that $\phi(n)$ is the number of positive integers less than or equal to n that are relatively prime to n. Let S denote the set of integers $1, 2, \cdot \cdot \cdot , n$, that is, the set of integers i satisfying $1 \leq i \leq n$. We separate S into subsets S_d, where $d|n$, by putting i into S_d if $(i, n) = d$. Then each element of S is in exactly one S_d. Moreover, i is in S_d if and only if i is of the form jd with $1 \leq j \leq n/d$ and $(j, n/d) = 1$. Therefore there are exactly $\phi(n/d)$ elements in S_d. Since there are n elements in S, we have $n = \sum_{d|n} \phi(n/d)$, which we can write as $n = \sum_{d|n} \phi(d)$. This is Theorem 2.17. Then, by Theorem 4.7,

$$\phi(n) = \sum_{d|n} \mu(d) \frac{n}{d}, \qquad \frac{\phi(n)}{n} = \sum_{d|n} \frac{\mu(d)}{d}.$$

Also the function $\mu(d)/d$ is multiplicative, and therefore so is $\phi(n)/n$ by Theorem 4.4. Hence $\phi(n)$ is multiplicative, and we have Theorem 2.15. Finally, using the foregoing equation with n replaced by p^e, we have

$$\phi(p^e) = \sum_{d|p^e} \mu(d) \frac{p^e}{d} = \sum_{f=0}^{e} \mu(p^f) \frac{p^e}{p^f}$$

$$= \mu(1)p^e + \mu(p)p^{e-1} = p^e - p^{e-1} = p^e \left(1 - \frac{1}{p}\right)$$

if $e \geq 1$, and hence

$$\phi(p_1^{e_1} p_2^{e_2} \cdot \cdot \cdot p_r^{e_r}) = p_1^{e_1} p_2^{e_2} \cdot \cdot \cdot p_r^{e_r} \left(1 - \frac{1}{p_1}\right)\left(1 - \frac{1}{p_2}\right) \cdot \cdot \cdot \left(1 - \frac{1}{p_r}\right)$$

since $\phi(n)$ is multiplicative. This is Theorem 2.16.

Problems

1. Find a positive integer n such that $\mu(n) + \mu(n + 1) + \mu(n + 2) = 3$.
2. Prove that $\mu(n)\mu(n + 1)\mu(n + 2)\mu(n + 3) = 0$ if n is a positive integer.
3. Evaluate $\sum_{j=1}^{\infty} \mu(j!)$.

4. Prove Theorem 4.8 by defining $G(n)$ as $\sum_{d|n} f(d)$, then applying Theorem 4.7 to write $f(n) = \sum_{d|n} \mu(d)G(n/d)$. Thus $\sum_{d|n} \mu(d)G(n/d) = \sum_{d|n} \mu(d)F(n/d)$. Use this to show that $F(1) = G(1)$, $F(2) = G(2)$, $F(3) = G(3)$, and so on.

5. If k denotes the number of distinct prime factors of a positive integer n, prove that $\sum_{d|n} |\mu(d)| = 2^k$.

6. If $F(n) = \sum_{d|n} f(d)$ for every positive integer n, prove that $f(n) = \sum_{d|n} \mu(n/d)F(d)$.

7. Let n have the distinct prime factors p_1, p_2, $\cdots$, p_k. Prove that $\sum_{d|n} \mu(d)\tau(d) = (-1)^k$. Similarly, evaluate $\sum_{d|n} \mu(d)\sigma(d)$.

8. If n is any even integer, prove that $\sum_{d|n} \mu(d)\phi(d) = 0$.

9. By use of the algebraic identity $(x + 1)^2 - x^2 = 2x + 1$, establish that
$$(n + 1)^2 - 1^2 = \sum_{x=1}^{n} \{(x+1)^2 - x^2\} = \sum_{x=1}^{n} (2x + 1)$$ and so derive the result $\sum_{x=1}^{n} x = n(n + 1)/2$.

10. By use of the algebraic identity $(x + 1)^3 - x^3 = 3x^2 + 3x + 1$, establish that $(n + 1)^3 - 1^3 = \sum_{x=1}^{n} \{(x + 1)^3 - x^3\} = \sum_{x=1}^{n} (3x^2 + 3x + 1)$, and so derive the result $\sum_{x=1}^{n} x^2 = n(n + 1)(2n + 1)/6$. (The results of this and the previous problem can be established by other methods, mathematical induction, for example.)

11. Let $S(n)$ denote the sum of the squares of the positive integers $\leq n$ and prime to n. Prove that
$$\sum_{j=1}^{n} j^2 = \sum_{d|n} d^2 S\left(\frac{n}{d}\right) = \sum_{d|n} \frac{n^2}{d^2} S(d).$$

    Suggestion: separate the integers $\leq n$ into classes, so that all integers k such that $(k, n) = d$ are in the same class.

12. Combine the results of the two preceding problems to get
$$\sum_{d|n} \frac{S(d)}{d^2} = \frac{1}{6}\left(2n + 3 + \frac{1}{n}\right).$$

Then apply the Moebius inversion formula to get

$$\frac{S(n)}{n^2} = \sum_{d|n} \frac{1}{6} \mu(d) \left(\frac{2n}{d} + 3 + \frac{d}{n}\right).$$

13. Prove that $f(n) = n\mu(n)$ is a multiplicative function and that $\sum_{d|n} d\mu(d) = (-1)^k \phi(n) p_1 p_2 \cdots p_k/n$ where $p_1, p_2, \cdots, p_k$ are the distinct prime factors of n.

14. Combine the results of the two preceding problems to get $S(n) = n^2\phi(n)/3 + (-1)^k\phi(n)p_1p_2 \cdots p_k/6$ for $n > 1$, where as before $p_1p_2, \cdots, p_k$ are the prime factors of n. *Suggestion:* use the formula $\sum_{d|n} \mu(d)/d = \phi(n)/n$.

15. Given any positive integer k, prove that there exist infinitely many integers n such that

$$\mu(n + 1) = \mu(n + 2) = \mu(n + 3) = \cdots = \mu(n + k).$$

4.4   Recurrence Functions

A particular sort of numerical function can be defined as follows. If a, b, x_0, x_1 are arbitrary numbers, perhaps even complex, we let $f(0) = x_0$, $f(1) = x_1$, and $f(n + 1) = af(n) + bf(n - 1)$ for $n \geq 1$. This determines $f(n)$ uniquely, depending only on a, b, x_0, x_1. For convenience we will write x_n in place of $f(n)$ and we have $x_{n+1} = ax_n + bx_{n-1}$. Such a relation is called a recurrence or recursion formula.

In order to get a simpler relationship we write this last equation in the form

$$x_{n+1} - kx_n = (a - k)(x_n - kx_{n-1}) + (b + ak - k^2)x_{n-1}.$$

If k_1 and k_2 are the roots of $k^2 - ak - b = 0$, then $k_1 + k_2 = a$ and we have

$$x_{n+1} - k_1 x_n = k_2(x_n - k_1 x_{n-1}),$$

$$x_{n+1} - k_2 x_n = k_1(x_n - k_2 x_{n-1}),$$

and hence

$$x_{n+1} - k_1 x_n = k_2^n(x_1 - k_1 x_0),$$

$$x_{n+1} - k_2 x_n = k_1^n(x_1 - k_2 x_0).$$

Subtracting   we   find $(k_2 - k_1)x_n = (x_1 - k_1 x_0)k_2^n - (x_1 - k_2 x_0)k_1^n$.

Therefore, if $k_2 \neq k_1$, we have

$$(4.1) \qquad x_n = \frac{(x_1 - k_1 x_0)k_2^n - (x_1 - k_2 x_0)k_1^n}{k_2 - k_1}, \qquad k_2 \neq k_1.$$

Thus we have a formula for finding the value of x_n directly in terms of a, b, x_0, x_1 without having to compute the values of x_2, x_3, $\cdots$, x_{n-1}. However, this formula has no meaning if $k_2 = k_1$. In this case we might try holding k_1 and n fixed and letting k_2 approach k_1, hoping that this will suggest a solution that we can then verify. We regard the above equation as having the form

$$x_n = \frac{g(k_2)}{h(k_2)}$$

with $g(k_1) = h(k_1) = 0$, and we apply L'Hospital's rule in the form

$$\lim_{k_2 \to k_1} \frac{g(k_2)}{h(k_2)} = \lim_{k_2 \to k_1} \frac{g'(k_2)}{h'(k_2)}$$

if the limit on the right exists. This gives us

$$\lim_{k_2 \to k_1} x_n = \lim_{k_2 \to k_1} \{ n(x_1 - k_1 x_0)k_2^{n-1} + x_0 k_1^n \}$$
$$= nx_1 k_1^{n-1} - nx_0 k_1^n + x_0 k_1^n.$$

Now we can set $y_n = nx_1 k_1^{n-1} - nx_0 k_1^n + x_0 k_1^n$ and check whether or not y_n actually is the solution. Since $k_1 = k_2$ is the only root of $k^2 - ak - b = 0$ we have $a = 2k_1$, $b = -k_1^2$. We have $y_0 = x_0$, $y_1 = x_1$, and, for $n \geq 1$,

$$y_{n+1} = (n + 1)x_1 k_1^n - (n + 1)x_0 k_1^{n+1} + x_0 k_1^{n+1}$$
$$= 2k_1(nx_1 k_1^{n-1} - nx_0 k_1^n + x_0 k_1^n)$$
$$\qquad - k_1^2 \{ (n - 1)x_1 k_1^{n-2} - (n - 1)x_0 k_1^{n-1} + x_0 k_1^{n-1} \}$$
$$= ay_n + by_{n-1}.$$

Now, for $n \geq 1$, we have $y_{n+1} - x_{n+1} = a(y_n - x_n) + b(y_{n-1} - x_{n-})$ and $y_0 - x_0 = 0$, $y_1 - x_1 = 0$. This implies $y_{n+1} - x_{n+1} = 0$ for $n + 1 = 2, 3, 4, \cdots$, and we have

$$x_n = y_n = nx_1 k_1^{n-1} - (n - 1)x_0 k_1^n, \qquad k_1 = k_2.$$

We have found formulas for x_n in both cases. If a, b, x_0, x_1 are integers then so are all the x_n, since $x_n = ax_{n-1} + bx_{n-2}$.

The Fibonacci numbers $F_0, F_1, \cdots$ are defined by $F_0 = 0, F_1 = 1,$ $F_{n+1} = F_n + F_{n-1}$. In this case we have $k^2 - k - 1 = 0, k_1 = (1 - \sqrt{5})/2, k_2 = (1 + \sqrt{5})/2$, and, by (4.1),

$$F_n = \frac{1}{\sqrt{5}} \left\{ \left(\frac{1 + \sqrt{5}}{2} \right)^n - \left(\frac{1 - \sqrt{5}}{2} \right)^n \right\}.$$

As another example we consider the sequence $0, 1, 3, 8, 21, \cdots$, for which $x_0 = 0, x_1 = 1, a = 3, b = -1$. Then $k_1 = (3 - \sqrt{5})/2,$ $k_2 = (3 + \sqrt{5})/2$, and

$$x_n = \frac{1}{\sqrt{5}} \left\{ \left(\frac{3 + \sqrt{5}}{2} \right)^n - \left(\frac{3 - \sqrt{5}}{2} \right)^n \right\}.$$

But $0 < \{ (3 - \sqrt{5})/2 \}^n \leq 1$, and x_n is an integer so that in this case we can write the solution as

$$x_n = \left[\frac{1}{\sqrt{5}} \left(\frac{3 + \sqrt{5}}{2} \right)^n \right].$$

Problems

1. Without using the results of this section find a formula for x_n if $x_{n+1} = ax_n$. Also if $x_{n+1} = bx_{n-1}$.
2. Find a formula for x_n if $x_{n+1} = 2x_n - x_{n-1}$, $x_0 = 0$, $x_1 = 1$. Also if $x_0 = 1$, $x_1 = 1$. Then do the same for $x_{n+1} = 2x_n + 3x_{n-1}$.
3. Write the first ten terms of the Fibonacci series. Prove in general that any two consecutive terms are relatively prime.
4. Prove that the Fibonacci numbers satisfy the inequalities

$$\left(\frac{1 + \sqrt{5}}{2} \right)^{n-1} < F_{n+1} < \left(\frac{1 + \sqrt{5}}{2} \right)^n,$$

if $n > 1$. *Suggestion:* write α for $(1 + \sqrt{5})/2$, and observe that $\alpha^2 = \alpha + 1 > F_2 + F_1 = F_3$, $\alpha^3 = \alpha^2 + \alpha > F_3 + F_2 = F_4$. Then use induction.
5. Prove that for $n \geq 2$,

$$F_n = \binom{n-1}{0} + \binom{n-2}{1} + \binom{n-3}{2} + \binom{n-4}{3} + \cdots + \binom{n-j}{j-1},$$

where the sum of the binomial coefficients on the right terminates with the largest j such that $2j \leqq n + 1$. *Suggestion:* use the fact that $\binom{m}{r} = \binom{m-1}{r-1} + \binom{m-1}{r}$.

6. Prove that $F_1 + F_2 + F_3 + \cdots + F_n = F_{n+2} - 1$.

7. Prove that $F_{n-1}F_{n+1} - F_n^2 = (-1)^n$.

8. Prove that $F_{m+n} = F_{m-1}F_n + F_m F_{n+1}$ for any positive integers m and n. Then prove that $F_m | F_n$ if $m | n$. *Suggestion:* let $n = mq$ and use induction on q.

9. Consider the sequence $1, 2, 3, 5, 8, \cdots = F_2, F_3, F_4, F_5, F_6, \cdots$. Prove that every positive integer can be written as a sum of distinct terms from this sequence. *Suggestion:* for k not in the sequence, let n be such that $F_{n-1} < k < F_n$. Show that $0 < k - F_{n-1} < F_{n-2}$. Prove the statement by induction.

10. Let $f(n)$ denote the number of sequences $a_1, a_2, \cdots, a_n$ that can be constructed where each a_j is $+1$, -1, or 0, subject to the restrictions that no two consecutive terms can be $+1$, and no two consecutive terms can be -1. Prove that $f(n)$ is the integer nearest to $\frac{1}{2}(1 + \sqrt{2})^{n+1}$. *Suggestion:* prove that $f(n) = 2f(n - 1) + f(n - 2)$.

11. (a) Let S_n be a set of integers x, $1 \leqq x \leqq n$, such that no member of S_n divides another member of S_n. Show that S_n can have $[(n + 1)/2]$ members, but no more.

    (b) Find the maximum size of S_n if the x are also restricted to be odd.

    (c) Show that if $2^k a$, a odd, is in the S_n of (a) and if S_n is of maximum size, then $n < 3^{k+1}a$.

    (d) Show that an S_n of (a) can be of less than maximum size, and yet be maximal in the sense that no new member can be adjoined to S_n.

12. Let $f(n)$ be the sum of the first n terms of the sequence $0, 1, 1, 2, 2, 3, 3, 4, 4, \cdots$. Construct a table for $f(n)$. Prove that $f(n) = [n^2/4]$. For x, y integers, $x > y$, prove that $xy = f(x + y) - f(x - y)$. Thus the process of multiplication can be replaced by an addition, a subtraction, looking up two numbers in the table, and subtracting them.

13. Use the ideas of this section to find a formula for x_n if $x_0 = 1$, $x_1 = 2$, $x_2 = 1$ and $x_{n+1} = x_n + 4x_{n-1} - 4x_{n-2}$. *Suggestion:* consider the expression $x_{n+1} + kx_n + lx_{n-1}$.

Chapter 5

Some Diophantine Equations

5.1 Diophantine Equations

There are many problems and puzzles whose solutions require more than just finding all the solutions of some equation. They are worded in such a way that the desired solutions must satisfy other conditions. For example, we notice that $\frac{26}{65} = \frac{2\not6}{\not65} = \frac{2}{5}$ is correct although this cancelling of the 6 violates the rules of algebra. Our problem is to find all the positive fractions that behave in this way. That is, we are to determine x, y, z in such a way that $\frac{10x + y}{10y + z} = \frac{x}{z}$. This reduces to $(y - x)z = 10(y - z)x$, but we are only interested in solutions such that x, y, and z are positive integers less than 10. We will not carry out the solution. It is not hard to see that the solutions are $\frac{19}{95}, \frac{16}{64}, \frac{26}{65}, \frac{49}{98}$, and the fractions of the form $\frac{10x + x}{10x + x}$.

In the foregoing problem the equation $(y - x)z = 10(y - z)x$ is an indeterminate equation. It has many algebraic solutions, and we are required to sort out the solutions in which x, y, and z are positive integers less than 10. Such a problem is called a Diophantine problem and we say we are solving a Diophantine equation. This particular problem is merely a curiosity, but there are many important Diophantine equations. In general, the added restrictions are that the solutions are to be integers or, sometimes, rational. Frequently the solutions are also to be positive.

There are endless varieties of Diophantine equations, and there is no general method of solution. We will discuss a few of the simplest equations. We will also consider some related problems. For example Theorem 5.6 states, in effect, that the equation $x_1^2 + x_2^2 + x_3^2 + x_4^2 = n$ has at least one solution, with x_1, x_2, x_3, x_4 integers, for each positive integer n. However, we will not attempt to find all the integral solutions.

Pell's equation, $x^2 - dy^2 = N$, will be discussed in Chapter 7.

5.2   The Equation $ax + by = c$

Any linear equation in two variables having integral coefficients can be put in the form $ax + by = c$. The problem is trivial unless neither a nor b is zero, so we can suppose $a \neq 0$, $b \neq 0$. We let g denote (a, b). Then Theorem 1.3 shows that there exist integers x_0 and y_0 such that $ax_0 + by_0 = g$. Numerical values for x_0 and y_0 can be obtained conveniently by applying the Euclidean algorithm, Theorem 1.11, to the integers $|a|$ and $|b|$.

Now if $g \nmid c$, then $ax + by = c$ clearly has no solution in integers. If $g | c$, we use our solution x_0, y_0 of $ax + by = g$ to get a solution $x_1 = (c/g)x_0$, $y_1 = (c/g)y_0$ of $ax + by = c$. In order to find all integral solutions we let r, s denote any integral solution. Then we have $ar + bs = c = ax_1 + by_1$, and hence

$$(5.1) \qquad \frac{a}{g}(r - x_1) = -\frac{b}{g}(s - y_1).$$

But $(a/g, b/g) = 1$ by Corollary 1.7, and hence $(a/g)|(s - y_1)$ and $(b/g)|(r - x_1)$ by Theorem 1.9. This implies $s - y_1 = (a/g)u$ and $r - x_1 = (b/g)t$ for some integers u, t, and then (5.1) implies $u = -t$. Therefore every integral solution r, s of $ax + by = c$ can be written in the form $r = x_1 + (b/g)t$, $s = y_1 - (a/g)t$. Since these values clearly satisfy $ax + by = c$, we have solved the Diophantine equation. Note that the equation has solutions if and only if (a, b) divides c.

Problems

1. Prove that all solutions of $3x + 5y = 1$ can be written in the form $x = 2 + 5t$, $y = -1 - 3t$; also in the form $x = 2 - 5t$, $y = -1 + 3t$; also in

the form $x = -3 + 5t$, $y = 2 - 3t$. Prove that $x = a + bt$, $y = c + dt$ is a form of the general solution if and only if a, c is a solution and either $b = 5$, $d = -3$, or $b = -5$, $d = 3$.

2. Find all solutions of $10x - 7y = 17$.

3. If $ax + by = c$ is solvable, prove that it has a solution x_0, y_0 with $0 \leq x_0 < |b|$.

4. Prove that $ax + by = a + c$ is solvable if and only if $ax + by = c$ is solvable.

5. Consider the equation $ax + by = c$. Since we can divide out any common factor of the coefficients, we may presume that $(a, b, c) = 1$. Prove that the equation is solvable if and only if $(a, b) = 1$. Then, assuming that $(a, b) = 1$, prove that the general solution is $x = x_1 + bt$, $y = y_1 - at$ where x_1, y_1 is any particular solution.

6. Prove that $ax + by = c$ is solvable if and only if $(a, b) = (a, b, c)$.

7. Given that $ax + by = c$ has two solutions, (x_0, y_0) and (x_1, y_1) with $x_1 = 1 + x_0$, and given that $(a, b) = 1$, prove that $b = \pm 1$.

8. Interpreted geometrically, the solutions of $ax + by = c$ in integers are certain points on the straight line represented by the equation in an x, y coordinate system. If $(a, b) = 1$, prove that any segment of the line of length $(a^2 + b^2)^{\frac{1}{2}}$ contains at least one of these points with integral coordinates.

9. Find necessary and sufficient conditions that

$$x + b_1 y + c_1 z = d_1, \qquad x + b_2 y + c_2 z = d_2$$

have at least one simultaneous solution in integers x, y, z, assuming that the coefficients are integers with $b_1 \neq b_2$.

10. Give an independent proof that $ax + by = c$ has at least one solution in integers x, y if $(a, b) | c$, by using induction on max (a, b). *Suggestion:* if $0 < a < b$ then $ax + by = c$ is solvable if and only if $a(x - y) + (b - a)y = c$ is solvable.

5.3 Positive Solutions

Let us suppose that a, b, and c are positive, that $(a, b) | c$, and that we are asked to find all solutions r, s of $ax + by = c$ in positive integers. We solve as in Section 5.2, and have only to restrict t in such a way as to make r and s positive. We merely restrict t to the range $-(g/b)x_1 < t < (g/a)y_1$. The smallest allowable value for t is $[-(g/b)x_1 + 1]$ and the largest value is $-[(-g/a)y_1 + 1]$. The number of solutions is then

$$N = - \left[-\frac{g}{a} y_1 + 1 \right] - \left[-\frac{g}{b} x_1 + 1 \right] + 1$$

$$= - \left(\left[-\frac{g}{a} y_1 \right] + \left[-\frac{g}{b} x_1 \right] + 1 \right)$$

from which we find, by use of Theorem 4.1d, that

$$- \left(\left[-\frac{g}{a} y_1 - \frac{g}{b} x_1 \right] + 1 \right) \leqq N \leqq - \left[-\frac{g}{a} y_1 - \frac{g}{b} x_1 \right].$$

Since $-(g/a)y_1 - (g/b)x_1 = -(g/ab)(by_1 + ax_1) = -(gc)/(ab)$ we finally have

$$- \left[-\frac{gc}{ab} \right] - 1 \leqq N \leqq - \left[-\frac{gc}{ab} \right].$$

These inequalities do not constitute a precise formula for N, but they do specify two consecutive integers one of which must be N. Note that there will always be at least one positive solution of $ax + by = c$ if $g|c$ and $gc > ab$.

Problems

1. Find all solutions in positive integers:
   (a) $5x + 3y = 52$;
   (b) $15x + 7y = 111$;
   (c) $40x + 63y = 521$;
   (d) $123x + 57y = 531$;
   (e) $12x + 501y = 1$;
   (f) $12x + 501y = 274$;
   (g) $97x + 98y = 1000$.
2. Prove that $101x + 37y = 3819$ has a positive solution in integers.
3. Given that $(a, b) = 1$ and that a and b are of opposite sign, prove that $ax + by = c$ has infinitely many positive solutions for any value of c.
4. Let a, b, c be positive integers. Prove that there is no solution of $ax + by = c$ in positive integers if $a + b > c$.
5. The theory in the text states that one of the formulas

$$N = - \left[-\frac{gc}{ab} \right] - 1, \qquad N = - \left[-\frac{gc}{ab} \right]$$

is correct. Prove that neither formula is correct in all cases.

6. Let a, b, c be positive integers such that $(a, b) = 1$. Assuming that c/ab is not an integer, prove that the number N of solutions of $ax + by = c$ in positive integers is $[c/ab]$ or $[c/ab] + 1$. Assuming further that c/a is an integer, prove that $N = [c/ab]$. *Suggestion:* if c/a is an integer, then a specific solution of $ax + by = c$ can be found easily, for example, $x_1 = c/a$, $y_1 = 0$.

7. Let a, b, c be positive integers such that $(a, b) = 1$. Assuming that c/ab is an integer, prove that $N = -1 + c/ab$.

8. Modify the theory of this section so as to treat the number, say N_0, of solutions in non-negative integers of $ax + by = c$, where a, b, c are positive integers such that $(a, b)|c$. *Suggestion:* observe that t is restricted to the range $-(g/b)x_1 \leq t \leq (g/a)y_1$. The smallest allowable value for t is $-[(g/b)x_1]$ and the largest value is $[(g/a)y_1]$. The final inequalities turn out to be

$$\left[\frac{gc}{ab}\right] \leq N_0 \leq \left[\frac{gc}{ab}\right] + 1.$$

9. Let a and b be positive integers satisfying $(a, b) = 1$. Consider the set S of integers $\{ax + by\}$, where x and y range over all non-negative integers. Prove that the set S contains all integers greater than $c = ab - a - b$, but not c itself.

10. In the preceding problem, restrict x and y to be positive integers, yielding the set $S' = \{ax + by\}$. What is the largest integer missing from the set S'?

5.4 Other Linear Equations

Consider the equation

$$(5.2) \qquad a_1x_1 + a_2x_2 + \cdots + a_kx_k = c, \qquad k > 2,$$

and let g denote the greatest common divisor $(a_1, a_2, \cdots, a_k)$. If the equation has a solution, then clearly $g|c$. Conversely, by Theorem 1.5 there exist $y_1, y_2, \cdots, y_k$ such that $a_1y_1 + a_2y_2 + \cdots + a_ky_k = g$. If $g|c$ then $c = gr$ for some integer r and $x_1 = ry_1$, $x_2 = ry_2, \cdots$, $x_k = ry_k$ is a solution of (5.2). Thus (5.2) has solutions if and only if $g|c$.

To find solutions of (5.2) we reduce it to the case of Section 5.2 with two unknowns. We can suppose that the a_i are not zero, and that $(a_1, a_2, \cdots, a_k)|c$. We write

$$(5.3) \qquad x_{k-1} = \alpha u + \beta v, \qquad x_k = \gamma u + \delta v,$$

where we shall choose integers α, β, γ, δ in such a way that $\alpha\delta - \beta\gamma = 1$.

Then we will have $u = \delta x_{k-1} - \beta x_k$ and $v = -\gamma x_{k-1} + \alpha x_k$. Thus, u, v are integers if and only if x_{k-1}, x_k are. If we take

$$\beta = \frac{a_k}{(a_{k-1}, a_k)}, \qquad \delta = \frac{-a_{k-1}}{(a_{k-1}, a_k)},$$

then $(\beta, \delta) = 1$, and we can solve $\alpha\delta - \beta\gamma = 1$ for α, γ by the method of Section 5.2. However, we need only one pair of values for α, γ, not the general solution.

Equation (5.2) now reduces to

$$(5.4) \quad a_1 x_1 + a_2 x_2 + \cdots + a_{k-2} x_{k-2} + (a_{k-1}\alpha + a_k\gamma)u = c,$$

with one less unknown, and we note that

$$a_{k-1}\alpha + a_k\gamma = -(a_{k-1}, a_k)\alpha\delta + (a_{k-1}, a_k)\beta\gamma = -(a_{k-1}, a_k),$$

$$(a_1, a_2, \cdots, a_{k-2}, (a_{k-1}, a_k)) = (a_1, a_2, \cdots, a_k).$$

Thus the new equation, (5.4), has the same properties as equation (5.2), that the g.c.d. of its coefficients divides c and that no coefficient is zero. If $k > 3$ this reduction process can be applied to equation (5.4) to produce an equation with $k - 2$ variables, and hence repetitions of the process finally lead to an equation with two unknowns.

Furthermore we may note from Section 5.2 that if a linear equation in two unknowns has a solution, its general solution is given in terms of a single parameter t. Similarly the solutions of (5.2), with k unknowns, are expressed in terms of $k - 1$ parameters. This can be proved by induction on k. For if any equation such as (5.4), in $k - 1$ unknowns, has solutions $x_1, x_2, \cdots, x_{k-2}, u$ in terms of $k - 2$ parameters, $v_1, v_2, \cdots, v_{k-2}$, then, by (5.3), the solutions of (5.2) are given by $x_1, x_2, \cdots, x_{k-2}, \alpha u + \beta v, \gamma u + \delta v$. These involve the $k - 1$ parameters $v_1, v_2, \cdots, v_{k-2}, v$. It is easy to see that the solutions have the form $x_i = b_i + d_{i,1}v_1 + d_{i,2}v_2 + \cdots + d_{i,k-1}v_{k-1}$ where we have written v_{k-1} for v.

If we are asked to solve a system of s equations in r unknowns,

$$(5.5) \quad a_{j,1}x_1 + a_{j,2}x_2 + \cdots + a_{j,r}x_r = c_j, \qquad j = 1, 2, \cdots, s,$$

we start by solving the first equation, $j = 1$. If it has a solution, it will be of the form

$$x_i = b_i + d_{i,1}v_1 + d_{i,2}v_2 + \cdots + d_{i,r-1}v_{r-1}, \qquad i = 1, 2, \cdots, r.$$

We substitute these in the remaining equations and solve the second equation, $j = 2$, for $v_1, v_2, \cdots, v_{r-1}$ in terms of $r - 2$ new parameters. Repetition of this process allows us to solve the system (5.5). Of course, if we encounter an equation that has no solutions, then the system (5.5) has no solutions.

Problem

1. Solve the equations:
   (a) $x + 2y + 3z = 1$ (b) $x + 2y + 3z = 10$
   (c) $5x - 2y - 4z = 1$ (d) $5x - 2y - 4z = 10$
   (e) $3x - 6y + 5z = 11$ (f) $6x + 48y - 78z = 5$

5.5   The Equation $x^2 + y^2 = z^2$

We wish to solve the equation $x^2 + y^2 = z^2$ in positive integers. Consider such a solution x, y, z and write g for (x, y). Then $g^2 | z^2$ and hence $g | z$, and since $(x, y, z) = ((x, y), z)$ holds in general, we see that $(x, y, z) = g$. By symmetry we have $(x, y, z) = (x, y) = (y, z) = (x, z) = g$, and

$$\left(\frac{x}{g}\right)^2 + \left(\frac{y}{g}\right)^2 = \left(\frac{z}{g}\right)^2, \qquad \left(\frac{x}{g}, \frac{y}{g}\right) = \left(\frac{y}{g}, \frac{z}{g}\right) = \left(\frac{x}{g}, \frac{z}{g}\right) = 1.$$

A solution x_1, y_1, z_1 having the property that these three are relatively prime in pairs is called a primitive solution. Thus every solution x, y, z can be written in the form gx_1, gy_1, gz_1 where x_1, y_1, z_1 is some primitive solution. Conversely, if x_1, y_1, z_1 is a primitive solution, then gx_1, gy_1, gz_1 is a solution if g is a positive integer. Thus we need look only for primitive solutions, and this we now do.

Now x and y cannot both be even. They cannot both be odd either, for if they were we would have $x^2 \equiv 1 \pmod 4$, $y^2 \equiv 1 \pmod 4$, and therefore $z^2 \equiv 2 \pmod 4$, which is impossible.

Since x and y enter the equations symmetrically we can now restrict our attention to primitive solutions for which y is even, x and z odd.

Then we have

(5.6)
$$\frac{z+x}{2}\frac{z-x}{2} = \left(\frac{y}{2}\right)^2.$$

Now
$$\left(\frac{z+x}{2},\frac{z-x}{2}\right)\Big|\left(\frac{z+x}{2} + \frac{z-x}{2}\right) = z$$

and
$$\left(\frac{z+x}{2},\frac{z-x}{2}\right)\Big|\left(\frac{z+x}{2} - \frac{z-x}{2}\right) = x$$

and therefore
$$\left(\frac{z+x}{2},\frac{z-x}{2}\right) = 1.$$

This with equation (5.6) shows that $(z+x)/2 = r^2$ and $(z-x)/2 = s^2$ for some positive integers r, s. We also see that $(r, s) = 1, r > s, x = r^2 - s^2, y = 2rs, z = r^2 + s^2$. Also, since z is odd, r and s are of opposite parity, one is even, the other odd.

Conversely, let r and s be any two integers such that $(r, s) = 1$, $r > s > 0$, r and s of opposite parity. Then if $x = r^2 - s^2$, $y = 2rs$, $z = r^2 + s^2$, we have x, y, z positive and

$$x^2 + y^2 = (r^2 - s^2)^2 + (2rs)^2 = (r^2 + s^2)^2 = z^2.$$

It is easy to see that $(x, y) = 1$ and that y is even. Therefore, x, y, z is a primitive solution with y even. Thus we have the following result.

Theorem 5.1 *The positive primitive solutions of $x^2 + y^2 = z^2$ with y even are $x = r^2 - s^2$, $y = 2rs$, $z = r^2 + s^2$, where r and s are arbitrary integers of opposite parity with $r > s > 0$ and $(r, s) = 1$.*

Problems

1. Find all primitive solutions of $x^2 + y^2 = z^2$ having $0 < z < 30$.
2. Prove that if $x^2 + y^2 = z^2$, then one of x, y is a multiple of 3 and one of x, y, z is a multiple of 5.
3. Any solution of $x^2 + y^2 = z^2$ in positive integers is called a Pythagorean triple because there is a right triangle whose sides have corresponding lengths. Find all Pythagorean triples whose terms form (*a*) an arithmetic progression, (*b*) a geometric progression.
4. If n is any integer ≥ 3, show that there is a Pythagorean triple with n as one of its members.

5. For which positive integers n are there solutions to the equation $x^2 - y^2 = n$?

6. Prove that every integer n can be expressed in the form $n = x^2 + y^2 - z^2$.

7. Prove that $x^2 + y^2 = z^4$ has infinitely many solutions with $(x, y, z) = 1$.

8. Show that all solutions of $x^2 + 2y^2 = z^2$ in positive integers with $(x, y, z) = 1$ are given by $x = |u^2 - 2v^2|$, $y = 2uv$, $z = u^2 + 2v^2$, where u and v are arbitrary positive integers such that u is odd and $(u, v) = 1$. *Suggestion:* any solution has y even, because y odd implies $z^2 - x^2 \equiv 2 \pmod 8$, which is impossible. Hence x and z are odd, and the proof of Theorem 5.1 can be used as a model.

9. Show that $(x, y) > 1$ if x, y, z satisfies $\dfrac{1}{x^2} + \dfrac{1}{y^2} = \dfrac{1}{z^2}$.

10. Show that if $\dfrac{1}{x^2} + \dfrac{1}{y^2} = \dfrac{1}{z^2}$, then $xy \equiv 0 \pmod{60}$.

11. Prove that the positive solutions of $\dfrac{1}{x^2} + \dfrac{1}{y^2} = \dfrac{1}{z^2}$, $(x, y, z) = 1$ are given by

$$x = r^4 - s^4, \quad y = 2rs(r^2 + s^2), \quad z = rs(r^2 - s^2)$$

or

$$x = 2rs(r^2 + s^2), \quad y = r^4 - s^4, \quad z = rs(r^2 - s^2)$$

where $r > s > 0$, $(r, s) = 1$, and r and s of opposite parity.

12. Prove that no Pythagorean triple of integers belongs to an isosceles right triangle, but that there are infinitely many primitive Pythagorean triples for which the acute angles of the corresponding triangles are, for any given positive ϵ, within ϵ of $\pi/4$.

5.6   The Equation $x^4 + y^4 = z^2$

In trying to solve the equation $x^4 + y^4 = z^2$ in positive integers, we can restrict ourselves to solutions x, y, z for which $(x, y) = 1$, just as in Section 5.5. Then $(x^2)^2 + (y^2)^2 = z^2$ and x^2, y^2, z is a primitive solution of the equation of Section 5.5. We can assume that y^2, and hence y, is even. Then there are two integers u and v such that $x^2 = u^2 - v^2$, $y^2 = 2uv$, $z = u^2 + v^2$, $u > v > 0$, $(u, v) = 1$ and u and v are of opposite parity. If u were even, then v would be odd, and we would have $x^2 \equiv 0 - 1 \equiv 3 \pmod 4$. Since this is impossible we have u odd and v even. Then

$$\left(\frac{y}{2}\right)^2 = u \cdot \frac{v}{2}, \qquad \left(u, \frac{v}{2}\right) = 1,$$

and hence, for some integers r and s,

$$u = r^2, \quad \frac{v}{2} = s^2, \quad y = 2rs, \quad (r, s) = 1, \quad r > 0, s > 0, \quad r \text{ odd.}$$

Also $x^2 + v^2 = u^2$ so we have $x^2 + 4s^4 = r^4$. Since $(r, 2s) = 1$ we can apply Section 5.5 to this equation. There are integers ρ and σ such that

$$x = \rho^2 - \sigma^2, \quad 2s^2 = 2\rho\sigma, \quad r^2 = \rho^2 + \sigma^2, \quad (\rho, \sigma) = 1, \quad \rho > \sigma > 0.$$

Since $\rho\sigma = s^2$, we can write $\rho = f^2$, $\sigma = g^2$ with some $f > 0$, $g > 0$ $(f, g) = 1$. Then we have $r^2 = f^4 + g^4$, which looks just like our original equation. In trying to solve the equation we have tried to reduce it to something simpler but have ended up with an equation of the same form. At first glance this seems rather profitless, but we may have gained something. We started with the solution x, y, z and ended with the solution f, g, r. We may have found a different solution. In fact we have $z = u^2 + v^2 = r^4 + 4s^4 > r^4$, so $z > r$ and f, g, r is a different solution. More than this, we have obtained a solution with $z > r > 0$. Now if we apply the entire reduction to the new solution we obtain still another solution f_1, g_1, r_1 with $r > r_1 > 0$. Continuing in the same way we obtain a whole sequence of solutions with corresponding r_i such that $r > r_1 > r_2 > \cdots > 0$. But all the r_i are integers, and hence $r_r \leqq 0$. Thus the assumption that there was a solution has led us to a contradiction. We have not solved the equation but have shown that it has no solution x, y, z in positive integers with $(x, y) = 1$.

If x, y, z were any integral solution of the equation with $xy \neq 0$, then $|x|/g$, $|y|/g$, $|z|/g^2$ where $g = (x, y)$ would be a solution in positive integers with $(|x|/g, |y|/g) = 1$.

Therefore, any solution x, y, z will be such that $xy = 0$ and so we have proved the following proposition.

Theorem 5.2 *The only integral solutions of $x^4 + y^4 = z^2$ are the trivial solutions $x = 0$, y, $z = \pm y^2$ and x, $y = 0$, $z = \pm x^2$.*

The method used in the proof of this theorem is sometimes called "proof by descent" or "Fermat's method of infinite descent." This type of proof, which also occurs at other places in number theory, is based on the principle that every nonempty set of positive integers contains a least element. It may also be noted that the proof could have been written in a slightly different form as a reduction to a contradiction. Thus, if we had presumed that the initial solution x, y, z had been selected as that one with least positive z, the procedure would have led us to another solution f, g, r with $0 < r < z$, which is clearly a contradiction.

The fact that $x^4 + y^4 = z^2$ has no positive solutions implies that $x^4 + y^4 = z^4$ has no positive solutions. This is a particular case of a famous statement of Fermat. It is often called Fermat's last theorem, and it states that for $n > 2$, the equations $x^n + y^n = z^n$ have no integral solutions other than the trivial solutions in which one variable is zero. We have found the solutions for $n = 2$ and have proved the statement for $n = 4$. It is known that the statement is true for a great many values of n, but it has neither been proved nor disproved in general.

Problems

1. For any positive integer $n \equiv 0 \pmod 4$, prove that $x^n + y^n = z^n$ has no solutions with $xy \neq 0$.
2. Prove that $x^4 + 4y^4 = z^2$ has no solutions with $xy \neq 0$. *Suggestions:* use the method of proof of Theorem 5.2.
3. Prove that $x^4 - y^4 = z^2$ has no solutions with $yz \neq 0$.
4. Consider an integral right triangle, that is, a right triangle the lengths of whose sides form a Pythagorean triple. Prove that the area is not a perfect square.
5. Prove that there are no positive integers a and b such that both $a^2 + b^2$ and $a^2 - b^2$ are perfect squares.

5.7 Sum of Four Squares

Our aim in this section is not to solve a Diophantine equation but only to show that the equation $x_1^2 + x_2^2 + x_3^2 + x_4^2 = n$ has at least one integral solution whenever n is a positive integer. We start with an algebraic identity.

Lemma 5.3 *We have*

$$(5.7) \quad (x_1^2 + x_2^2 + x_3^2 + x_4^2)(y_1^2 + y_2^2 + y_3^2 + y_4^2)$$
$$= (x_1y_1 + x_2y_2 + x_3y_3 + x_4y_4)^2 + (x_1y_2 - x_2y_1 + x_3y_4 - x_4y_3)^2$$
$$+ (x_1y_3 - x_3y_1 + x_4y_2 - x_2y_4)^2 + (x_1y_4 - x_4y_1 + x_2y_3 - x_3y_2)^2.$$

Proof. This identity, discovered by Euler, can be verified by just multiplying out both sides.

This identity shows that if X and Y can be expressed as sums of four squares, then so can their product XY. Since $1 = 1^2 + 0^2 + 0^2 + 0^2$ and $2 = 1^2 + 1^2 + 0^2 + 0^2$, we need prove only that every odd prime can be expressed as a sum of four squares. The proof can be broken up into two steps.

Theorem 5.4 *Let p denote any odd prime. There is an integer m such that $1 \leq m < p$ and $mp = x_1^2 + x_2^2 + x_3^2 + x_4^2$ for some integers x_1, x_2, x_3, x_4.*

Proof. Consider the sets S_1 consisting of 0^2, 1^2, 2^2, $\cdots$, $\{(p-1)/2\}^2$ and S_2 consisting of $-0^2 - 1$, $-1^2 - 1$, $-2^2 - 1$, $\cdots$, $-\{(p-1)/2\}^2 - 1$. Since $x^2 \equiv y^2 \pmod{p}$ implies $p \mid (x - y)$ or $p \mid (x + y)$, we see that no two numbers of S_1 are congruent modulo p. Also no two numbers of S_2 are congruent modulo p. Now S_1 and S_2 together consist of $p + 1$ integers. Since there are only p distinct residue classes modulo p we see that some number, say x^2, is congruent modulo p to some number, $-y^2 - 1$, of S_2. Then $x^2 + y^2 + 1 \equiv 0 \pmod{p}$, $0 \leq x \leq (p-1)/2$, $0 \leq y \leq (p-1)/2$, and we have

$$x^2 + y^2 + 1 = mp, \qquad 1 \leq m = \frac{1}{p}(x^2 + y^2 + 1)$$

$$\leq \frac{1}{p}\left(2\left(\frac{p-1}{2}\right)^2 + 1\right) < \frac{1}{p}\left(\frac{p^2}{2} + 1\right) < p.$$

Theorem 5.5 *If m is the least integer satisfying Theorem 5.4, then $m = 1$.*

Proof. There certainly is at least one such m. If m is even, then so is $mp = x_1^2 + x_2^2 + x_3^2 + x_4^2$, and hence either none, two, or four of the x_i are even. If exactly two of the x_i are even, we can number the x_i in such a way that x_1 and x_2 are the even ones. Then in all cases $x_1 \pm x_2$ and $x_3 \pm x_4$ are even, and

$$\left(\frac{x_1 + x_2}{2}\right)^2 + \left(\frac{x_1 - x_2}{2}\right)^2 + \left(\frac{x_3 + x_4}{2}\right)^2 + \left(\frac{x_3 - x_4}{2}\right)^2 = \frac{m}{2}p.$$

Therefore m is not least if it is even.

Now consider the possibility $m > 1$. Since m is odd we have $3 \leq m < p$. For $1 \leq i \leq 4$, we define numbers y_i by

$$(5.8) \qquad y_i \equiv x_i \pmod{m}, \qquad -\frac{m-1}{2} \leq y_i \leq \frac{m-1}{2}.$$

Then $y_1^2 + y_2^2 + y_3^2 + y_4^2 \equiv x_1^2 + x_2^2 + x_3^2 + x_4^2 \equiv 0 \pmod{m}$ since $x_1^2 + x_2^2 + x_3^2 + x_4^2 = mp$, and we can write

$$(5.9) \quad y_1^2 + y_2^2 + y_3^2 + y_4^2 = mn, \qquad 0 \leq n \leq \frac{1}{m} 4 \left(\frac{m-1}{2}\right)^2 < m.$$

If n were zero, we would have $y_1 = y_2 = y_3 = y_4 = 0$ by (5.9), and then $x_1 \equiv x_2 \equiv x_3 \equiv x_4 \equiv 0 \pmod{m}$ by (5.8). This would imply $mp = x_1^2 + x_2^2 + x_3^2 + x_4^2 \equiv 0 \pmod{m^2}$, hence $p \equiv 0 \pmod{m}$, which is impossible since $3 \leq m < p$. Therefore we have $n > 0$.

Using Theorem 5.3 we see that

$$(5.10) \qquad m^2 np = (x_1^2 + x_2^2 + x_3^2 + x_4^2)(y_1^2 + y_2^2 + y_3^2 + y_4^2)$$
$$= A_1^2 + A_2^2 + A_3^2 + A_4^2,$$

where the A_i denote the expressions whose squares appear on the right side of (5.7). Using (5.8) we easily find that $A_i \equiv 0 \pmod{m}$ for $i = 1, 2, 3, 4$. Dividing (5.10) by m^2 we get

$$np = \left(\frac{A_1}{m}\right)^2 + \left(\frac{A_2}{m}\right)^2 + \left(\frac{A_3}{m}\right)^2 + \left(\frac{A_4}{m}\right)^2$$

with $0 < n < m$. This shows that m is not least if $m > 1$. Hence $m = 1$ and the theorem is proved.

Collecting our results and noting that $7 = 2^2 + 1^2 + 1^2 + 1^2$ requires four squares, we obtain the following theorem:

Theorem 5.6 *Every positive integer is a sum of four squares, and fewer than four squares will not suffice.*

Problems

1. Prove that no integer of the form $8k + 7$ can be expressed as a sum of three squares.

2. Prove that no integer of the form $4^m(8k + 7)$ is expressible as a sum of three squares. (*Remark:* these are the only integers not expressible as sums of three squares, but the proof of this result is not given in this book.)

5.8 Waring's Problem

Waring considered the question as to whether the results of Section 5.7 can be generalized to higher powers. He conjectured that 9 cubes, 19 fourth powers, etc. would suffice. Hilbert proved that for each positive integer k there is a number g such that g kth powers will suffice. If $g(k)$ denotes the least number of kth powers that will suffice, then $g(2) = 4$, as we have just seen. It is known that $g(3) = 9$, and the value of $g(k)$ is also known for $k \geq 6$ apart from a possible exceptional circumstance relating to the fractional part of $(3/2)^k$. For the cases $k = 4$ and 5 it is known that $19 \leq g(4) \leq 35$ and $37 \leq g(5) \leq 54$. However, except for $g(2)$ and $g(3)$, the known proofs of these results involve much more complicated methods. The proofs lean heavily on the theory of functions of a complex variable, and they belong to the part of number theory called the analytic theory of numbers. There is a good account of the history of the problem in the notes at the end of Chapter 21 of Hardy and Wright's *An Introduction to the Theory of Numbers.*

Problem

1. Prove that $g(k) \geq 2^k + [3^k/2^k] - 2$. *Suggestion:* express the number $n = 2^k[3^k/2^k] - 1$ as a sum of kth powers.

5.9 Sum of Fourth Powers

There is one small result connected with Waring's problem that we can obtain simply. We will prove $g(4) \leq 50$. This is far from the known result, $g(4) \leq 35$, but it is of some interest because the proof is elementary, and because it proves the existence of $g(4)$.

Summing the identity $(x_i + x_j)^4 + (x_i - x_j)^4 = 2x_i^4 + 12x_i^2x_j^2 +$

$2x_j^4$ we find

$$\sum_{1 \leq i < j \leq 4} ((x_i + x_j)^4 + (x_i - x_j)^4)$$

$$= 2 \sum_{i=1}^{4} (4 - i)x_i^4 + 6 \sum_{i=1}^{4} \sum_{\substack{j=1 \\ j \neq i}}^{4} x_i^2 x_j^2 + 2 \sum_{j=1}^{4} (j - 1)x_j^4$$

$$= 2 \sum_{i=1}^{4} (4 - i + i - 1)x_i^4 + 6 \sum_{i=1}^{4} \sum_{\substack{j=1 \\ j \neq i}}^{4} x_i^2 x_j^2$$

$$= 6 \sum_{i=1}^{4} x_i^4 + 6 \sum_{i=1}^{4} \sum_{\substack{j=1 \\ j \neq i}}^{4} x_i^2 x_j^2$$

$$= 6 \sum_{i=1}^{4} \sum_{j=1}^{4} x_i^2 x_j^2 = 6 \left(\sum_{i=1}^{4} x_i^2 \right)^2.$$

The left side is a sum of 12 fourth powers. This with Theorem 5.6 shows that every number of the form $6m^2$ is a sum of 12 fourth powers. But Theorem 5.6 also shows that every positive integer of the form $6l$ can be expressed as a sum of four numbers of the form $6m^2$, and hence as a sum of 48 fourth powers.

Furthermore the integers $j = 0, 1, 2, 81, 16, 17$ form a complete residue system modulo 6, and each one is the sum of at most 2 fourth powers. Then every integer $n > 81$ can be written in the form $6l + j$ with l positive, and hence can be expressed as a sum of at most 50 fourth powers. For $0 < n \leq 50$ we have $n = \sum_{i=1}^{n} 1^4$, and for $50 < n \leq 81$ we have $n = 2^4 + 2^4 + 2^4 + \sum_{i=1}^{n-48} 1^4$. In all cases n is expressed as a sum of at most 50 fourth powers.

5.10 Sum of Two Squares

Not every positive integer is a sum of two squares. We will determine just which integers are sums of two squares and will find the number of solutions of $x^2 + y^2 = n$.

A solution x, y of $x^2 + y^2 = n$ will be called primitive if $(x, y) = 1$. We restrict n to be positive, and we let

$N(n)$ = number of solutions of $x^2 + y^2 = n$,

$P(n)$ = number of non-negative, primitive solutions of $x^2 + y^2 = n$,

$Q(n)$ = number of primitive solutions of $x^2 + y^2 = n$.

In counting solutions we consider x_1, y_1 and x_2, y_2 as distinct if $x_1 \neq x_2$ or $y_1 \neq y_2$. It may be noted that, for $n > 1$, $P(n)$ is actually the number of positive primitive solutions of $x^2 + y^2 = n$, since neither x nor y can be zero.

Theorem 5.7 *We have* $N(1) = Q(1) = 4, P(1) = 2$, *and, for* $n > 1$, $Q(n) = 4P(n)$ *and*

$$N(n) = \sum_{d^2 \mid n} Q\left(\frac{n}{d^2}\right).$$

Proof. Since $1 = (\pm 1)^2 + 0^2 = 0^2 + (\pm 1)^2$ and there are no other solutions, we have $N(1) = Q(1) = 4$ and $P(1) = 2$.

If $n > 1$ and x, y is a non-negative primitive solution, then $x \geq 1$, $y \geq 1$, and $\pm x$, $\pm y$ is a primitive solution for all choices of the signs. From this it follows that $Q(n) = 4P(n)$.

If x, y is any solution of $x^2 + y^2 = n$, and if $g = (x, y)$, then $g^2 \mid n$, $(x/g, y/g) = 1$, and $(x/g)^2 + (y/g)^2 = n/g^2$. From this it is easy to see that

$$N(n) = \sum_{d^2 \mid n} Q\left(\frac{n}{d^2}\right).$$

Theorem 5.8 *Suppose* $n > 1$. *Each non-negative primitive solution of* $x^2 + y^2 = n$ *determines a unique* s *modulo* n *such that* $sy \equiv x$ (mod n). *Furthermore,* $s^2 \equiv -1$ (mod n), *and different non-negative primitive solutions determine different* s *modulo* n.

Proof. If x, y is a non-negative primitive solution, then $(y, n) = 1$ and hence $sy \equiv x$ (mod n) determines a unique s modulo n. Furthermore if y' is a solution of $yy' \equiv 1$ (mod n), then $s \equiv xy'$ (mod n), and we have $s^2 \equiv x^2 y'^2 \equiv -y^2 y'^2 \equiv -1$ (mod n).

We must still show that different solutions determine different s. Suppose that x, y and u, v are both non-negative primitive solutions and that $sy \equiv x \pmod{n}$ and $sv \equiv u \pmod{n}$. Then we have $xv \equiv syv \equiv yu \pmod{n}$. But since $n > 1$, any non-negative primitive solution is a positive solution and so we have $1 \leq x < \sqrt{n}$, $1 \leq v < \sqrt{n}$. Hence $1 \leq xv < n$, and similarly $1 \leq yu < n$. Therefore $xv = yu$, and hence $x = u$, $y = v$, since $(x, y) = (u, v) = 1$ and all the numbers are positive.

Theorem 5.9 *Suppose $n > 1$, $s^2 \equiv -1 \pmod{n}$. There is a non-negative primitive solution x, y of $x^2 + y^2 = n$ such that $sy \equiv x \pmod{n}$.*

Proof. Consider the set of integers $u - sv$ where u and v run through all integral values such that $0 \leq u \leq \sqrt{n}$, $0 \leq v \leq \sqrt{n}$. There are $(1 + [\sqrt{n}])^2 > n$ different pairs u, v. Therefore, there are two pairs u_1, v_1 and u_2, v_2 such that $u_1 - sv_1 \equiv u_2 - sv_2 \pmod{n}$. Let us set $v_2 - v_1 = v_0$, $u_2 - u_1 = u_0$. We then have $sv_0 \equiv u_0 \pmod{n}$ and $|u_0| \leq \sqrt{n}$, $|v_0| \leq \sqrt{n}$. Furthermore, since u_1, v_1 and u_2, v_2 are different pairs, u_0 and v_0 cannot both be zero. Also, we can show that at least one of $|u_0|$ and $|v_0|$ is less than $\sqrt{n}$. This is obvious if n is not a square. If n is a square and $|u_0| = |v_0| = \sqrt{n}$, we have $s\sqrt{n} \equiv \pm\sqrt{n} \pmod{n}$, and hence $s \equiv \pm 1 \pmod{\sqrt{n}}$, $s^2 \equiv 1 \pmod{\sqrt{n}}$. But $s^2 \equiv -1 \pmod{n}$, so we have $s^2 \equiv -1 \pmod{\sqrt{n}}$, and hence $1 \equiv -1 \pmod{\sqrt{n}}$. Therefore $\sqrt{n} = 2$ and $n = 4$, but this cannot occur since there is no integer s such that $s^2 \equiv -1 \pmod{4}$.

The bounds for u_0 and v_0 imply the inequality $1 < u_0^2 + v_0^2 < 2n$. The congruence $sv_0 \equiv u_0 \pmod{n}$ implies $u_0^2 + v_0^2 \equiv s^2 v_0^2 + v_0^2 \equiv v_0^2(s^2 + 1) \equiv 0 \pmod{n}$. Together these imply $u_0^2 + v_0^2 = n$.

Now let $g = (u_0, v_0)$. Then $g^2 | n$ and $s(v_0/g) \equiv (u_0/g) \pmod{n/g}$, and hence

$$\frac{n}{g^2} \equiv \frac{u_0^2 + v_0^2}{g^2} \equiv \left(s\frac{v_0}{g}\right)^2 + \left(\frac{v_0}{g}\right)^2 \equiv -\left(\frac{v_0}{g}\right)^2 + \left(\frac{v_0}{g}\right)^2 \equiv 0 \left(\bmod \frac{n}{g}\right).$$

This is possible only if $g = 1$, and we have $(u_0, v_0) = 1$.

Finally, if u_0 and v_0 have the same sign we let $x = |u_0|$, $y = |v_0|$. If u_0 and v_0 have opposite signs we let $x = |v_0|$, $y = |u_0|$. In both cases we see that x, y is a non-negative primitive solution. In the first case we have $sy \equiv s(\pm v_0) \equiv \pm u_0 \equiv x \pmod{n}$. In the second case we have $sy \equiv s(\pm u_0) \equiv \pm s(sv_0) \equiv \mp v_0 \equiv x \pmod{n}$.

The last two theorems show that there is a one to one correspondence between the non-negative primitive solutions of $x^2 + y^2 = n$ and the solutions of the congruence $s^2 \equiv -1 \pmod{n}$. Combining this with Theorem 5.7 we have the following.

Theorem 5.10 *Let* $R(n)$ *denote the number of roots of* $s^2 \equiv -1 \pmod{n}$. *Then* $P(n) = R(n)$ *for* $n > 1$, $P(1) = 2$, $R(1) = 1$, $Q(1) = 4$, $Q(n) = 4R(n)$ *for* $n \geq 1$, *and* $N(n) = 4 \sum_{d^2 \mid n} R(n/d^2)$.

Theorem 5.11 *The functions* $R(n)$ *and* $N(n)/4$ *are multiplicative functions.*

Proof. The fact that $R(n)$ is multiplicative follows directly from Theorem 2.14. To show that $N(n)/4$ is multiplicative, we consider any two positive relatively prime integers n_1 and n_2. Then

$$\frac{1}{4} N(n_1 n_2) = \sum_{d^2 \mid n_1 n_2} R\left(\frac{n_1 n_2}{d^2}\right) = \sum_{d_1^2 \mid n_1} \sum_{d_2^2 \mid n_2} R\left(\frac{n_1}{d_1^2} \frac{n_2}{d_2^2}\right)$$

$$= \sum_{d_1^2 \mid n_1} \sum_{d_2^2 \mid n_2} R\left(\frac{n_1}{d_1^2}\right) R\left(\frac{n_2}{d_2^2}\right) = \sum_{d_1^2 \mid n_1} R\left(\frac{n_1}{d_1^2}\right) \sum_{d_2^2 \mid n_2} R\left(\frac{n_2}{d_2^2}\right)$$

$$= \frac{1}{4} N(n_1) \frac{1}{4} N(n_2).$$

Theorem 5.12 *Let* $h(1) = 1$, $h(2^e) = 0$, $h(p^e) = (-1)^{\{(p-1)/2\}e}$, p *an odd prime,* $e \geq 1$. *Let* $h(n)$ *for composite* n *be determined in such a way that* $h(n)$ *is a multiplicative function. Then* $N(n) = 4 \sum_{d \mid n} h(d)$.

Proof. It is interesting to note that $h(n)$ as defined above is actually totally multiplicative.

By Theorem 4.4, $\sum_{d \mid n} h(d)$ is multiplicative. Since $N(n)/4$ is also multiplicative, we have only to verify that $N(n) = 4 \sum_{d \mid n} h(d)$ for n a prime power. The congruence $s^2 \equiv -1 \pmod{2}$ has the one solution $s \equiv 1 \pmod{2}$. For $e > 1$ the congruence $s^2 \equiv -1 \pmod{2^e}$ has no solutions since $s^2 \equiv -1 \pmod{4}$ has none. Therefore by

Theorem 5.10,

$$N(2^e) = 4 \sum_{f=0}^{[e/2]} R(2^{e-2f}) = 4$$

since non-zero terms will occur only for $e - 2f = 0$ or 1. Correspondingly we have

$$4 \sum_{d|2^e} h(d) = 4 \sum_{f=0}^{e} h(2^f) = 4h(1) = 4.$$

We now consider an odd prime p. From Theorem 2.11 we see that $s^2 \equiv -1 \pmod{p}$ has two solutions if $p \equiv 1 \pmod 4$, and no solutions if $p \equiv 3 \pmod 4$. We apply Section 2.6 to the polynomial $f(x) = x^2 + 1$, with $f'(x) = 2x$. Since $(2s, p) = 1$ we find that $s^2 \equiv -1 \pmod{p^e}$ has the same number of solutions for all $e \geq 1$. That is

$$R(p^e) = R(p) = \begin{cases} 2 \text{ if } p \equiv 1 \pmod 4 \\ 0 \text{ if } p \equiv 3 \pmod 4, \end{cases} \quad e \geq 1.$$

Then, by Theorem 5.10, if e is even we have

(5.11) $$N(p^e) = 4 \sum_{f=0}^{e/2} R(p^{e-2f}) = 4\frac{e}{2} R(p) + 4R(1)$$

$$= \begin{cases} 4e + 4 \text{ if } p \equiv 1 \pmod 4 \\ 4 \qquad \text{ if } p \equiv 3 \pmod 4, \end{cases}$$

and if e is odd we have

(5.12) $$N(p^e) = 4 \sum_{f=0}^{(e-1)/2} R(p^{e-2f}) = 4\frac{e+1}{2} R(p)$$

$$= \begin{cases} 4e + 4 \text{ if } p \equiv 1 \pmod 4 \\ 0 \qquad \text{ if } p \equiv 3 \pmod 4. \end{cases}$$

Corresponding to this we also have

$$(5.13) \quad 4 \sum_{d \mid p^e} h(d) = 4 \sum_{f=0}^{e} h(p^f) = 4h(1) + 4 \sum_{f=1}^{e} (-1)^{\{(p-1)/2\}f}$$

$$= \begin{cases} 4 + 4e & \text{if } p \equiv 1 \pmod 4 \\ 4 & \text{if } p \equiv 3 \pmod 4, \ e \text{ even} \\ 0 & \text{if } p \equiv 3 \pmod 4, \ e \text{ odd.} \end{cases}$$

A comparison of (5.11) and (5.12) with (5.13) completes the proof of the theorem.

Corollary 5.13 $N(n)$ *is four times the excess of the number of divisors of n of the form $4j + 1$ over those of the form $4j + 3$.*

Proof. If $d = 1$, then $h(d) = 1$. If d is even, then $h(d) = 0$. If d is odd and d is the product of the primes $p_1, p_2, \cdots, p_k$, not necessarily distinct, then $h(d) = 1$ or -1 according as an even or an odd number of the p_i are of the form $4j + 3$. But also, in this case, $d \equiv p_1 p_2 \cdots p_k \equiv 1$ or $3 \pmod 4$, according as an even or an odd number of the p_i are of the form $4j + 3$. Since $N(n) = 4 \sum_{d \mid n} h(d)$, the corollary follows.

Corollary 5.14 *The equation $x^2 + y^2 = n$ is solvable if and only if the canonical factoring of n into prime powers contains no factor p^e with p of the form $4j + 3$ and e odd.*

Proof. This follows at once from (5.11) and (5.12) and Theorem 5.11.

Problems

1. Evaluate $N(n)$, $P(n)$ and $Q(n)$ for $n = 100$, 101, and 102.
2. Prove that if n is square-free, $N(n) = Q(n)$.
3. Prove that the number of representations of an integer $m > 1$ as a sum of two squares of positive relatively prime integers equals the number of solutions of the congruence $x^2 \equiv -1 \pmod m$.
4. Corollary 5.13 implies that every positive integer has at least as many divisors of the form $4j + 1$ as of the form $4j + 3$. Prove this fact directly.
5. For a given positive integer K, prove that there is an integer n such that
   (a) $N(n) = K$ if and only if $K \equiv 0 \pmod 4$;
   (b) $P(n) = K$ if and only if K has the form 2^m with $m \geq 0$;
   (c) $Q(n) = K$ if and only if K has the form 2^m with $m \geq 2$.

6. Prove that if an integer n is divisible by a prime of the form $4k + 3$, then $Q(n) = 0$.

7. Suppose that q is any positive divisor of n, and that n is expressible as $n = a^2 + b^2$ with $(a, b) = 1$. Prove that there exist integers c and d such that $c^2 + d^2 = q$ with $(c, d) = 1$.

5.11   The Equation $4x^2 + y^2 = n$

The ideas and methods of Section 5.10 can be greatly extended. The quadratic form $x^2 + y^2$ is only a special case of an extended theory. However, it is probably the most interesting case, and we will do no more than consider a few direct consequences and applications.

In this section we will restrict our attention to positive $n \equiv 1 \pmod 4$. If $x^2 + y^2 = n$, then one of x and y is odd, the other is even. If x is even, we let $u = x/2$, $v = y$; if y is even, we let $u = y/2$, $v = x$. In both cases we have $4u^2 + v^2 = n$. Since $x^2 + y^2 = y^2 + x^2$ and $x \neq y$, we see that exactly two solutions of $x^2 + y^2 = n$ correspond to one solution of $4u^2 + v^2 = n$. Also $(x, y) = (2u, v) = (u, v)$ since v is odd. If we define $N'(n)$, $P'(n)$, $Q'(n)$ for the equation $4x^2 + y^2 = n$, just as we defined $N(n)$, $P(n)$, $Q(n)$ for $x^2 + y^2 = n$, we have

$$N'(n) = \frac{N(n)}{2}, \quad P'(n) = \frac{P(n)}{2}, \quad Q'(n) = \frac{Q(n)}{2}.$$

Theorem 5.15 *Let n be an integer, $n > 1$, $n \equiv 1 \pmod 4$. If n is a prime, then $4x^2 + y^2 = n$ has exactly one non-negative solution, and it is a primitive solution. If n is not a prime, then $4x^2 + y^2 = n$ has either no primitive solutions, more than one non-negative primitive solution, or it has one non-negative primitive solution and at least one non-negative non-primitive solution.*

Proof. If n is a prime, we use Theorems 5.12 and 5.10 to obtain

$$N'(n) = \frac{N(n)}{2} = 2(h(n) + h(1)) = 4, \quad P'(n) = \frac{P(n)}{2} = \frac{R(n)}{2} = 1.$$

Therefore $4x^2 + y^2 = n$ has just one non-negative primitive solution, say u, v. Then, changing signs of u and v, we find three other solutions. Since $N'(n) = 4$ we see that $4x^2 + y^2 = n$ has just one non-negative solution, and it is primitive.

If n is composite, and if some prime $p \equiv 3 \pmod 4$ divides n, then, by Theorem 5.10, $Q'(n) = Q(n)/2 = 2R(n) = 0$. Thus $4x^2 + y^2 = n$ has no primitive solutions in this case.

If $n = p_1^{e_1} p_2^{e_2} \cdots p_r^{e_r}$, $p_i \equiv 1 \pmod 4$, $e_i > 0$, $r > 1$, then $P'(n) = P(n)/2 = R(n)/2 = 2^{r-1} > 1$, and $4x^2 + y^2 = n$ has more than one non-negative primitive solution.

If $n = p^e$, $e > 1$, $p \equiv 1 \pmod 4$, then

$$N'(n) = \frac{N(n)}{2} = 2 \sum_{f=0}^{e} h(p^f) = 2(e + 1) \geq 6$$

and $P'(n) = P(n)/2 = R(p^e)/2 = 1$. Therefore $4x^2 + y^2 = n$ has just one non-negative primitive solution, and it has more than four solutions. It must have some non-primitive solution, u, v. Then $|u|$, $|v|$ is a non-negative non-primitive solution. This completes the proof.

The problem of deciding whether or not some number is a prime has always been of interest to many. If the number is large, it can present quite a problem, and it has led to the development of various methods and machines. No matter how far these go, there is always someone trying to push a little further. Theorem 5.15 is a criterion for primality. Given $n \equiv 1 \pmod 4$, we look for non-negative solutions of $4x^2 + y^2 = n$. If we find a non-primitive solution or two non-negative solutions, we can stop looking further; n is composite. If we find no solutions, n is again composite. If we find exactly one non-negative solution, it will be primitive, and n is a prime.

If we find a non-primitive solution x, y of $4x^2 + y^2 = n$ we not only know that n is composite, but also we know a factor (x, y) of n. If we find two non-negative primitive solutions u, v and μ, ν we can also find a factor of n. Since $2u$, v and 2μ, ν are different non-negative primitive solutions of $x^2 + y^2 = n$, they determine different s and t such that $sv \equiv 2u \pmod n$, $t\nu \equiv 2\mu \pmod n$ by Theorem 5.8. Then $s^2 \equiv t^2 \equiv -1 \pmod n$, $s \not\equiv t \pmod n$, and

$$2(s - t)(u\nu + v\mu) \equiv (s - t)(sv\nu + vt\nu) \equiv (s - t)(s + t)v\nu$$
$$\equiv (s^2 - t^2)v\nu \equiv 0 \pmod n,$$

which implies that $u\nu + v\mu$ and n have a common factor > 1. If g denotes $(u\nu + v\mu, n)$, then

$$1 < g \leqq u\nu + v\mu \leqq \left[\frac{\sqrt{n}}{2}\right][\sqrt{n}] + \left[\frac{\sqrt{n}}{2}\right][\sqrt{n}] < n,$$

and g is a proper factor of n.

When looking for non-negative solutions of $4x^2 + y^2 = n$, we can restrict x to $0 \leq x \leq \sqrt{n}/2$ and we need only check whether $n - 4x^2$ is a perfect square. But we don't even need to try all these values of x. Since y is odd, we have $y^2 \equiv 1 \pmod 8$. Therefore x must satisfy $n - 4x^2 \equiv 1 \pmod 8$, which is equivalent to $x^2 \equiv (n - 1)/4 \pmod 2$. Thus x is even if $n \equiv 1 \pmod 8$, x is odd if $n \equiv 5 \pmod 8$. In either case we have halved the number of x that must be tried.

Going further, if c is odd and positive then, $n - 4x^2 \equiv y^2 \pmod c$, and we can exclude all x for which $n - 4x^2$ is a quadratic nonresidue modulo c. For example 2 and 3 are nonresidues modulo 5, and we can exclude x for which $n - 4x^2 \equiv 2$ or $3 \pmod 5$, that is $x^2 \equiv 2 - n$ or $3 - n \pmod 5$. If $n \equiv 3 \pmod 5$ this excludes x such that $x^2 \equiv -1$ or $0 \pmod 5$, that is $x \equiv 0, 2, 3 \pmod 5$.

Let us consider a simple example. We take $n = 4993$. Then we can restrict x to $0 \leq x < 71/2 < 36$. Since $n \equiv 1 \pmod 8$, we take x even. Since $n \equiv 3 \pmod 5$ we can exclude all $x \equiv 0, 2, 3 \pmod 5$. Writing down the even numbers $0, 2, 4, \cdots, 34$ and scratching out the $x \equiv 0, 2, 3 \pmod 5$, we find that we need test only $x = 4, 6, 14, 16, 24, 26, 34$. This list can be cut down further if we use other values of c. For example, $c = 7$ eliminates 6 and 34, and $c = 11$ eliminates 14. This is hardly worthwhile for an n of this size. In any event we have only a few values to check. It will be found that $x = 16$ gives $n - 4x^2 = 3969 = 63^2$ and that there are no other solutions. Therefore 4993 is a prime.

For larger values of n one would probably use more values of c. If one is going to use this method very much, it is advisable to make short tables showing which x are excluded by various values of c. If the method is carried out systematically, and if a table of squares is available, it is a useful test for primality of n that are not too large. This test was based on the equation $4x^2 + y^2 = n$, and it is useful only for $n \equiv 1 \pmod 4$. There are other tests, based on other equations, valid for other n.

5.12   The Equation $ax^2 + by^2 + cz^2 = 0$

Although the theorem we give concerning this equation goes back to Legendre, our proof is a recent one (see the bibliography at the end of the book).

Theorem 5.16 *Let a, b, c be non-zero integers such that the product abc is square-free. Necessary and sufficient conditions that $ax^2 + by^2 + cz^2 = 0$ have a solution in integers x, y, z, not all zero, are that a, b, c do not have the same sign, and that $-bc$, $-ac$, $-ab$ are quadratic residues modulo a, b, c, respectively.*

Before giving the proof of this result we establish two lemmas.

Lemma 5.17 *Let λ, μ, ν be positive real numbers with product $\lambda\mu\nu = m$ an integer. Then any congruence $\alpha x + \beta y + \gamma z \equiv 0 \pmod{m}$ has a solution x, y, z, not all zero, such that $|x| \leq \lambda$, $|y| \leq \mu$, $|z| \leq \nu$.*

Proof. Let x range over the values $0, 1, \cdots, [\lambda]$, y over $0, 1, \cdots, [\mu]$, and z over $0, 1, \cdots, [\nu]$. This gives us $(1 + [\lambda])(1 + [\mu])(1 + [\nu])$ different triples x, y, z. Now $(1 + [\lambda])(1 + [\mu])(1 + [\nu]) > \lambda\mu\nu = m$ by Theorem 4.1a and hence there must be some two triples x_1, y_1, z_1 and x_2, y_2, z_2 such that $\alpha x_1 + \beta y_1 + \gamma z_1 \equiv \alpha x_2 + \beta y_2 + \gamma z_2 \pmod{m}$. Then we have $\alpha(x_1 - x_2) + \beta(y_1 - y_2) + \gamma(z_1 - z_2) \equiv 0 \pmod{m}$, $|x_1 - x_2| \leq [\lambda] \leq \lambda$, $|y_1 - y_2| \leq \mu$, $|z_1 - z_2| \leq \nu$.

Lemma 5.18 *Suppose that $ax^2 + by^2 + cz^2$ factors into linear factors modulo m and also modulo n; that is*

$$ax^2 + by^2 + cz^2 \equiv (\alpha_1 x + \beta_1 y + \gamma_1 z)(\alpha_2 x + \beta_2 y + \gamma_2 z) \pmod{m},$$

$$ax^2 + by^2 + cz^2 \equiv (\alpha_3 x + \beta_3 y + \gamma_3 z)(\alpha_4 x + \beta_4 y + \gamma_4 z) \pmod{n}.$$

If $(m, n) = 1$ then $ax^2 + by^2 + cz^2$ factors into linear factors modulo mn.

Proof. Using Theorem 2.14, we can choose α, β, γ, α', β', γ' to satisfy

$$\alpha \equiv \alpha_1, \beta \equiv \beta_1, \gamma \equiv \gamma_1, \alpha' \equiv \alpha_2, \beta' \equiv \beta_2, \gamma' \equiv \gamma_2 \pmod{m},$$

$$\alpha \equiv \alpha_3, \beta \equiv \beta_3, \gamma \equiv \gamma_3, \alpha' \equiv \alpha_4, \beta' \equiv \beta_4, \gamma' \equiv \gamma_4 \pmod{n}.$$

Then the congruence

$$ax^2 + by^2 + cz^2 \equiv (\alpha x + \beta y + \gamma z)(\alpha' x + \beta' y + \gamma' z)$$

holds modulo m and modulo n, and hence it holds modulo mn.

Proof of Theorem 5.16. If $ax^2 + by^2 + cz^2 = 0$ has a solution x_0, y_0, z_0 not all zero, then a, b, c are not of the same sign. Dividing x_0, y_0, z_0 by (x_0, y_0, z_0) we have a solution x_1, y_1, z_1 with $(x_1, y_1, z_1) = 1$.

Next we prove that $(c, x_1) = 1$. If this were not so there would be a prime p dividing both c and x_1. Then $p \nmid b$ since $p|c$ and abc is square-free. Therefore $p|by_1^2$ and $p \nmid b$, hence $p|y_1^2$, $p|y_1$, and then $p^2|(ax_1^2 + by_1^2)$ so that $p^2|cz_1^2$. But c is square-free so $p|z_1$. We have concluded that p is a factor of x_1, y_1, and z_1 contrary to $(x_1, y_1, z_1) = 1$. Consequently, we have $(c, x_1) = 1$.

Let u be chosen to satisfy $ux_1 \equiv 1 \pmod{c}$. Then the equation $ax_1^2 + by_1^2 + cz_1^2 = 0$ implies $ax_1^2 + by_1^2 \equiv 0 \pmod{c}$, and multiplying this by u^2b we get $u^2b^2y_1^2 \equiv -ab \pmod{c}$. Thus we have established that $-ab$ is a quadratic residue modulo c. A similar proof shows that $-bc$ and $-ac$ are quadratic residues modulo a and b respectively.

Conversely, let us assume that $-bc$, $-ac$, $-ab$ are quadratic residues modulo a, b, c respectively. Note that this property does not change if a, b, c are replaced by their negatives. Since a, b, c are not of the same sign, we can change the signs of all of them, if necessary, in order to have one positive and two of them negative. Then, perhaps with a change of notation, we can arrange it so that a is positive and b and c are negative.

Define r as a solution of $r^2 \equiv -ab \pmod{c}$, and a_1 as a solution of $aa_1 \equiv 1 \pmod{c}$. These solutions exist because of our assumptions on a, b, c. Then we can write

$$ax^2 + by^2 \equiv aa_1(ax^2 + by^2) \equiv a_1(a^2x^2 + aby^2) \equiv a_1(a^2x^2 - r^2y^2)$$

$$\equiv a_1(ax - ry)(ax + ry) \equiv (x - a_1ry)(ax + ry) \pmod{c},$$

$$ax^2 + by^2 + cz^2 \equiv (x - a_1ry)(ax + ry) \pmod{c}.$$

Thus $ax^2 + by^2 + cz^2$ is the product of two linear factors modulo c, and similarly modulo a and modulo b. Applying Lemma 5.18 twice, we conclude that $ax^2 + by^2 + cz^2$ can be written as the product of two linear factors modulo abc. That is, there exist numbers α, β, γ, α', β', γ' such that

$$(5.14) \quad ax^2 + by^2 + cz^2 \equiv (\alpha x + \beta y + \gamma z)(\alpha' x + \beta' y + \gamma' z) \pmod{abc}.$$

Now we apply Lemma 5.17 to the congruence

(5.15) $\alpha x + \beta y + \gamma z \equiv 0 \pmod{abc}$,

using $\lambda = \sqrt{bc}$, $\mu = \sqrt{|ac|}$, $\nu = \sqrt{|ab|}$. Thus we get a solution x_1, y_1, z_1 of the congruence (5.15) with $|x_1| \leq \sqrt{bc}$, $|y_1| \leq \sqrt{|ac|}$, $|z_1| \leq \sqrt{|ab|}$. But abc is square-free, so $\sqrt{bc}$ is an integer only if it is 1, and similarly for $\sqrt{|ac|}$ and $\sqrt{|ab|}$. Therefore we have

$|x_1| \leq \sqrt{bc}$, $x_1^2 \leq bc$ with equality possible only if $b = c = -1$,

$|y_1| \leq \sqrt{|ac|}$, $y_1^2 \leq -ac$ with equality possible only if $a = 1$, $c = -1$,

$|z_1| \leq \sqrt{|ab|}$, $z_1^2 \leq -ab$ with equality possible only if $a = 1$, $b = -1$.

Hence, since a is positive and b and c are negative, we have, unless $b = c = -1$,

$$ax_1^2 + by_1^2 + cz_1^2 \leq ax_1^2 < abc,$$

and

$$ax_1^2 + by_1^2 + cz_1^2 \geq by_1^2 + cz_1^2 > b(-ac) + c(-ab) = -2abc.$$

Leaving aside the special case when $b = c = -1$, we have

$$-2abc < ax_1^2 + by_1^2 + cz_1^2 < abc.$$

Now x_1, y_1, z_1 is a solution of (5.15) and so also, because of (5.14), a solution of

$$ax^2 + by^2 + cz^2 \equiv 0 \pmod{abc}.$$

Thus the above inequalities imply that

$$ax_1^2 + by_1^2 + cz_1^2 = 0 \quad \text{or} \quad ax_1^2 + by_1^2 + cz_1^2 = -abc.$$

In the first case we have our solution of $ax^2 + by^2 + cz^2 = 0$. In the second case we readily verify that x_2, y_2, z_2, defined by $x_2 = -by_1 + x_1z_1$, $y_2 = ax_1 + y_1z_1$, $z_2 = z_1^2 + ab$, form a solution. In case $x_2 = y_2 = z_2 = 0$ one can easily find a proper solution.

Finally we must dispose of the special case $b = c = -1$. The conditions on a, b, c now imply that -1 is a quadratic residue modulo a, in other words, that $R(a)$ of Theorem 5.10 is positive. By Theorem 5.10 this implies that $Q(a)$ is positive and hence that the equation $y^2 + z^2 = a$ has a solution y_1, z_1. Then $x = 1$, $y = y_1$, $z = z_1$ is a solution of $ax^2 + by^2 + cz^2 = 0$ since $b = c = -1$.

Problem

1. Show that in the proof of Theorem 5.16 we have established more than the theorem stated, that the following stronger result is implied. Let a, b, c be non-zero integers not of the same sign such that the product abc is square-free. Then the following three conditions are equivalent.

   (a) $ax^2 + by^2 + cz^2 = 0$ has a solution x, y, z not all zero;

   (b) $ax^2 + by^2 + cz^2$ factors into linear factors modulo abc;

   (c) $-bc$, $-ac$, $-ab$ are quadratic residues modulo a, b, c respectively.

5.13   Binary Quadratic Forms

A form is a homogeneous polynomial, that is, a polynomial in several variables, all of whose terms are of the same degree. A quadratic form f has terms of degree two, and is therefore an expression of the type

$$(5.16) \qquad f(x_1, x_2, \cdots, x_n) = \sum_{i,j=1}^{n} a_{ij}x_ix_j.$$

We restrict our attention to quadratic forms with integral coefficients a_{ij}. If $f(x_1, x_2, \cdots, x_n)$ assumes only positive values whenever x_1, x_2, $\cdots$, x_n are replaced by any set of integers other than $0, 0, \cdots$, 0, then f is said to be a positive form. Similarly f is called a negative form if its value is negative when $x_1, x_2, \cdots, x_n$ are replaced by integers not all zero. A definite form is one which is either positive or negative. For example $x_1^2 + x_2^2$, or $x^2 + y^2$ in other notation, is a positive form, and $-x^2 - 3y^2$ is a negative form; both are definite forms. The form $x^2 - y^2$ is an indefinite form. Sometimes positive forms are called positive definite, and negative forms negative definite. Clearly if f is positive then $-f$ is negative, and conversely. Hence there is no need to study both positive and negative forms because the properties of one kind follow from the properties of the other.

A quadratic form (5.16) is said to represent an integer m if there are integers $b_1, b_2, \cdots, b_n$ such that $f(b_1, b_2, \cdots, b_n) = m$. For example, $x^2 + y^2$ represents 5 but not 6. Every quadratic form represents 0 because $f(0, 0, \cdots, 0) = 0$. The form f is called a zero form if $f(b_1, b_2, \cdots, b_n) = 0$ for some integers $b_1, b_2, \cdots, b_n$, not all zero. By definition a definite form is not a zero form. Theorem 5.16 gave necessary and sufficient conditions that $ax^2 + by^2 + cz^2$ be a zero form for a wide class of integers a, b, c.

A positive form is said to be universal if it represents all positive integers. Thus, according to Theorem 5.6, $x_1^2 + x_2^2 + x_3^2 + x_4^2$ is a universal form. Although we will not prove it, it is a fact that no form of the type $ax^2 + by^2 + cz^2$ can be universal. The arithmetic theory of quadratic forms includes such problems as to determine which forms are universal, to determine or characterize the class of integers represented by a quadratic form that is not universal, and to determine how many ways an integer can be represented by a quadratic form. For example, Corollary 5.14 determined the class of integers represented by the form $x^2 + y^2$, and Corollary 5.13 determined the number of representations.

A form involving two variables is called a binary form. The rest of this chapter deals with binary quadratic forms, that is forms of the type

$$(5.17) \qquad f(x, y) = ax^2 + bxy + cy^2.$$

We do not intend to do more than just give an introduction to a part of the theory dealing with binary quadratic forms. The use of matrices would simplify a few of our proofs. However, for the little that we shall do, the simplification is not enough to offset the work that would be required in introducing matrices.

Theorem 5.19 *The quadratic form* $f(x, y) = ax^2 + bxy + cy^2$ *is positive if and only if its discriminant* $b^2 - 4ac$ *is negative,* $a > 0$, *and* $c > 0$.

Proof. Since $f(1, 0) = a$ and $f(0, 1) = c$, we see that f is not positive if $a \leq 0$ or if $c \leq 0$. We can now suppose $a > 0$, $c > 0$, and can write

$$(5.18) \qquad f(x, y) = \frac{1}{4a} ((2ax + by)^2 + (4ac - b^2)y^2).$$

This shows that $f(-b, 2a) = (4ac - b^2)a$ and hence, since $a > 0$, that f is not positive if $4ac - b^2 \leq 0$. On the other hand, if $b^2 - 4ac < 0$, it shows that $f(x, y)$ is never negative no matter what integers may be substituted for x and y. Moreover $f(x, y) = 0$ then holds if and only if $2ax + by = 0$ and $(4ac - b^2)y^2 = 0$. These equations imply that $y = 0$ and $x = 0$ if $a > 0$, $b^2 - 4ac < 0$.

The quadratic form $x^2 - dy^2$ with $d > 0$ has discriminant $4d > 0$, and it is clearly indefinite. Pell's equation $x^2 - dy^2 = n$, $d > 0$, d not a perfect square, will be discussed in Section 7.8. For fixed d and n it turns out that the equation has either no solution or an infinite number of solutions. On the other hand it is easy to see that $x^2 - y^2 = n$ has no solutions if $n \equiv 2 \pmod 4$, and only a finite number of solutions, $x = (t + n/t)/2$, $y = (t - n/t)/2$, $t | n$, $t \equiv n \pmod 2$, if $n \not\equiv 2 \pmod 4$. The first situation does not arise in the case of definite forms, as shown in the following theorem.

Theorem 5.20 *Let f be a positive quadratic form. Then the number of representations of an integer m by f is finite, possibly zero.*

Proof. We will show that there is only a finite number of pairs of integers for which $f(x, y) \leq m$. We can suppose $m > 0$. Using (5.18) we see that $f(x, y) \leq m$ implies $(4ac - b^2)y^2 \leq 4am$, and hence

$$-2 \left(\frac{am}{4ac - b^2} \right)^{\frac{1}{2}} \leq y \leq 2 \left(\frac{am}{4ac - b^2} \right)^{\frac{1}{2}}.$$

This restricts y to a finite number of values. For each such y we then have $(2ax + by)^2 \leq 4am - (4ac - b^2)y^2$, which then restricts $2ax + by$ and hence x to a finite number of values.

Corollary 5.21 *Let f be a positive quadratic form. Then the smallest positive integer represented by f can be found in a finite number of steps.*

Proof. Since a is represented by f we just take $m = a - 1$ in the proof of Theorem 5.20, find all y and x that are allowed, and then determine the least value of $f(x, y)$.

For example, if $f(x, y) = 5x^2 + 14xy + 11y^2$, then $b^2 - 4ac = -24 < 0$ and y is limited to $-\sqrt{30}/3 \leq y \leq \sqrt{30}/3$. Hence $y = -1, 0, 1$. For $y = -1$ we have $(10x - 14)^2 \leq 56$ from which we find $x = 1$ or 2, $f(x, -1) = 2$ or 3. For $y = 0$ we find $x = 0$, $f(0, 0) = 0$. For $y = 1$ we find $x = -2$ or -1, $f(x, 1) = 3$ or 2. Therefore the least positive integer represented by f is 2.

If in the quadratic form $f(x, y) = 5x^2 + 14xy + 11y^2$ we replace x by $-X + 2Y$ and y by $X - Y$, we get the form $F(X, Y) = 2X^2 + 3Y^2$. Now the transformation

$$(5.19) \qquad\qquad x = -X + 2Y, \qquad y = X - Y$$

can be solved for X and Y to give the inverse transformation

$$X = x + 2y, \qquad Y = x + y.$$

The transformation (5.19) has the special property that its inverse also has integral coefficients; both (5.19) and its inverse are integral transformations. If X and Y are replaced by integers, then (5.19) gives a pair of integers for x and y to make the value of $f(x, y)$ the same as that of $F(X, Y)$. The inverse transformation works the other way, giving integers X and Y corresponding to integers x and y.

It follows that any integer represented by f can also be represented by F, and conversely. Furthermore, the number of representations is the same in both cases. The form F is considerably simpler than f. By trial, it is easy to verify that all the solutions of $F(X, Y) = 14$ are $(1, 2)$, $(1, -2)$, $(-1, 2)$, $(-1, -2)$. Then (5.19) gives us the solutions of $f(x, y) = 14$, namely $(3, -1)$, $(-5, 3)$, $(5, -3)$, $(-3, 1)$.

The quadratic form F is said to be equivalent to f. Anything we can say about representations by F can be carried over to f by virtue of (5.19) and its inverse. If we study F there is no need to study f or any other equivalent form. This example suggests the desirability of studying transformations and equivalence of forms more closely.

Problems

1. Determine the class of integers represented by each of the following forms:
   (a) $2x^2 + 2y^2$;
   (b) $2x^2 - 2y^2$;
   (c) $x^2 - xy$;
   (d) $2x^2 + 2y^2 + 2z^2 + 2t^2$.
2. Prove that $x^2 - 2xy + y^2$ is a zero form. Determine the class of integers represented by this form.
3. If C is any class of integers, finite or infinite, let mC denote the class obtained by multiplying each integer of C by the integer m. Prove that if C is the class of integers represented by any form f, then mC is the class represented by mf.
4. Prove that $ax^2 + bxy + cy^2$ is a positive form if and only if $a > 0$ and $b^2 - 4ac < 0$. (Observe that this problem shows that the condition $c > 0$ in Theorem 5.19 is superfluous.)
5. Prove that $ax^2 + bxy + cy^2$ is a positive form if and only if $c > 0$ and $b^2 - 4ac < 0$.

6. Prove that the form $ax^2 + bxy + cy^2$ is negative if and only if $a < 0$ and $b^2 - 4ac < 0$.

7. Prove that the form $ax^2 + bxy + cy^2$ is definite if and only if $b^2 - 4ac < 0$.

8. Prove that $x^2 + 7xy + y^2$ is neither a definite form nor a zero form.

9. Find all solutions of the Diophantine equations
   (a) $5x^2 + 14xy + 11y^2 = 35$;
   (b) $5x^2 + 14xy + 11y^2 = 46$.

10. Find the least positive integer represented by the positive form $7x^2 + 25xy + 23y^2$.

11. If $f(x, y)$ is a positive binary quadratic form, prove that $f(\alpha, \beta)$ is positive for every pair of real numbers α, β except 0, 0.

12. Let $f(x, y) = ax^2 + bxy + cy^2$ be a quadratic form with $a > 0$ and $b^2 - 4ac = 0$. Given also that $(a, b, c) = 1$, prove that the integers represented by f are precisely the numbers m^2, with $m = 0, 1, 2, \cdots$. Hence, removing the restriction that $(a, b, c) = 1$, prove that the integers represented by f are all numbers of the form dm^2, where $d = (a, b, c)$.

5.14   Equivalence of Quadratic Forms

Theorem 5.22 *The inverse of an integral transformation*

$$(5.20) \qquad\qquad x = \alpha X + \beta Y, \qquad y = \gamma X + \delta Y$$

is also an integral transformation if and only if $\Delta = \pm 1$ *where* Δ *is the determinant of the transformation,*

$$\Delta = \begin{vmatrix} \alpha & \beta \\ \gamma & \delta \end{vmatrix} = \alpha\delta - \beta\gamma.$$

Proof. The inverse exists if and only if (5.20) can be solved uniquely for X and Y, hence if and only if $\Delta \neq 0$. Then if the inverse does exist we can solve to get

$$(5.21) \qquad\qquad X = \frac{\delta}{\Delta} x - \frac{\beta}{\Delta} y, \qquad Y = -\frac{\gamma}{\Delta} x + \frac{\alpha}{\Delta} y.$$

If $\Delta = \pm 1$ then (5.21) is an integral transformation.

Now suppose that (5.21) is an integral transformation. Let p be any prime, and let p^k be the highest power of p that divides Δ. If p does not divide Δ, then $k = 0$. Since the coefficients in (5.21) are integers, we conclude that

$$p^k | \delta, \quad p^k | \beta, \quad p^k | \gamma, \quad p^k | \alpha.$$

It follows that

$$p^{2k} | \alpha\delta, \quad p^{2k} | \beta\gamma, \quad p^{2k} | \Delta.$$

But p^k is the highest power of p that divides Δ, so we have $2k \leqq k$, which implies $k = 0$. Thus no prime divides Δ, and hence $\Delta = \pm 1$.

This theorem shows that if F is a quadratic form obtained from a form f by means of (5.20) with $\Delta = \pm 1$, then, just as in Section 5.13, the problem of representing integers by f can be reduced to that of representing them by F.

Definition 5.1 *A quadratic form $f(x, y) = ax^2 + bxy + cy^2$ is equivalent to a form $g(x, y) = Ax^2 + Bxy + Cy^2$ if there is an integral transformation* (5.20), *with determinant $\Delta = \pm 1$, that carries $f(x, y)$ into $g(X, Y)$. In case f is equivalent to g we write $f \sim g$.*

Applying (5.20) to f and multiplying out we find

$$(5.22) \quad A = a\alpha^2 + b\alpha\gamma + c\gamma^2, \quad B = 2a\alpha\beta + b(\alpha\delta + \beta\gamma) + 2c\gamma\delta,$$

$$C = a\beta^2 + b\beta\delta + c\delta^2,$$

if (5.20) carries $f(x, y)$ into $g(X, Y)$.

The next theorem shows that this equivalence is a true equivalence relation: it is reflexive, symmetric, and transitive.

Theorem 5.23 *Let f, g, and h be binary quadratic forms. Then*

(a) $f \sim f$,
(b) *if $f \sim g$ then $g \sim f$,*
(c) *if $f \sim g$ and $g \sim h$ then $f \sim h$.*

Proof. (a) The identity transformation $x = X$, $y = Y$ has determinant 1, and it carries $f(x, y)$ into $f(X, Y)$.

(b) We can suppose that (5.20) is the transformation that carries $f(x, y)$ into $g(X, Y)$. Then, by (5.21) the inverse transformation that carries $g(X, Y)$ back into $f(x, y)$ has determinant

$$\frac{\delta}{\Delta}\frac{\alpha}{\Delta} - \frac{\beta}{\Delta}\frac{\gamma}{\Delta} = \frac{1}{\Delta} = \pm 1.$$

(c) We suppose that (5.20) with $\Delta = \pm 1$ carries $f(x, y)$ into $g(X, Y)$ and that the transformation $X = \alpha_1 u + \beta_1 v$, $Y = \gamma_1 u + \delta_1 v$, with $\Delta_1 = \alpha_1 \delta_1 - \beta_1 \gamma_1 = \pm 1$ carries $g(X, Y)$ into $h(u, v)$. If we eliminate X and Y, we find

$$x = (\alpha\alpha_1 + \beta\gamma_1)u + (\alpha\beta_1 + \beta\delta_1)v,$$

$$y = (\gamma\alpha_1 + \delta\gamma_1)u + (\gamma\beta_1 + \delta\delta_1)v,$$

and this transformation carries $f(x, y)$ into $h(u, v)$. An easy computation shows that the determinant of this transformation is equal to $(\alpha\delta - \beta\gamma)(\alpha_1\delta_1 - \beta_1\gamma_1) = \pm 1$. Therefore $f(x, y)$ is equivalent to $h(x, y)$.

Theorem 5.24 *If $f \sim g$, then the discriminants of f and g are equal.*

Proof. We suppose that (5.20) carries $f(x, y)$ into $g(X, Y)$ as in Definition 5.1. It is possible to compute the discriminant $B^2 - 4AC$ of g, using (5.22), to obtain $B^2 - 4AC = (\alpha\delta - \beta\gamma)^2(b^2 - 4ac)$, but it is simpler to use the ordinary rule for multiplying determinants,

$$\begin{vmatrix} \alpha & \gamma \\ \beta & \delta \end{vmatrix} \begin{vmatrix} 2a & b \\ b & 2c \end{vmatrix} \begin{vmatrix} \alpha & \beta \\ \gamma & \delta \end{vmatrix} = \begin{vmatrix} 2a\alpha + b\gamma & b\alpha + 2c\gamma \\ 2a\beta + b\delta & b\beta + 2c\delta \end{vmatrix} \begin{vmatrix} \alpha & \beta \\ \gamma & \delta \end{vmatrix}$$

$$= \begin{vmatrix} 2A & B \\ B & 2C \end{vmatrix}.$$

Evaluating the determinants we find $(\alpha\delta - \beta\gamma)^2(4ac - b^2) = 4AC - B^2$. Since $(\alpha\delta - \beta\gamma)^2 = \Delta^2 = 1$ we have $b^2 - 4ac = B^2 - 4AC$.

In light of Theorem 5.23 we can separate all binary quadratic forms into equivalence classes, putting two forms f and g into the same class if $f \sim g$. Part (b) of Theorem 5.23 assures that f and g represent the same set of integers if f and g are in the same class, and that there is a one to one correspondence between the representations by f and those by g. In other words it suffices to consider just one representative form from each equivalence class. Clearly, if one form in a class is positive then so are all the others in that class. Also two forms in the same class have the same discriminants.

The next thing that it is desirable to have is some way of picking one unique representative form from each equivalence class. In the case of positive binary quadratic forms, this can be done in a fairly simple way. The whole theory connected with positive forms is quite elegant. For this reason we will restrict our attention to positive forms from now on.

Definition 5.2 *A positive binary quadratic form* $ax^2 + bxy + cy^2$ *is a reduced form if* $0 \le b \le a \le c$.

For example, $x^2 + y^2$ is a reduced form.

Theorem 5.25 *To each positive binary quadratic form there corresponds an equivalent reduced form.*

Proof. Consider any positive binary quadratic form $g(x, y) = Ax^2 + Bxy + Cy^2$. We shall show that there is an equivalent form $ax^2 + bxy + cy^2$ with $0 \le |b| \le a \le c$. This will suffice because in case b is negative, the transformation $x = -X$, $y = Y$ will carry $ax^2 + bxy + cy^2$ into a reduced form.

Let a denote the least positive integer represented by g. In Corollary 5.21 we saw how a can be found. There are integers α and β such that $A\alpha^2 + B\alpha\gamma + C\gamma^2 = a$. Note that $(\alpha, \gamma) = 1$; for if $(\alpha, \gamma) = d$, then $F(\alpha/d, \gamma/d) = a/d^2$, which implies $d = 1$ since a was minimal. Then by Theorem 1.3 there are integers β and δ such that $\alpha\delta - \beta\gamma = 1$, and we use these to construct the transformation $x = \alpha u + \beta v$, $y = \gamma u + \delta v$ of determinant 1. This transformation carries $g(x, y)$ into

$$h(u, v) = A(\alpha u + \beta v)^2 + B(\alpha u + \beta v)(\gamma u + \delta v) + C(\gamma u + \delta v)^2$$
$$= au^2 + kuv + mv^2,$$

say, where a is the integer defined above.

Now, for any integer j the transformation $u = x - jy$, $v = y$ has determinant 1, and it carries $h(u, v)$ into

$$f(x, y) = ax^2 + (k - 2aj)xy + (aj^2 - kj + m)y^2.$$

If we take j to be the nearest integer to $k/2a$, we have

$$-\frac{1}{2} \le \frac{k}{2a} - j \le \frac{1}{2}, \quad -a \le k - 2aj \le a, \quad |k - 2aj| \le a$$

and we can write

$$f(x, y) = ax^2 + bxy + cy^2, \qquad |b| \le a.$$

Now $g \sim f$, g is positive, and $f(0, 1) = c$. Therefore g represents c, and c is positive, hence $c \ge a$.

Theorem 5.26 *If two reduced forms are equivalent they are identical.*

Proof. Let $ax^2 + bxy + cy^2$ and $Ax^2 + Bxy + Cy^2$ be equivalent reduced forms. We can suppose that $a \geq A$ and that (5.20) is the transformation carrying one into the other. Then the coefficients satisfy (5.22).

First we prove that $a = A$. We have $0 \leq b \leq a \leq c$, and using the simple inequality $\alpha^2 + \gamma^2 \geq 2|\alpha\gamma|$ we find

$$(5.23) \quad A = a\alpha^2 + b\alpha\gamma + c\gamma^2 \geq a\alpha^2 + c\gamma^2 - b|\alpha\gamma|$$
$$\geq a\alpha^2 + a\gamma^2 - b|\alpha\gamma| \geq 2a|\alpha\gamma| - b|\alpha\gamma| \geq a|\alpha\gamma|.$$

Since $a \geq A > 0$ it follows that $|\alpha\gamma| \leq 1$. If $|\alpha\gamma| = 0$ we have

$$(5.24) \quad A = a\alpha^2 + c\gamma^2 \geq a\alpha^2 + a\gamma^2 \geq a$$

because α and γ are not both zero. If $|\alpha\gamma| = 1$, then (5.23) reduces immediately to the same result, $A \geq a$. Thus we have $A \geq a$ in both cases, and this with $a \geq A$ implies that $a = A$.

Now that we have $a = A > 0$ we need only prove $b = B$ or $c = C$, since one follows from the other because $b^2 - 4ac = B^2 - 4AC$ by Theorem 5.24. Thus the case $c = C$ requires no further proof. Since $a = A$ we can interchange the forms if necessary and can assume $c > C$. Then we have $c > a$ since $C \geq A = a$. This rules out the possibility $|\alpha\gamma| = 1$, for if $|\alpha\gamma| = 1$ then $c\gamma^2 > a\gamma^2$, and (5.23) would then imply $A > a|\alpha\gamma| = a$. Now that we have $|\alpha\gamma| = 0$, we can prove that $\gamma = 0$, for otherwise we would again have $c\gamma^2 > a\gamma^2$ and (5.24) would imply $A > a$.

We have narrowed the possibilities down to $a = A$, $a < c$, $\gamma = 0$. Since the determinant $\Delta = \alpha\delta - \beta\gamma$ is ± 1, we also have $\alpha\delta = \pm 1$. Then by (5.22) we have $B = 2a\alpha\beta \pm b$. There are two cases.

First, suppose that $B = 2a\alpha\beta + b$. Then $0 \leq b \leq a$ and $0 \leq B \leq A = a$ imply that $-a \leq B - b \leq a$. But $B - b = 2a\alpha\beta$ is a multiple of $2a$ so we have $B - b = 0$, $b = B$.

Second, suppose that $B = 2a\alpha\beta - b$. This time we find $0 \leq B + b \leq 2a$ and $B + b$ is a multiple of $2a$. We have either $B + b = 0$ or $B + b = 2a$. Since $0 \leq b \leq a$ and $0 \leq B \leq a$ we have $b = B = 0$ if $B + b = 0$, and $b = B = a$ if $B + b = 2a$. Again we have $b = B$.

This completes the proof since we have $a = A$, $b = B$, $c = C$ in every case.

The last two theorems show that Definition 5.2 does just what we wanted. It supplies us with one and just one representative for each equivalence class of positive binary quadratic forms. It should be noted that Definition 5.1 is not the only way in which the positive binary quadratic forms can be put into equivalence classes. In fact, some authors demand that the transformation have determinant 1 in their definition of equivalence. They then use a slightly different definition of a reduced form in order that Theorems 5.25 and 5.26 still hold under their definitions of equivalence and of reduced forms.

Theorem 5.27 *There are only finitely many reduced forms having a given discriminant.*

Proof. Let $-d$ be any negative integer. If $ax^2 + bxy + cy^2$ is a reduced form with discriminant $-d$, then $b^2 - 4ac = -d$ and $0 \leq b \leq a \leq c$. Thus we have $d = 4ac - b^2 \geq 4ac - ac \geq 3a^2$ as well as $0 \leq b \leq a$, so that there are at most $\sqrt{d/3}$ possible values for $a > 0$, and at most $a + 1$ values for b corresponding to each a. Finally there is at most one c, for each a, b, such that $4ac - b^2 = d$.

Let us find all reduced forms with $d \leq 16$. We have $1 \leq a \leq \sqrt{16/3}$, $a = 1$ or 2. Corresponding to $a = 1$, $b = 0$ we have $d = 4c$, and we can take $c = 1, 2, 3,$ or 4. Corresponding to $a = 1$, $b = 1$ we have $d = 4c - 1$, and again we can take $c = 1, 2, 3,$ or 4. Similarly we find $a = 2$, $b = 0, d = 8c, c = 2$, and $a = 2, b = 1, d = 8c - 1, c = 2$, and $a = 2$, $b = 2, d = 8c - 4, c = 2$. Listing the reduced forms according to the values of d we get the following table.

$$d = 3,\ x^2 + xy + y^2$$
$$d = 4,\ x^2 + y^2$$
$$d = 7,\ x^2 + xy + 2y^2$$
$$d = 8,\ x^2 + 2y^2$$
$$d = 11,\ x^2 + xy + 3y^2$$
$$d = 12,\ x^2 + 3y^2,\ 2x^2 + 2xy + 2y^2$$
$$d = 15,\ x^2 + xy + 4y^2,\ 2x^2 + xy + 2y^2$$
$$d = 16,\ x^2 + 4y^2,\ 2x^2 + 2y^2.$$

For $d = 3, 4, 7, 8, 11$, there is just one reduced form of discriminant $-d$. For these values of d, any positive form with discriminant $-d$ will represent the same set of integers as the corresponding reduced form represents. For example, Corollary 5.14 determined the set of integers represented by $x^2 + y^2$, and this is the set represented by any positive form of discriminant -4.

The case $d = 12$ is a little different since there are two reduced forms of discriminant -12. But in the first form $x^2 + 3y^2$ the coefficients are relatively prime whereas in the second form $2x^2 + 2xy + 2y^2$ the coefficients are all divisible by 2. From (5.22) it is obvious that any form equivalent to $2x^2 + 2xy + 2y^2$ will also have all its coefficients divisible by 2. Also by (5.22) any positive form with discriminant -12, having all its coefficients divisible by 2, will be equivalent to a reduced form having all its coefficients divisible by 2, hence it is equivalent to $2x^2 + 2xy + 2y^2$. Therefore we can make the statement: Suppose f is a positive form of discriminant -12. If the coefficients of f are relatively prime, then f represents the same class as does $x^2 + 3y^2$. If the coefficients are not relatively prime, then f represents the same class as does $2x^2 + 2xy + 2y^2$. The case $d = 16$ can be treated in a similar way.

The case $d = 15$ is still different, and harder. Here we have two reduced forms, and in both of them the coefficients are relatively prime. There are ways of distinguishing between forms equivalent to one or the other reduced form without having to actually produce the reduced form by going through the steps of the proof of Theorem 5.25. However, we shall not go into this.

This is as far as we will pursue the topic of quadratic forms. There is more that can be done. For one thing, we have not discussed the question of how to determine the class of integers represented by a reduced form. The methods used to obtain Corollary 5.14 can be extended to give some information. A further study of the transformation introduced in the present section is also very useful.

Problems

1. Prove that the following forms are equivalent:
   $$ax^2 + bxy + cy^2, \quad cx^2 + bxy + ay^2, \quad ax^2 - bxy + cy^2, \quad cx^2 - bxy + ay^2.$$
2. Find the reduced form equivalent to
   (a) $3x^2 + 7xy + 5y^2$;

(b) $2x^2 - 5xy + 4y^2$;

(c) $2x^2 + xy + 6y^2$;

(d) $3x^2 + xy + y^2$.

3. Prove that there are no binary quadratic forms with discriminant congruent to 2 or 3 modulo 4.

4. Find the reduced form equivalent to $7x^2 + 25xy + 23y^2$.

5. Prove that to any given positive binary quadratic form there corresponds infinitely many equivalent forms.

6. Prove that there is only one reduced form of discriminant -43. Hence prove that any two positive binary quadratic forms of discriminant -43 are equivalent.

7. Prove that any two positive binary quadratic forms of discriminant -67 are equivalent.

8. Denote the positive form $ax^2 + bxy + cy^2$ bv $[a, b, c]$. Prove that, as a variation of the method of Theorem 5.25, the reduced form equivalent to $[a, b, c]$ can be obtained by a finite sequence of operations of three types:

(1) in case $a > c$, the replacement of $[a, b, c]$ by $[c, b, a]$;

(2) in case $|b| > a$, the replacement of $[a, b, c]$ by $[a, b - 2aj, c_1]$, where j is chosen so that $|b - 2aj| \leq a$, and c_1 is determined by the equality of the discriminants, $b^2 - 4ac = (b - 2aj)^2 - 4ac_1$;

(3) in case $b < 0$, the replacement of $[a, b, c]$ by $[a, -b, c]$.

Chapter 6

Farey Fractions

6.1 Farey Sequences

Let us construct a table in the following way. In the first row we write $0/1$ and $1/1$. For $n = 2, 3, \cdots$ we use the rule: Form the nth row by copying the $(n-1)$st in order, but insert the fraction $(a+a')/(b+b')$ between the consecutive fractions a/b and a'/b' of the $(n-1)$st row if $b+b' \leq n$. Thus, since $1+1 \leq 2$ we insert $(0+1)/(1+1)$ between $0/1$ and $1/1$ and obtain $0/1$, $1/2$, $1/1$, for the second row. The third row is $0/1$, $1/3$, $1/2$, $2/3$, $1/1$. To obtain the fourth row we insert $(0+1)/(1+3)$ and $(2+1)/(3+1)$ but not $(1+1)/(3+2)$ and $(1+2)/(2+3)$. The first five rows of the table are:

$\frac{0}{1}$										$\frac{1}{1}$
$\frac{0}{1}$					$\frac{1}{2}$					$\frac{1}{1}$
$\frac{0}{1}$			$\frac{1}{3}$		$\frac{1}{2}$		$\frac{2}{3}$			$\frac{1}{1}$
$\frac{0}{1}$		$\frac{1}{4}$	$\frac{1}{3}$		$\frac{1}{2}$		$\frac{2}{3}$	$\frac{3}{4}$		$\frac{1}{1}$
$\frac{0}{1}$	$\frac{1}{5}$	$\frac{1}{4}$	$\frac{1}{3}$	$\frac{2}{5}$	$\frac{1}{2}$	$\frac{3}{5}$	$\frac{2}{3}$	$\frac{3}{4}$	$\frac{4}{5}$	$\frac{1}{1}$

Up to this row, at least, the table has a number of interesting properties. All the fractions that appear are in reduced form; all reduced fractions a/b such that $0 \leq a/b \leq 1$ and $b \leq n$ appear in the nth row; if a/b and a'/b' are consecutive fractions in the nth row, then $a'b - ab' = 1$ and $b + b' > n$. We will prove all these properties for the entire table.

Theorem 6.1 *If a/b and a'/b' are consecutive fractions in the nth row, say with a/b to the left of a'/b', then $a'b - ab' = 1$.*

Proof. It is true for $n = 1$. Suppose it is true for the $(n - 1)$st row. Any consecutive fractions in the nth row will be either a/b, a'/b' or a/b, $(a + a')/(b + b')$, or $(a + a')/(b + b')$, a'/b' where a/b and a'/b' are consecutive fractions in the $(n - 1)$st row. But then we have $a'b - ab' = 1$, $(a + a')b - a(b + b') = a'b - ab' = 1$, $a'(b + b') - (a + a')b' = a'b - ab' = 1$, and the theorem is proved by mathematical induction.

Corollary 6.2 *Every a/b in the table is in reduced form, that is, $(a, b) = 1$.*

Corollary 6.3 *The fractions in each row are listed in order of their size.*

Theorem 6.4 *If a/b and a'/b' are consecutive fractions in any row, then among all rational fractions with values between these two, $(a + a')/(b + b')$ is the unique fraction with smallest denominator.*

Proof. In the first place, the fraction $(a + a')/(b + b')$ will be the first fraction to be inserted between a/b and a'/b' as we continue to further rows of the table. It will first appear in the $(b + b')$th row. Therefore we have

$$\frac{a}{b} < \frac{a + a'}{b + b'} < \frac{a'}{b'}$$

by Corollary 6.3.

Now consider any fraction x/y between a/b and a'/b' so that $a/b < x/y < a'/b'$. Then

$$(6.1) \quad \frac{a'}{b'} - \frac{a}{b} = \left(\frac{a'}{b'} - \frac{x}{y}\right) + \left(\frac{x}{y} - \frac{a}{b}\right)$$

$$= \frac{a'y - b'x}{b'y} + \frac{bx - ay}{by} \geq \frac{1}{b'y} + \frac{1}{by} = \frac{b + b'}{bb'y},$$

and therefore

$$\frac{b + b'}{bb'y} \leqq \frac{a'b - ab'}{bb'} = \frac{1}{bb'},$$

which implies $y \geqq b + b'$. If $y > b + b'$ then x/y does not have least denominator among fractions between a/b and a'/b'. If $y = b + b'$, then the inequality in (6.1) must become equality and we have $a'y - b'x = 1$ and $bx - ay = 1$. Solving, we find $x = a + a'$, $y = b + b'$, and hence $(a + a')/(b + b')$ is the unique rational fraction lying between a/b and a'/b'.

Theorem 6.5 *If $0 \leqq x \leqq y$, $(x, y) = 1$, then the fraction x/y appears in the yth and all later rows.*

Proof. This is obvious if $y = 1$. Suppose it is true for $y = y_0 - 1$, with $y_0 > 1$. Then if $y = y_0$, the fraction x/y cannot be in the $(y - 1)$st row by definition and so it must lie in value between two consecutive fractions a/b and a'/b' of the $(y - 1)$st row. Thus $a/b < x/y < a'/b'$. Since

$$\frac{a}{b} < \frac{a + a'}{b + b'} < \frac{a'}{b'}$$

and a/b, a'/b' are consecutive, the fraction $(a + a')/(b + b')$ is not in the $(y - 1)$st row and hence $b + b' > y - 1$ by our induction hypothesis. But $y \geqq b + b'$ by Theorem 6.4, and so we have $y = b + b'$. Then the uniqueness part of Theorem 6.4 shows that $x = a + a'$. Therefore $x/y = (a + a')/(b + b')$ enters in the yth row, and it is then in all later rows.

Corollary 6.6 *The nth row consists of all reduced rational fractions a/b such that $0 \leqq a/b \leqq 1$ and $0 < b \leqq n$. The fractions are listed in order of their size.*

Definition 6.1 *The sequence of all reduced fractions with denominators not exceeding n, listed in order of their size, is called the Farey sequence of order n.*

The nth row of our table gives that part of the Farey sequence of order n that lies between 0 and 1, and so the entire Farey sequence of order n can be obtained from the nth row by adding and subtracting integers. For example, the Farey sequence of order 2 is

$$\cdots , \frac{-3}{1}, \frac{-5}{2}, \frac{-2}{1}, \frac{-3}{2}, \frac{-1}{1}, \frac{-1}{2}, \frac{0}{1}, \frac{1}{2}, \frac{1}{1}, \frac{3}{2}, \frac{2}{1}, \frac{5}{2}, \frac{3}{1}, \cdots .$$

This definition of the Farey sequences seems to be the most convenient. However, some authors prefer to restrict the fractions to the interval from 0 to 1; they define the Farey sequences to be just the rows of our table.

Any reduced fraction with positive denominator $\leq n$ is a member of the Farey sequence of order n and can be called a Farey fraction of order n. Note that consecutive fractions a/b and a'/b' in the Farey sequence of order n satisfy the equality of Theorem 6.1 and also the inequality $b + d > n$.

Problems

1. Let a/b and a'/b' be the fractions immediately to the left and the right of the fraction $1/2$ in the Farey sequence of order n. Prove that $b = b' = 1 + 2[(n-1)/2]$, that is b is the greatest odd integer $\leq n$. Also prove that $a + a' = b$.

2. Prove that the number of Farey fractions a/b of order n satisfying the inequalities $0 \leq a/b \leq 1$ is $1 + \sum_{j=1}^{n} \phi(j)$, and that their sum is exactly half of this value.

3. Let a/b, a'/b', a''/b'' be any three consecutive fractions in the Farey sequence of order n. Prove that $a'/b' = (a + a'')/(b + b'')$.

4. Let a/b and a'/b' run through all pairs of adjacent fractions in the Farey sequence of order $n > 1$. Prove that

$$\min \left(\frac{a'}{b'} - \frac{a}{b} \right) = \frac{1}{n(n-1)} \quad \text{and} \quad \max \left(\frac{a'}{b'} - \frac{a}{b} \right) = \frac{1}{n}.$$

5. Consider two rational numbers a/b and c/d such that $ad - bc = 1$, $b > 0$, $d > 0$. Define n as max (b, d), and prove that a/b and c/d are adjacent fractions in the Farey sequence of order n.

6. Prove that the two fractions described in the preceding problem are not necessarily adjacent in the Farey sequence of order $n + 1$.

7. Consider the fractions from $0/1$ to $1/1$ inclusive in the Farey sequence of order n. Reading from left to right, let the denominators of these fractions be $a_1, a_2, \cdots , a_k$ so that $a_1 = 1$ and $a_k = 1$. Prove that $\sum_{j=1}^{n-1} (a_j a_{j+1})^{-1} = 1$.

6.2   Rational Approximations

Theorem 6.7 *If a/b and c/d are Farey fractions of order n such that no other Farey fraction of order n lies between them, then*

$$\left| \frac{a}{b} - \frac{a+c}{b+d} \right| = \frac{1}{b(b+d)} \leq \frac{1}{b(n+1)},$$

and

$$\left| \frac{c}{d} - \frac{a+c}{b+d} \right| = \frac{1}{d(b+d)} \leq \frac{1}{d(n+1)}.$$

Proof. We have

$$\left| \frac{a}{b} - \frac{a+c}{b+d} \right| = \frac{|ad-bc|}{b(b+d)} = \frac{1}{b(b+d)} \leq \frac{1}{b(n+1)}$$

by Theorem 6.1 and the fact that $b + d \geq n + 1$. The second formula is proved in a similar way.

Theorem 6.8 *If n is a positive integer and x is real, there is a rational number a/b such that $0 < b \leq n$ and*

$$\left| x - \frac{a}{b} \right| \leq \frac{1}{b(n+1)}.$$

Proof. Consider the set of all Farey fractions of order n and all of the fractions $(a + c)/(b + d)$ as described in Theorem 6.7. For some fractions a/b and c/d, the number x will lie in the closed interval between a/b and $(a + c)/(b + d)$. Then, by Theorem 6.7,

$$\left| x - \frac{a}{b} \right| \leq \left| \frac{a}{b} - \frac{a+c}{b+d} \right| \leq \frac{1}{b(n+1)}.$$

Theorem 6.9 *If ξ is real and irrational, there are infinitely many rational numbers a/b such that*

$$\left| \xi - \frac{a}{b} \right| < \frac{1}{b^2}.$$

Proof. For each $n = 1, 2, \cdots$ we can find an a_n and a b_n by Theorem 6.8 such that $0 < b_n \leq n$ and

$$\left| \xi - \frac{a_n}{b_n} \right| \leq \frac{1}{b_n(n+1)} < \frac{1}{b_n^2}.$$

Many of the b_n may be equal to each other, but there will be infinitely many distinct ones. For if there were not infinitely many distinct ones, there would be only a finite number of distinct values taken by $|\xi - a_n/b_n|$, $n = 1, 2, 3, \cdots$. Then there would be a least one among these values, and it would be the value of $|\xi - a_n/b_n|$ for some n, say $n = k$. We would have $|\xi - a_n/b_n| \geq |\xi - a_k/b_k|$ for all $n = 1, 2, 3, \cdots$. But $|\xi - a_k/b_k| > 0$ since ξ is irrational, and we can find an n sufficiently large that

$$\frac{1}{n+1} < \left| \xi - \frac{a_k}{b_k} \right|.$$

This leads to a contradiction since we would now have

$$\left| \xi - \frac{a_k}{b_k} \right| \leq \left| \xi - \frac{a_n}{b_n} \right| \leq \frac{1}{b_n(n+1)} \leq \frac{1}{n+1} < \left| \xi - \frac{a_k}{b_k} \right|.$$

The condition that ξ be irrational is necessary in the theorem. For if x is any rational number, we can write $x = r/s$, $s > 0$. Then if a/b is any fraction such that $a/b \neq r/s$, $b > s$, we have

$$\left| \frac{r}{s} - \frac{a}{b} \right| = \frac{|rb - as|}{sb} \geq \frac{1}{sb} > \frac{1}{b^2}.$$

Hence all fractions a/b, $b > 0$, satisfying $|x - a/b| < 1/b^2$ have denominators $b \leq s$, and there can only be a finite number of such fractions.

The result of Theorem 6.9 can be improved, as Theorem 6.11 will show. Different proofs of Theorems 6.11 and 6.12 are given in Section 7.6.

Lemma 6.10 *If x and y are positive integers then not both of the two inequalities*

$$\frac{1}{xy} \geq \frac{1}{\sqrt{5}}\left(\frac{1}{x^2} + \frac{1}{y^2} \right) \quad and \quad \frac{1}{x(x+y)} \geq \frac{1}{\sqrt{5}}\left(\frac{1}{x^2} + \frac{1}{(x+y)^2} \right)$$

can hold.

Proof. The two inequalities can be written as

$$\sqrt{5}\, xy \geq y^2 + x^2, \qquad \sqrt{5}\, x(x+y) \geq (x+y)^2 + x^2.$$

Adding these inequalities, we get $\sqrt{5}(x^2 + 2xy) \geq 3x^2 + 2xy + 2y^2$, hence $2y^2 - 2(\sqrt{5} - 1)xy + (3 - \sqrt{5})x^2 \leq 0$. Multiplying this by 2 we put it in the form $4y^2 - 4(\sqrt{5} - 1)xy + (5 - 2\sqrt{5} + 1)x^2 \leq 0$, $(2y - (\sqrt{5} - 1)x)^2 \leq 0$. This is impossible for positive integers x and y because $\sqrt{5}$ is irrational.

Theorem 6.11 (*Hurwitz*) *Given any irrational number* ξ, *there exist infinitely many different rational numbers* h/k *such that*

(6.2)
$$\left| \xi - \frac{h}{k} \right| < \frac{1}{\sqrt{5}\,k^2}.$$

Proof. Let n be a positive integer. There exist two consecutive fractions a/b and c/d in the Farey sequence of order n, such that $a/b < \xi < c/d$. Either $\xi < (a + c)/(b + d)$ or $\xi > (a + c)/(b + d)$.

Case I. $\xi < (a + c)/(b + d)$. Suppose that

$$\xi - \frac{a}{b} \geq \frac{1}{b^2\sqrt{5}}, \quad \frac{a + c}{b + d} - \xi \geq \frac{1}{(b + d)^2\sqrt{5}}, \quad \frac{c}{d} - \xi \geq \frac{1}{d^2\sqrt{5}}.$$

Adding inequalities we obtain

$$\frac{c}{d} - \frac{a}{b} \geq \frac{1}{d^2\sqrt{5}} + \frac{1}{b^2\sqrt{5}}, \quad \frac{a + c}{b + d} - \frac{a}{b} \geq \frac{1}{(b + d)^2\sqrt{5}} + \frac{1}{b^2\sqrt{5}},$$

hence

$$\frac{1}{bd} = \frac{cb - ad}{bd} = \frac{c}{d} - \frac{a}{b} \geq \frac{1}{\sqrt{5}}\left(\frac{1}{b^2} + \frac{1}{d^2}\right)$$

and

$$\frac{1}{b(b + d)} = \frac{(a + c)b - (b + d)a}{b(b + d)} \geq \frac{1}{\sqrt{5}}\left(\frac{1}{b^2} + \frac{1}{(b + d)^2}\right).$$

These two inequalities contradict Lemma 6.10. Therefore at least one of a/b, c/d, $(a + c)/(b + d)$ will serve as h/k in this case.

Case II. $\xi > (a + c)/(b + d)$. Suppose that

$$\xi - \frac{a}{b} \geq \frac{1}{b^2\sqrt{5}}, \quad \xi - \frac{a + c}{b + d} \geq \frac{1}{(b + d)^2\sqrt{5}}, \quad \frac{c}{d} - \xi \geq \frac{1}{d^2\sqrt{5}}.$$

Adding as before, we obtain

$$\frac{c}{d} - \frac{a}{b} \geqq \frac{1}{d^2 \sqrt{5}} + \frac{1}{b^2 \sqrt{5}}, \qquad \frac{c}{d} - \frac{a+c}{b+d} \geqq \frac{1}{d^2 \sqrt{5}} + \frac{1}{(b+d)^2 \sqrt{5}},$$

hence

$$\frac{1}{bd} \geqq \frac{1}{\sqrt{5}}\left(\frac{1}{d^2} + \frac{1}{b^2}\right), \qquad \frac{1}{d(b+d)} \geqq \frac{1}{\sqrt{5}}\left(\frac{1}{(b+d)^2} + \frac{1}{d^2}\right),$$

which also contradicts Lemma 6.10. Again at least one of a/b, c/d, $(a+c)/(b+d)$ will serve as h/k.

We have shown the existence of some h/k that satisfies (6.2). This h/k depends on our choice of n. In fact h/k is either a/b, c/d, or $(a+c)/(b+d)$, where a/b and c/d are consecutive fractions in the Farey sequence of order n, and $a/b < \xi < c/d$. Using Theorem 6.7 we see that either

$$\left|\xi - \frac{h}{k}\right| \leqq \frac{1}{b(n+1)} \quad \text{or} \quad \left|\xi - \frac{h}{k}\right| \leqq \frac{1}{d(n+1)}.$$

In either case we have

$$\left|\xi - \frac{h}{k}\right| \leqq \frac{1}{n+1}.$$

We want to establish that there are infinitely many h/k that satisfy (6.2). Suppose that we have any h_1/k_1 that satisfies (6.2). Then $\left|\xi - \dfrac{h_1}{k_1}\right|$ is positive, and we can choose $n > 1 \Big/ \left|\xi - \dfrac{h_1}{k_1}\right|$. The Farey sequence of order n then yields an h/k that satisfies (6.2) and such that

$$\left|\xi - \frac{h}{k}\right| \leqq \frac{1}{n+1} < \left|\xi - \frac{h_1}{k_1}\right|.$$

This shows that there exist infinitely many rational numbers h/k that satisfy (6.2) since, given any rational number, we can find another that is closer to ξ.

Theorem 6.12 *The constant* $\sqrt{5}$ *in Theorem 6.11 is the best possible. In other words Theorem 6.11 does not hold if* $\sqrt{5}$ *is replaced by any larger value.*

Proof. We need only exhibit one ξ for which $\sqrt{5}$ cannot be replaced by a larger value. Let us take $\xi = \frac{1}{2}(1 + \sqrt{5})$. Then

$$(x - \xi)\left(x - \frac{1 - \sqrt{5}}{2}\right) = x^2 - x - 1.$$

For integers h, k with $k > 0$, we then have

$$(6.3) \quad \left|\frac{h}{k} - \xi\right|\left|\frac{h}{k} - \xi + \sqrt{5}\right| = \left|\left(\frac{h}{k} - \xi\right)\left(\frac{h}{k} - \frac{1 - \sqrt{5}}{2}\right)\right|$$

$$= \left|\frac{h^2}{k^2} - \frac{h}{k} - 1\right| = \frac{1}{k^2}\left|h^2 - hk - k^2\right|.$$

The expression on the left in (6.3) is not zero because both ξ and $\sqrt{5} - \xi$ are irrational. The expression $\left|h^2 - hk - k^2\right|$ is a non-negative integer. Therefore $\left|h^2 - hk - k^2\right| \geq 1$ and we have

$$(6.4) \quad \left|\frac{h}{k} - \xi\right|\left|\frac{h}{k} - \xi + \sqrt{5}\right| \geq \frac{1}{k^2}.$$

Now suppose we have an infinite sequence of rational numbers h_j/k_j, $k_j > 0$, and a positive real number m such that

$$(6.5) \quad \left|\frac{h_j}{k_j} - \xi\right| < \frac{1}{mk_j^2}.$$

Then $k_j\xi - \dfrac{1}{mk_j} < h_j < k_j\xi + \dfrac{1}{mk_j}$, and this implies that there are only a finite number of h_j corresponding to each value of k_j. Therefore we have $k_j \to \infty$ as $j \to \infty$. Also, by (6.4), (6.5) and the triangle inequality we have

$$\frac{1}{k_j^2} \leq \left|\frac{h_j}{k_j} - \xi\right|\left|\frac{h_j}{k_j} - \xi + \sqrt{5}\right| < \frac{1}{mk_j^2}\left(\frac{1}{mk_j^2} + \sqrt{5}\right),$$

hence

$$m < \frac{1}{mk_j^2} + \sqrt{5},$$

and therefore

$$m \leq \lim_{j \to \infty}\left(\frac{1}{mk_j^2} + \sqrt{5}\right) = \sqrt{5}.$$

Problems

1. Prove that for every real number x there are infinitely many pairs of integers a, b, with b positive such that $|bx - a| < (\sqrt{5}\, b)^{-1}$.

2. Let ξ be irrational. Let $\lambda > 0$ and $\alpha > 2$ be real numbers. Prove that there are only finitely many rationals h/k satisfying

$$\left| \xi - \frac{h}{k} \right| < \frac{1}{\lambda k^\alpha}.$$

3. Suppose $h = a$, $k = b$ is a solution of the inequality (6.2) for some irrational ξ. Prove that only a finite number of pairs h, k in the set $\{h = ma, k = mb; m = 1, 2, 3, \cdots\}$ satisfy (6.2).

4. Let $\alpha > 1$ be a real number. Suppose that for some real number β there are infinitely many rational numbers h/k such that $|\beta - h/k| < k^{-\alpha}$. Prove that β is irrational.

5. Prove that the following are irrational:

$$\sum_{j=1}^{\infty} 2^{-3^i}, \qquad \sum_{j=1}^{\infty} 2^{-j!}.$$

Chapter 7

Simple Continued Fractions

7.1 The Euclidean Algorithm

Given any rational fraction u_0/u_1, in lowest terms so that $(u_0, u_1) = 1$ and $u_1 > 0$, we apply the Euclidean algorithm as formulated in Theorem 1.11 to get

$$(7.1) \qquad
\begin{aligned}
u_0 &= u_1 a_0 + u_2, &\quad 0 &< u_2 < u_1 \\
u_1 &= u_2 a_1 + u_3, &\quad 0 &< u_3 < u_2 \\
u_2 &= u_3 a_2 + u_4, &\quad 0 &< u_4 < u_3 \\
u_{j-1} &= u_j a_{j-1} + u_{j+1}, &\quad 0 &< u_{j+1} < u_j \\
u_j &= u_{j+1} a_j.
\end{aligned}$$

The notation has been altered from that of Theorem 1.11 by the replacement of b, c by u_0, u_1, of r_1, r_2, $\cdots$, r_j by u_2, u_3, $\cdots$, u_{j+1}, and of q_1, q_2, $\cdots$, q_{j+1} by a_0, a_1, $\cdots$, a_j. The form (7.1) is a little more suitable for our present purposes. If we write ξ_i in place of u_i/u_{i+1} for all values of i in the range $0 \leq i \leq j$, then equations (7.1) become

$$(7.2) \qquad \xi_i = a_i + \frac{1}{\xi_{i+1}}, \quad 0 \leq i \leq j - 1; \quad \xi_j = a_j.$$

If we take the first two of these equations, those for which $i = 0$ and $i = 1$, and eliminate ξ_1, we get

$$\xi_0 = a_0 + \cfrac{1}{a_1 + \cfrac{1}{\xi_2}}.$$

In this result we replace ξ_2 by its value from (7.2), and then we continue with the replacement of ξ_3, ξ_4, $\cdot$ $\cdot$ $\cdot$, to get

$$(7.3) \qquad \frac{u_0}{u_1} = \xi_0 = a_0 + \cfrac{1}{a_1 + \cfrac{}{\cdots \cfrac{}{+ \cfrac{1}{a_{j-1} + \cfrac{1}{a_j}}}}}.$$

This is a continued fraction expansion of ξ_0, or of u_0/u_1. The integers a_i are called the partial quotients since they are the quotients in the repeated application of the division algorithm in equations (7.1). We presumed that the rational fraction u_0/u_1 had positive denominator u_1, but we cannot make a similar assumption about u_0. Hence a_0 may be positive, negative, or zero. However, since $0 < u_2 < u_1$, we note that the quotient a_1 is positive, and similarly the subsequent quotients a_2, a_3, $\cdot$ $\cdot$ $\cdot$, a_j are positive integers. In case $j \geq 1$, that is if the set (7.1) contains more than one equation, then $a_j = u_j/u_{j+1}$ and $0 < u_{j+1} < u_j$ imply that $a_j > 1$.

We shall use the notation $\langle a_0, a_1, \cdot \cdot \cdot , a_j \rangle$ to designate the continued fraction in (7.3). In general, if x_0, x_1, $\cdot$ $\cdot$ $\cdot$, x_j are any real numbers, all positive except perhaps x_0, we shall write

$$\langle x_0, x_1, \cdot \cdot \cdot , x_j \rangle = x_0 + \cfrac{1}{x_1 + \cfrac{}{\cdots \cfrac{}{+ \cfrac{1}{x_{j-1} + \cfrac{1}{x_j}}}}}.$$

Such a finite continued fraction is said to be simple if all the x_i are integers. The following obvious formulas are often useful:

$$\langle x_0, x_1, \cdot \cdot \cdot , x_j \rangle = x_0 + \frac{1}{\langle x_1, \cdot \cdot \cdot , x_j \rangle}$$

$$= \left\langle x_0, x_1, \cdot \cdot \cdot , x_{j-2}, x_{j-1} + \frac{1}{x_j} \right\rangle.$$

The symbol $[x_0, x_1, \cdot\cdot\cdot, x_j]$ is often used to represent a continued fraction. We use the notation $\langle x_0, x_1, \cdot\cdot\cdot, x_j \rangle$ to avoid confusion with the least common multiple and the greatest integer.

Problems

1. Expand the rational fractions $17/3$, $3/17$, and $8/1$ into finite simple continued fractions.
2. Prove that the set (7.1) consists of exactly one equation if and only if $u_1 = 1$ Under what circumstances is $a_0 = 0$?
3. Convert into rational numbers: $\langle 2, 1, 4 \rangle$; $\langle -3, 2, 12 \rangle$; $\langle 0, 1, 1, 100 \rangle$.
4. Given positive integers b, c, d with $c > d$, prove that $\langle a, c \rangle < \langle a, d \rangle$ but $\langle a, b, c \rangle > \langle a, b, d \rangle$ for any integer a.
5. Let $a_1, a_2 \cdot\cdot\cdot, a_n$ and c be positive real numbers. Prove that

$$\langle a_0, a_1, \cdot\cdot\cdot, a_n \rangle > \langle a_0, a_1, \cdot\cdot\cdot, a_n + c \rangle$$

holds if n is odd, but is false if n is even.

7.2 Uniqueness

In the last section we saw that such a fraction as $51/22$ can be expanded into a simple continued fraction, $51/22 = \langle 2, 3, 7 \rangle$. It can be verified that $51/22$ can also be expressed as $\langle 2, 3, 6, 1 \rangle$, but it turns out that these are the only two representations of $51/22$. In general, we note that the simple continued fraction expansion (7.3) has an alternate form,

$$(7.4) \quad \frac{u_0}{u_1} = \langle a_0, a_1, \cdot\cdot\cdot, a_{j-1}, a_j \rangle = \langle a_0, a_1, \cdot\cdot\cdot, a_{j-1}, a_j - 1, 1 \rangle.$$

The following result establishes that these are the only two simple continued fraction expansions of a fixed rational number.

Theorem 7.1 *If* $\langle a_0, a_1, \cdot\cdot\cdot, a_j \rangle = \langle b_0, b_1, \cdot\cdot\cdot, b_n \rangle$ *where these finite continued fractions are simple, and if* $a_j > 1$ *and* $b_n > 1$, *then* $j = n$ *and* $a_i = b_i$ *for* $i = 0, 1, \cdot\cdot\cdot, n$.

Proof. We write y_i for the continued fraction $\langle b_i, b_{i+1}, \cdot\cdot\cdot, b_n \rangle$ and observe that

$$(7.5) \quad y_i = \langle b_i, b_{i+1}, \cdot\cdot\cdot, b_n \rangle = b_i + \frac{1}{\langle b_{i+1}, b_{i+2}, \cdot\cdot\cdot, b_n \rangle}$$

$$= b_i + \frac{1}{y_{i+1}}.$$

Thus we have $y_i > b_i$ and $y_i > 1$ for $i = 1, 2, \cdots, n - 1$, and $y_n = b_n > 1$. Consequently $b_i = [y_i]$ for all values of i in the range $0 \leq i \leq n$. The hypothesis that the continued fractions are equal can be written in the form $y_0 = \xi_0$, where we are using the notation of equation (7.3). Now the definition of ξ_i as u_i/u_{i+1} implies that $\xi_{i+1} > 1$ for all values of $i \geq 0$, and so $a_i = [\xi_i]$ for $0 \leq i \leq j$ by equations (7.2). It follows from $y_0 = \xi_0$ that, taking integral parts, $b_0 = [y_0] = [\xi_0] = a_0$. By equations (7.2) and (7.5) we get

$$\frac{1}{\xi_1} = \xi_0 - a_0 = y_0 - b_0 = \frac{1}{y_1}, \quad \xi_1 = y_1, \quad a_1 = [\xi_1] = [y_1] = b_1.$$

This gives us the start of a proof by mathematical induction. We now establish that $\xi_i = y_i$ and $a_i = b_i$ imply that $\xi_{i+1} = y_{i+1}$ and $a_{i+1} = b_{i+1}$. To see this, we again use equations (7.2) and (7.5) to write

$$\frac{1}{\xi_{i+1}} = \xi_i - a_i = y_i - b_i = \frac{1}{y_{i+1}}, \quad \xi_{i+1} = y_{i+1}, \quad a_{i+1} = [\xi_{i+1}]$$

$$= [y_{i+1}] = b_{i+1}.$$

It must also follow that the continued fractions have the same length, that is, that $j = n$. For suppose that, say, $j < n$. From the preceding argument we have $\xi_j = y_j$, $a_j = b_j$. But $\xi_j = a_j$ by (7.2) and $y_j > b_j$ by (7.5), and so we have a contradiction. If we had assumed $j > n$, a symmetrical contradiction would have arisen, and thus j must equal n, and the theorem is proved.

Theorem 7.2 *Any finite simple continued fraction represents a rational number. Conversely any rational number can be expressed as a finite simple continued fraction, and in exactly two ways.*

Proof. The first assertion can be established by mathematical induction on the number of terms in the continued fraction, by use of the formula

$$\langle a_0, a_1, \cdots, a_j \rangle = a_0 + \frac{1}{\langle a_1, a_2, \cdots, a_j \rangle}.$$

The second assertion follows from the development of u_0/u_1 into a finite simple continued fraction in Section 7.1, together with equation (7.4) and Theorem 7.1.

Problem

1. Let $a_0, a_1, \cdots, a_n$ and $b_0, b_1, \cdots, b_{n+1}$ be positive integers. What are the conditions for

$$\langle a_0, a_1, \cdots, a_n \rangle < \langle b_0, b_1, \cdots, b_{n+1} \rangle?$$

7.3   Infinite Continued Fractions

Let $a_0, a_1, a_2, \cdots$ be an infinite sequence of integers, all positive except perhaps a_0. We define two sequences of integers $\{h_n\}$ and $\{k_n\}$ inductively as follows:

$$(7.6) \quad h_{-2} = 0, \quad h_{-1} = 1, \quad h_i = a_i h_{i-1} + h_{i-2} \quad \text{for } i \geq 0,$$

$$k_{-2} = 1, \quad k_{-1} = 0, \quad k_i = a_i k_{i-1} + k_{i-2} \quad \text{for } i \geq 0.$$

We note that $k_0 = 1$, $k_1 = a_1 k_0 \geq k_0$, $k_2 > k_1$, $k_3 > k_2$, etc., so that $1 = k_0 \leq k_1 < k_2 < k_3 < \cdots < k_n < \cdots$.

Theorem 7.3 *For any positive real number x,*

$$\langle a_0, a_1, \cdots, a_{n-1}, x \rangle = \frac{x h_{n-1} + h_{n-2}}{x k_{n-1} + k_{n-2}}.$$

Proof. If $n = 0$, the result is to be interpreted as

$$x = \frac{x h_{-1} + h_{-2}}{x k_{-1} + k_{-2}},$$

which is true by equations (7.6). If $n = 1$, the result is

$$\langle a_0, x \rangle = \frac{x h_0 + h_{-1}}{x k_0 + k_{-1}},$$

which can be verified from (7.6) and the fact that $\langle a_0, x \rangle$ stands for $a_0 + 1/x$. We establish the theorem in general by induction. Assuming that the result holds for $\langle a_0, a_1, \cdots, a_{n-1}, x \rangle$, we see that

$$\langle a_0, a_1, \cdots, a_n, x \rangle = \left\langle a_0, a_1, \cdots, a_{n-1}, a_n + \frac{1}{x} \right\rangle$$

$$= \frac{(a_n + 1/x) h_{n-1} + h_{n-2}}{(a_n + 1/x) k_{n-1} + k_{n-2}}$$

$$= \frac{x(a_n h_{n-1} + h_{n-2}) + h_{n-1}}{x(a_n k_{n-1} + k_{n-2}) + k_{n-1}} = \frac{x h_n + h_{n-1}}{x k_n + k_{n-1}}.$$

Theorem 7.4 *If we define* $r_n = \langle a_1, a_1, \cdots, a_n \rangle$ *for all integers* $n \geq 0$, *then* $r_n = h_n/k_n$.

Proof. We apply Theorem 7.3 with x replaced by a_n and then use equations (7.6) thus:

$$r_n = \langle a_0, a_1, \cdots, a_n \rangle = \frac{a_n h_{n-1} + h_{n-2}}{a_n k_{n-1} + k_{n-2}} = \frac{h_n}{k_n}.$$

Theorem 7.5 *The equations*

$$h_i k_{i-1} - h_{i-1} k_i = (-1)^{i-1} \quad and \quad r_i - r_{i-1} = \frac{(-1)^{i-1}}{k_i k_{i-1}}$$

hold for $i \geq 1$. *The identities*

$$h_i k_{i-2} - h_{i-2} k_i = (-1)^i a_i \quad and \quad r_i - r_{i-2} = \frac{(-1)^i a_i}{k_i k_{i-2}}$$

hold for $i \geq 2$. *The fraction* h_i/k_i *is reduced, that is* $(h_i, k_i) = 1$.

Proof. The equations (7.6) imply that $h_{-1} k_{-2} - h_{-2} k_{-1} = 1$. Continuing the proof by induction, we assume that $h_{i-1} k_{i-2} - h_{i-2} k_{i-1} = (-1)^{i-2}$. Again we use equations (7.6) to get $h_i k_{i-1} - h_{i-1} k_i = (a_i h_{i-1} + h_{i-2}) k_{i-1} - h_{i-1}(a_i k_{i-1} + k_{i-2}) = -(h_{i-1} k_{i-2} - h_{i-2} k_{i-1}) = (-1)^{i-1}$. This proves the first result stated in the theorem. We divide by $k_{i-1} k_i$ to get the second result, the formula for $r_i - r_{i-1}$. Furthermore, the fraction h_i/k_i is in lowest terms since any factor of h_i and k_i is also a factor of $(-1)^{i-1}$.

The other formulas can be derived in much the same way from (7.6), although we do not need induction in this case. First we observe that $h_0 k_{-2} - h_{-2} k_0 = a_0$, and that in general $h_i k_{i-2} - h_{i-2} k_i = (a_i h_{i-1} + h_{i-2}) k_{i-2} - h_{i-2}(a_i k_{i-1} + k_{i-2}) = a_i(h_{i-1} k_{i-2} - h_{i-2} k_{i-1}) = (-1)^i a_i$. The final identity can be obtained by dividing by $k_{i-2} k_i$.

Theorem 7.6 *The values* r_n *defined in Theorem 7.4 satisfy the infinite chain of inequalities* $r_0 < r_2 < r_4 < r_6 < \cdots < r_7 < r_5 < r_3 < r_1$. *Stated in words, the* r_n *with even subscripts form an increasing sequence, those with odd subscripts form a decreasing sequence, and every* r_{2n} *is less than every* r_{2j-1}. *Furthermore,* $\lim_{n \to \infty} r_n$ *exists, and for every* $j \geq 0$,

$$r_{2j} < \lim_{n \to \infty} r_n < r_{2j+1}.$$

Proof. The identities of Theorem 7.5 for $r_i - r_{i-1}$ and $r_i - r_{i-2}$ imply that $r_{2j} < r_{2j+2}$, $r_{2j-1} > r_{2j+1}$, and $r_{2j} < r_{2j-1}$ because the k_i are positive for $i \geq 0$ and the a_i are positive for $i \geq 1$. Thus we have $r_0 < r_2 < r_4 < \cdots$ and $r_1 > r_3 > r_5 > \cdots$. To prove that $r_{2n} < r_{2j-1}$, we put the previous results together in the form

$$r_{2n} < r_{2n+2j} < r_{2n+2j-1} \leqq r_{2j-1}.$$

The sequence r_0, r_2, r_4, $\cdots$ is monotonically increasing and is bounded above by r_1, and so has a limit. Analogously, the sequence $r_1, r_3, r_5, \cdots$ is monotonically decreasing and is bounded below by r_0, and so has a limit. These two limits are equal because, by Theorem 7.5, the difference $r_i - r_{i-1}$ tends to zero as i tends to infinity, since the integers k_i are increasing with i. Another way of looking at this is to observe that (r_0, r_1), (r_2, r_3), (r_4, r_5), $\cdots$ is a chain of nested intervals defining a real number, namely $\lim_{n \to \infty} r_n$.

These theorems suggest the following definition.

Definition 7.1 *An infinite sequence a_0, a_1, a_2, $\cdots$ of integers, all positive except perhaps for a_0, determines an infinite simple continued fraction $\langle a_0, a_1, a_2, \cdots \rangle$. The value of $\langle a_0, a_1, a_2, \cdots \rangle$ is defined to be* $\lim_{n \to \infty} \langle a_0, a_1, a_2, \cdots, a_n \rangle$.

This limit, being the same as $\lim_{n \to \infty} r_n$, exists by Theorem 7.6. Another way of writing this limit is $\lim_{n \to \infty} h_n/k_n$. The rational number $\langle a_0, a_1, \cdots, a_n \rangle = h_n/k_n = r_n$ is called the nth convergent to the infinite continued fraction. We say that the infinite continued fraction converges to the value $\lim_{n \to \infty} r_n$. In the case of a finite simple continued fraction $\langle a_0, a_1, \cdots, a_n \rangle$ we similarly call the number $\langle a_0, a_1, \cdots, a_m \rangle$ the mth convergent to $\langle a_0, a_1, \cdots, a_n \rangle$.

Theorem 7.7 *The value of any infinite simple continued fraction $\langle a_0, a_1, a_2, \cdots \rangle$ is irrational.*

Proof. Writing θ for $\langle a_0, a_1, a_2, \cdots \rangle$ we observe by Theorem 7.6 that θ lies between r_n and r_{n+1}, so that $0 < |\theta - r_n| < |r_{n+1} - r_n|$. Multiplying by k_n, and making use of the result from Theorem 7.5

that $\left|r_{n+1} - r_n\right| = (k_n k_{n+1})^{-1}$, we have

$$0 < \left|k_n \theta - h_n\right| < \frac{1}{k_{n+1}}.$$

Now suppose that θ were rational, say $\theta = a/b$ with integers a and b, $b > 0$. Then the above inequality would become, upon multiplication by b,

$$0 < \left|k_n a - h_n b\right| < \frac{b}{k_{n+1}}.$$

The integers k_n increase with n, so we could choose n sufficiently large so that $b < k_{n+1}$. Then the integer $\left|k_n a - h_n b\right|$ would lie between 0 and 1, which is impossible.

Suppose we have two different infinite simple continued fractions, $\langle a_0, a_1, a_2, \cdots \rangle$ and $\langle b_0, b_1, b_2, \cdots \rangle$. Can these converge to the same value? The answer is no, and we establish this in the next two results.

Lemma 7.8 *Let* $\theta = \langle a_1, a_1, a_2, \cdots \rangle$. *Then* $a_0 = [\theta]$. *Furthermore if* θ_1 *denotes* $\langle a_1, a_2, a_3, \cdots \rangle$ *then* $\theta = a_0 + 1/\theta_1$.

Proof. By Theorem 7.6 we see that $r_0 < \theta < r_1$, that is $a_0 < \theta < a_0 + 1/a_1$. Now $a_1 \geqq 1$, so we have $a_0 < \theta < a_0 + 1$, and hence $a_0 = [\theta]$. Also

$$\theta = \lim_{n \to \infty} \langle a_0, a_1, \cdots, a_n \rangle = \lim_{n \to \infty} \left(a_0 + \frac{1}{\langle a_1, \cdots, a_n \rangle} \right)$$

$$= a_0 + \frac{1}{\lim\limits_{n \to \infty} \langle a_1, \cdots, a_n \rangle} = a_0 + \frac{1}{\theta_1}.$$

Theorem 7.9 *Two distinct infinite simple continued fractions converge to different values.*

Proof. Let us suppose that $\langle a_0, a_1, a_2, \cdots \rangle = \langle b_0, b_1, b_2, \cdots \rangle = \theta$. Then by Lemma 7.8, $[\theta] = a_0 = b_0$ and

$$\theta = a_0 + \frac{1}{\langle a_1, a_2, \cdots \rangle} = b_0 + \frac{1}{\langle b_1, b_2, \cdots \rangle}.$$

Hence $\langle a_1, a_2, \cdot \cdot \cdot \rangle = \langle b_1, b_2, \cdot \cdot \cdot \rangle$. Repetition of the argument gives $a_1 = b_1$, and so by mathematical induction $a_n = b_n$ for all n.

Problems

1. Evaluate the infinite continued fraction $\langle 1, 1, 1, 1, \cdot \cdot \cdot \rangle$. *Suggestion:* by Lemma 7.8, we see that $\theta = 1 + 1/\theta$ in this case. This gives a quadratic equation, only one of whose roots is positive.
2. Evaluate the infinite continued fractions $\langle 2, 1, 1, 1, 1, \cdot \cdot \cdot \rangle$ and $\langle 2, 3, 1, 1, 1, 1, \cdot \cdot \cdot \rangle$. *Suggestion:* use the result of the preceding problem along with Lemma 7.8.
3. Evaluate the infinite continued fractions:
   - (a) $\langle 2, 2, 2, 2, \cdot \cdot \cdot \rangle$;   (b) $\langle 1, 2, 1, 2, 1, 2, \cdot \cdot \cdot \rangle$;
   - (c) $\langle 2, 1, 2, 1, 2, 1, \cdot \cdot \cdot \rangle$;   (d) $\langle 1, 3, 1, 2, 1, 2, 1, 2, \cdot \cdot \cdot \rangle$.
4. For $n \geq 1$, prove that $k_n/k_{n-1} = \langle a_n, a_{n-1}, \cdot \cdot \cdot, a_2, a_1 \rangle$. Find and prove a similar continued fraction expansion for h_n/h_{n-1}.

7.4   Irrational Numbers

We have shown that any infinite simple continued fraction represents an irrational number. Conversely, if we begin with an irrational number ξ, or ξ_0, we can expand it into an infinite simple continued fraction. To do this we define $a_0 = [\xi_0]$, $\xi_1 = 1/(\xi_0 - a_0)$, and next $a_1 = [\xi_1]$, $\xi_2 = 1/(\xi_1 - a_1)$, and so by an inductive definition

$$(7.7) \qquad a_i = [\xi_i], \qquad \xi_{i+1} = \frac{1}{\xi_i - a_i}.$$

The a_i are integers by definition, and the ξ_i are all irrational since the irrationality of ξ_1 is implied by that of ξ_0, that of ξ_2 by that of ξ_1, and so on. Furthermore, $a_i \geq 1$ for $i \geq 1$ because $a_{i-1} = [\xi_{i-1}]$ and the fact that ξ_{i-1} is irrational imply that

$$a_{i-1} < \xi_{i-1} < 1 + a_{i-1}, \quad 0 < \xi_{i-1} - a_{i-1} < 1,$$

$$\xi_i = \frac{1}{\xi_{i-1} - a_{i-1}} > 1, \quad a_i = [\xi_i] \geq 1.$$

Next we use repeated application of (7.7) in the form $\xi_i = a_i + 1/\xi_{i+1}$ to get the chain

$$\xi = \xi_0 = a_0 + \frac{1}{\xi_1} = \langle a_0, \xi_1 \rangle$$

$$= \left\langle a_0, a_1 + \frac{1}{\xi_2} \right\rangle = \langle a_0, a_1, \xi_2 \rangle$$

$$\cdots \cdots \cdots \cdots \cdots \cdots \cdots \cdots$$

$$= \left\langle a_0, a_1, \cdots, a_{m-2}, a_{m-1} + \frac{1}{\xi_m} \right\rangle = \langle a_0, a_1, \cdots, a_{m-1}, \xi_m \rangle.$$

This suggests, but does not establish, that ξ is the value of the infinite continued fraction $\langle a_0, a_1, a_2, \cdots \rangle$ determined by the integers a_i.

To prove this we use Theorem 7.3 to write

$$(7.8) \qquad \xi = \langle a_0, a_1, \cdots, a_{n-1}, \xi_n \rangle = \frac{\xi_n h_{n-1} + h_{n-2}}{\xi_n k_{n-1} + k_{n-2}}$$

with the h_i and k_i defined as in (7.6). By Theorem 7.5 we get

$$(7.9) \quad \xi - r_{n-1} = \xi - \frac{h_{n-1}}{k_{n-1}} = \frac{\xi_n h_{n-1} + h_{n-2}}{\xi_n k_{n-1} + k_{n-2}} - \frac{h_{n-1}}{k_{n-1}}$$

$$= \frac{-(h_{n-1}k_{n-2} - h_{n-2}k_{n-1})}{k_{n-1}(\xi_n k_{n-1} + k_{n-2})} = \frac{(-1)^{n-1}}{k_{n-1}(\xi_n k_{n-1} + k_{n-2})}.$$

This fraction tends to zero as n tends to infinity because the integers k_n are increasing with n, and ξ_n is positive. Hence $\xi - r_{n-1}$ tends to zero as n tends to infinity and then, by Definition 7.1,

$$\xi = \lim_{n \to \infty} r_n = \lim_{n \to \infty} \langle a_0, a_1, \cdots, a_n \rangle = \langle a_0, a_1, a_2, \cdots \rangle.$$

We summarize the results of the last two sections in the following theorem.

Theorem 7.10 *Any irrational number ξ is uniquely expressible, by the procedure that gave equations (7.7), as an infinite simple continued fraction $\langle a_0, a_1, a_2, \cdots \rangle$. Conversely any such continued fraction determined by integers a_i which are positive for all $i > 0$ represents an irrational number, ξ. The finite simple continued fraction $\langle a_0, a_1, \cdots, a_n \rangle$ has the rational value $h_n/k_n = r_n$, and is called the nth convergent to ξ. Equations (7.6) relate the h_i and k_i to the a_i. For $n = 0, 2, 4, \cdots$ these con-*

vergents form a monotonically increasing sequence with ξ as a limit. Similarly, for $n = 1, 3, 5, \cdots$ the convergents form a monotonically decreasing sequence tending to ξ. The denominators k_n of the convergents are an increasing sequence of positive integers for $n > 0$. Finally, with ξ_i defined by (7.7), we have $\langle a_0, a_1, \cdots \rangle = \langle a_0, a_1, \cdots, a_{n-1}, \xi_n \rangle$ and $\xi_n = \langle a_n, a_{n+1}, a_{n+2}, \cdots \rangle$.

Proof. Only the last equation is new, and it becomes obvious if we apply to ξ_n the process described at the opening of this section.

Problems

1. Expand each of the following as infinite simple continued fractions: $\sqrt{2}$, $\sqrt{2} - 1$, $\sqrt{2}/2$, $\sqrt{3}$, $1/\sqrt{3}$.

2. Given that two irrational numbers have identical convergents h_0/k_0, $h_1/k_1, \cdots$, up to h_n/k_n, prove that their continued fraction expansions are identical up to a_n.

3. Let α, β, γ be irrational numbers satisfying $\alpha < \beta < \gamma$. If α and γ have identical convergents h_0/k_0, $h_1/k_1, \cdots$, up to h_n/k_n, prove that β also has these same convergents up to h_n/k_n.

4. Let ξ be an irrational number with continued fraction expansion $\langle a_0, a_1, a_2, a_3, \cdots \rangle$. Let $b_1, b_2, b_3, \cdots$ be any finite or infinite sequence of positive integers. Prove that

$$\lim_{n \to \infty} \langle a_0, a_1, a_2, \cdots, a_n, b_1, b_2, b_3, \cdots \rangle = \xi.$$

5. In the notation used in the text, prove that

$$\xi_n = \langle a_n, a_{n+1}, a_{n+2}, \cdots \rangle.$$

6. Prove that for $n \geqq 1$,

$$\xi - \frac{h_n}{k_n} = (-1)^n k_n^{-2} \{ \xi_{n+1} + \langle 0, a_n, a_{n-1}, \cdots, a_2, a_1 \rangle \}^{-1}.$$

7. Prove that

$$k_n |k_{n-1}\xi - h_{n-1}| + k_{n-1} |k_n \xi - h_n| = 1.$$

7.5   Approximations to Irrational Numbers

Continuing to use the notation of the preceding sections, we now show that the convergents k_n/k_n form a sequence of "best" rational approximations to the irrational number ξ.

Theorem 7.11 *We have for any $n \geq 0$,*

$$\left| \xi - \frac{h_n}{k_n} \right| < \frac{1}{k_n k_{n+1}} \quad and \quad |\xi k_n - h_n| < \frac{1}{k_{n+1}}.$$

Proof. The second inequality follows from the first by multiplication by k_n. By (7.9) and (7.7) we see that

$$\left| \xi - \frac{h_n}{k_n} \right| = \frac{1}{k_n(\xi_{n+1} k_n + k_{n-1})} < \frac{1}{k_n(a_{n+1} k_n + k_{n-1})}.$$

Using (7.6), we replace $a_{n+1} k_n + k_{n-1}$ by k_{n+1} to obtain the first inequality.

Theorem 7.12 *The convergents h_n/k_n are successively closer to ξ, that is*

$$\left| \xi - \frac{h_n}{k_n} \right| < \left| \xi - \frac{h_{n-1}}{k_{n-1}} \right|.$$

In fact the stronger inequality $|\xi k_n - h_n| < |\xi k_{n-1} - h_{n-1}|$ holds.

Proof. To see that the second inequality is stronger in that it implies the first, we use $k_{n-1} \leq k_n$ to write

$$\left| \xi - \frac{h_n}{k_n} \right| = \frac{1}{k_n} |\xi k_n - h_n| < \frac{1}{k_n} |\xi k_{n-1} - h_{n-1}|$$

$$\leq \frac{1}{k_{n-1}} |\xi k_{n-1} - h_{n-1}| = \left| \xi - \frac{h_{n-1}}{k_{n-1}} \right|.$$

Now to prove the stronger inequality we observe that $a_n + 1 > \xi_n$ by (7.7), and so by (7.6),

$$\xi_n k_{n-1} + k_{n-2} < (a_n + 1)k_{n-1} + k_{n-2}$$
$$= k_n + k_{n-1} \leq a_{n+1} k_n + k_{n-1} = k_{n+1}.$$

This inequality and (7.9) imply that

$$\left| \xi - \frac{h_{n-1}}{k_{n-1}} \right| = \frac{1}{k_{n-1}(\xi_n k_{n-1} + k_{n-2})} > \frac{1}{k_{n-1} k_{n+1}}.$$

We multiply by k_{n-1} and use Theorem 7.11 to get

$$|\xi k_{n-1} - h_{n-1}| > \frac{1}{k_{n+1}} > |\xi k_n - h_n|.$$

The convergent h_n/k_n is the best approximation to ξ of all the rational fractions with denominator k_n or less. The following theorem states this in a different way.

Theorem 7.13 *If a/b is a rational number with positive denominator such that $|\xi - a/b| < |\xi - h_n/k_n|$ for some $n \geq 1$, then $b > k_n$. In fact if $|\xi b - a| < |\xi k_n - h_n|$ for some $n \geq 0$, then $b \geq k_{n+1}$.*

Proof. First we show that the second part of the theorem implies the first. Suppose that the first part is false so that there is an a/b with

$$\left| \xi - \frac{a}{b} \right| < \left| \xi - \frac{h_n}{k_n} \right| \quad \text{and} \quad b \leq k_n.$$

The product of these inequalities gives $|\xi b - a| < |\xi k_n - h_n|$. But the second part of the theorem says that this implies $b \geq k_{n+1}$, so we have a contradiction, since $k_n < k_{n+1}$ for $n \geq 1$.

To prove the second part of the theorem we proceed again by indirect argument, assuming that $|\xi b - a| < |\xi k_n - h_n|$ and $b < k_{n+1}$. Consider the linear equations in x and y,

$$xk_n + yk_{n+1} = b, \qquad xh_n + yh_{n+1} = a.$$

The determinant of coefficients is ± 1 by Theorem 7.5, and consequently these equations have an integral solution x, y. Moreover, neither x nor y is zero. For if $x = 0$ then $b = yk_{n+1}$, which implies that $y \neq 0$, in fact that $y > 0$ and $b \geq k_{n+1}$, in contradiction to $b < k_{n+1}$. If $y = 0$ then $a = xh_n$, $b = xk_n$, and

$$|\xi b - a| = |\xi x k_n - x h_n| = |x| \, |\xi k_n - h_n| \geq |k_n \xi - h_n|$$

since $|x| \geq 1$, and again we have a contradiction.

Next we prove that x and y have opposite signs. First, if $y < 0$, then $xk_n = b - yk_{n+1}$ shows that $x > 0$. Second, if $y > 0$, then $b < k_{n+1}$ implies that $b < yk_{n+1}$, and so xk_n is negative, whence $x < 0$. Now it follows from Theorem 7.10 that $\xi k_n - h_n$ and $\xi k_{n+1} - h_{n+1}$ have opposite signs, and hence $x(\xi k_n - h_n)$ and $y(\xi k_{n+1} - h_{n+1})$ have the same sign. From the equations defining x and y we get $\xi b - a = x(\xi k_n - h_n) + y(\xi k_{n+1} - h_{n+1})$. Since the two terms on the right have the same sign, the absolute value of the whole equals the sum of the separate absolute values. Thus

$$\left|\xi b - a\right| = \left|x(\xi k_n - h_n) + y(\xi k_{n+1} - h_{n+1})\right|$$
$$= \left|x(\xi k_n - h_n)\right| + \left|y(\xi k_{n+1} - h_{n+1})\right|$$
$$> \left|x(\xi k_n - h_n)\right| = \left|x\right|\left|\xi k_n - h_n\right| \geqq \left|\xi k_n - h_n\right|.$$

This is a contradiction, and so the theorem is established.

Theorem 7.14 *Let ξ denote any irrational number. If there is a rational number a/b with $b \geqq 1$ such that*

$$\left|\xi - \frac{a}{b}\right| < \frac{1}{2b^2},$$

then a/b equals one of the convergents of the simple continued fraction expansion of ξ.

Proof. It suffices to prove the result in the case $(a, b) = 1$. Let the convergents of the simple continued fraction expansion of ξ be h_j/k_j, and suppose that a/b is not a convergent. The inequalities $k_n \leqq b < k_{n+1}$ determine an integer n. For this n, the inequality $\left|\xi b - a\right| < \left|\xi k_n - b_n\right|$ is impossible because of Theorem 7.13.

Therefore we have

$$\left|\xi k_n - h_n\right| \leqq \left|\xi b - a\right| < \frac{1}{2b},$$

$$\left|\xi - \frac{h_n}{k_n}\right| < \frac{1}{2bk_n}.$$

Using the facts that $a/b \neq h_n/k_n$ and that $bh_n - ak_n$ is an integer, we find that

$$\frac{1}{bk_n} \leqq \frac{\left|bh_n - ak_n\right|}{bk_n} = \left|\frac{h_n}{k_n} - \frac{a}{b}\right| \leqq \left|\xi - \frac{h_n}{k_n}\right| + \left|\xi - \frac{a}{b}\right| < \frac{1}{2bk_n} + \frac{1}{2b^2}.$$

This implies $b < k_n$ which is a contradiction.

Theorem 7.15 *The nth convergent of $1/x$ is the reciprocal of the $(n - 1)$st convergent of x if x is any real number >1.*

Proof. We have $x = \langle a_0, a_1, \cdots \rangle$ and $1/x = \langle 0, a_0, a_1, \cdots \rangle$. If h_n/k_n and h'_n/k'_n are the convergents for x and $1/x$ respectively, then

$$h'_0 = 0, \quad h'_1 = 1, \quad h'_2 = a_1, \qquad h'_n = a_{n-1}h'_{n-1} + h'_{n-2}$$

$$k_0 = 1, \quad k_1 = a_1, \qquad k_{n-1} = a_{n-1}k_{n-2} + k_{n-3}$$

$$k'_0 = 1, \quad k'_1 = a_0, \quad k'_2 = a_0a_1 + 1, \qquad k'_n = a_{n-1}k'_{n-1} + k'_{n-2}$$

$$h_0 = a_0, \quad h_1 = a_0a_1 + 1, \quad h_{n-1} = a_{n-1}h_{n-2} + h_{n-3}.$$

The theorem now follows by mathematical induction.

Problems

1. Prove that the first assertion in Theorem 7.13 holds in case $n = 0$ if $k_1 > 1$.
2. Prove that the first assertion in Theorem 7.13 becomes false if "$b > k_n$" is replaced by "$b \geq k_{n+1}$". *Suggestion:* use $\xi = \pi^{-1}$ and $n = 1$.
3. Say that a rational number a/b with $b > 0$ is a "good approximation" to the irrational number ξ if

$$|\xi b - a| = \min_{\substack{\text{all } x \\ 0 < y \leq b}} |\xi y - x|,$$

where, as indicated, the minimum on the right is to be taken over all integers x and all y satisfying $0 < y \leq b$. Prove that every convergent to ξ is a "good approximation."
4. Prove that every "good approximation" to ξ is a convergent.
5. (a) Prove that if r/s lies between a/b and c/d, where the denominators of these rational fractions are positive, and if $ad - bc = \pm 1$, then $s > b$ and $s > d$.
   (b) Let ξ be an irrational with convergents $\{h_n/k_n\}$. Prove that the sequence

$$\frac{h_{n-1}}{k_{n-1}}, \frac{h_{n-1} + h_n}{k_{n-1} + k_n}, \frac{h_{n-1} + 2h_n}{k_{n-1} + 2k_n}, \cdots, \frac{h_{n-1} + a_{n+1}h_n}{k_{n-1} + a_{n+1}k_n} = \frac{h_{n+1}}{k_{n+1}}$$

is increasing if n is odd, decreasing if n is even. If a/b and c/d denote any consecutive pair of this sequence, prove that $ad - bc = \pm 1$. The terms of this sequence, except the first and last, are called the *secondary convergents*; here n runs through all values $0, 1, 2, \cdots$.
   (c) Say that a rational number a/b is a "fair approximation" to ξ if $|\xi - a/b| = \min |\xi - x/y|$, the minimum being taken over all integers x and y with $0 > y \leq b$. Prove that every good approximation is a fair approximation. Prove that every fair approximation is either a convergent or a secondary convergent to ξ.

(d) Prove that not every secondary convergent is a "fair approximation". *Suggestion:* consider $\xi = \sqrt{2}$.

(e) Say that an infinite sequence of rational numbers, $r_1, r_2, r_3, \cdots$ with limit ξ is an "approximating sequence" to an irrational number ξ if $|\xi - r_{j+1}| < |\xi - r_j|, j = 1, 2, 3, \cdots$, and if the positive denominators of the r_j are increasing with j. Prove that the "fair approximations" to ξ form an "approximating sequence."

(f) Let S_{n-1} denote the finite sequence of (b) with the first term deleted, so that S_{n-1} has a_{n+1} terms, the last term being h_{n+1}/k_{n+1}. Prove that the infinite sequence of rational numbers obtained by first taking the terms of S_0 in order, then the terms of S_2, then S_4, then S_6, $\cdots$, is also an "approximating sequence" to ξ. Prove also that this sequence is maximal in the sense that if any other rational number $< \xi$ is introduced into the sequence as a new member, we no longer have an approximating sequence.

(g) Establish analogous properties for the sequence obtained by taking the terms of $S_{-1}, S_1, S_3, S_5, \cdots$.

6. Let ξ be irrational, $\xi = \langle a_0, a_1, a_2, \cdots \rangle$. Verify that

$$-\xi = \langle -a_0 - 1, 1, a_1 - 1, a_2, a_3, \cdots \rangle \text{ if } a_1 > 1$$

and $-\xi = \langle -a_0 - 1, a_2 + 1, a_3, a_4, \cdots \rangle$ if $a_1 = 1$.

7.6 Best Possible Approximations

Theorem 7.11 provides another method of proving Theorem 6.9. For in the statement of Theorem 7.11 we can replace k_{n+1} by the smaller integer k_n to get the weaker, but still correct, inequality

$$\left| \xi - \frac{h_n}{k_n} \right| < \frac{1}{k_n^2}.$$

Moreover the process described in Section 7.4 enables us to determine for any given irrational ξ, as many convergents h_n/k_n as we please. We can also use continued fractions in other proofs of Theorems 6.11 and 6.12. First we give a simple lemma.

Lemma 7.16 *If x is real, $x > 1$, and $x + x^{-1} < \sqrt{5}$, then $x < \frac{1}{2}(\sqrt{5} + 1)$ and $x^{-1} > \frac{1}{2}(\sqrt{5} - 1)$.*

Proof. For real $x \geq 1$ we note that $x + x^{-1}$ increases with x, and $x + x^{-1} = \sqrt{5}$ if $x = \frac{1}{2}(\sqrt{5} + 1)$.

Theorem 7.17 (*Hurwitz*) *Given any irrational number ξ, there exist infinitely many rational numbers h/k such that*

(7.13)
$$\left| \xi - \frac{h}{k} \right| < \frac{1}{\sqrt{5}\, k^2}.$$

Proof. We will establish that, of every three consecutive convergents of the simple continued fraction expansion of ξ, at least one satisfies the inequality.

Let q_n denote k_n/k_{n-1}. We first prove that

(7.14)
$$q_j + q_j^{-1} < \sqrt{5}$$

if (7.13) is false for both $h/k = h_{j-1}/k_{j-1}$ and $h/k = h_j/k_j$. Suppose (7.13) is false for these two values of h/k. We have

$$\left| \xi - \frac{h_{j-1}}{k_{j-1}} \right| + \left| \xi - \frac{h_j}{k_j} \right| \geq \frac{1}{\sqrt{5}\, k_{j-1}^2} + \frac{1}{\sqrt{5}\, k_j^2}.$$

But ξ lies between h_{j-1}/k_{j-1} and h_j/k_j and hence we find, using Theorem 7.5, that

$$\left| \xi - \frac{h_{j-1}}{k_{j-1}} \right| + \left| \xi - \frac{h_j}{k_j} \right| = \left| \frac{h_{j-1}}{k_{j-1}} - \frac{h_j}{k_j} \right| = \frac{1}{k_{j-1}k_j}.$$

Combining these results we get

$$\frac{k_j}{k_{j-1}} + \frac{k_{j-1}}{k_j} \leqq \sqrt{5}.$$

Since the left side is rational we actually have a strict inequality, and (7.14) follows.

Now suppose (7.13) is false for $h/k = h_i/k_i$, $i = n - 1$, n, $n + 1$. We then have (7.14) for both $j = n$ and $j = n + 1$. By Lemma 7.16 we see that $q_n^{-1} > \frac{1}{2}(\sqrt{5} - 1)$ and $q_{n+1} < \frac{1}{2}(\sqrt{5} + 1)$, and, by (7.6) we find $q_{n+1} = a_{n+1} + q_n^{-1}$. This gives us

$$\tfrac{1}{2}(\sqrt{5} + 1) > q_{n+1} = a_{n+1} + q_n^{-1} > a_{n+1} + \tfrac{1}{2}(\sqrt{5} - 1)$$
$$\geqq 1 + \tfrac{1}{2}(\sqrt{5} - 1) = \tfrac{1}{2}(\sqrt{5} + 1)$$

and this is a contradiction.

Theorem 7.18 *The constant $\sqrt{5}$ in the preceding theorem is best possible. In other words Theorem 7.17 does not hold if $\sqrt{5}$ is replaced by any larger value.*

Proof. It suffices to exhibit an irrational number ξ for which $\sqrt{5}$ is the largest possible constant. Consider the irrational ξ whose continued fraction expansion is $\langle 1, 1, 1, \cdots \rangle$. We see that

$$\xi = 1 + \frac{1}{\langle 1, 1, \cdots \rangle} = 1 + \frac{1}{\xi}, \quad \xi^2 = \xi + 1, \quad \xi = \frac{1}{2}(\sqrt{5} + 1).$$

Using (7.7) we can prove by induction that $\xi_i = (\sqrt{5} + 1)/2$ for all $i \geq 0$, for if $\xi_i = (\sqrt{5} + 1)/2$ then

$$\xi_{i+1} = (\xi_i - a_i)^{-1} = (\tfrac{1}{2}(\sqrt{5} + 1) - 1)^{-1} = \tfrac{1}{2}(\sqrt{5} + 1).$$

A simple calculation yields $h_0 = k_0 = k_1 = 1$, $h_1 = k_2 = 2$. Equations (7.6) become $h_i = h_{i-1} + h_{i-2}$, $k_i = k_{i-1} + k_{i-2}$, and so by mathematical induction $k_n = h_{n-1}$ for $n \geq 1$. Hence we have

$$\lim_{n \to \infty} \frac{k_{n-1}}{k_n} = \lim_{n \to \infty} \frac{k_{n-1}}{h_{n-1}} = \frac{1}{\xi} = \frac{\sqrt{5} - 1}{2},$$

$$\lim_{n \to \infty} \left(\xi_{n+1} + \frac{k_{n-1}}{k_n} \right) = \frac{\sqrt{5} + 1}{2} + \frac{\sqrt{5} - 1}{2} = \sqrt{5}.$$

If c is any constant exceeding $\sqrt{5}$, then

$$\xi_{n+1} + \frac{k_{n-1}}{k_n} > c$$

holds for only a finite number of values of n. Thus, by (7.9),

$$\left| \xi - \frac{h_n}{k_n} \right| = \frac{1}{k_n^2(\xi_{n+1} + k_{n-1}/k_n)} < \frac{1}{ck_n^2}$$

holds for only a finite number of values of n. Thus there are only a finite number of rational numbers h/k satisfying $|\xi - h/k| < 1/(ck^2)$, because any such h/k is one of the convergents to ξ by Theorem 7.14.

Problems

1. Find two rational numbers a/b satisfying

$$\left| \sqrt{2} - \frac{a}{b} \right| < \frac{1}{\sqrt{5}\, b^2}$$

2. Find two rational numbers a/b satisfying

$$\left| \pi - \frac{a}{b} \right| < \frac{1}{\sqrt{5}\, b^2}.$$

3. Prove that the following is false for any constant $c > 2$: Given any irrational number ξ, there exist infinitely many rational numbers h/k such that

$$\left| \xi - \frac{h}{k} \right| < \frac{1}{k^c}.$$

4. Given any constant c, prove that there exists an irrational number ξ and infinitely many rational numbers h/k such that

$$\left| \xi - \frac{h}{k} \right| < \frac{1}{k^c}.$$

5. Prove that of every two consecutive convergents h_n/k_n to ξ with $n \geq 0$, at least one satisfies

$$\left| \xi - \frac{h}{k} \right| < \frac{1}{2k^2}.$$

Suggestion: use Lemma 7.16.

7.7 Periodic Continued Fractions

An infinite simple continued fraction $\langle a_0, a_1, a_2, \cdots \rangle$ is said to be periodic if there is an integer n such that $a_r = a_{n+r}$ for all sufficiently large integers r. Thus a periodic continued fraction can be written in the form

$$(7.15) \quad \langle b_0, b_1, b_2, \cdots, b_j, a_0, a_1, \cdots, a_{n-1}, a_0, a_1, \cdots, a_{n-1}, \cdots \rangle$$

$$= \langle b_0, b_1, b_2, \cdots, b_j, \overline{a_0, a_1, \cdots, a_{n-1}} \rangle,$$

where the bar over the $a_0, a_1, \cdots, a_{n-1}$ indicates that this block of integers is repeated indefinitely. For example $\langle \overline{2, 3} \rangle$ denotes $\langle 2, 3, 2, 3, 2, 3, \cdots \rangle$ and its value is easily computed. Writing θ for $\langle \overline{2, 3} \rangle$ we have

$$\theta = 2 + \cfrac{1}{3 + \cfrac{1}{\theta}}.$$

This is a quadratic equation in θ, and we discard the negative root to get the value $\theta = (3 + \sqrt{15})/3$. As a second example consider $\langle 4, 1, \overline{2, 3} \rangle$. Calling this ξ, we have $\xi = \langle 4, 1, \theta \rangle$, with θ as above, and so

$$\xi = 4 + (1 + \theta^{-1})^{-1} = 4 + \frac{\theta}{\theta + 1} = \frac{29 + \sqrt{15}}{7}.$$

These two examples illustrate the following result.

Theorem 7.19 *Any periodic simple continued fraction is a quadratic irrational number, and conversely.*

Proof. Let us write ξ for the periodic continued fraction of (7.15) and θ for its purely periodic part, $\theta = \langle \overline{a_0, a_1, \cdots, a_{n-1}} \rangle = \langle a_0, a_1, \cdots, a_{n-1}, \theta \rangle$. Then equation (7.8) gives

$$\theta = \frac{\theta h_{n-1} + h_{n-2}}{\theta k_{n-1} + k_{n-2}},$$

and this is a quadratic equation in θ. Hence θ is either a quadratic irrational number or a rational number, but the latter is ruled out by Theorem 7.7. Now ξ can be written in terms of θ,

$$\xi = \langle b_0, b_1, \cdots, b_j, \theta \rangle = \frac{\theta m + m'}{\theta q + q'}$$

where m'/q' and m/q are the last two convergents to $\langle b_0, b_1, \cdots, b_j \rangle$. But θ is of the form $(a + \sqrt{b})/c$, and hence ξ is of similar form because, as with θ, we can rule out the possibility that ξ is rational.

To prove the converse, let us begin with any quadratic irrational ξ, or ξ_0, of the form $\xi = \xi_0 = (a + \sqrt{b})/c$, with integers a, b, c, $b > 0$, $c \neq 0$. The integer b is not a perfect square since ξ is irrational. We multiply numerator and denominator by $|c|$ to get

$$\xi_0 = \frac{ac + \sqrt{bc^2}}{c^2} \quad \text{or} \quad \xi_0 = \frac{-ac + \sqrt{bc^2}}{-c^2}$$

according as c is positive or negative. Thus we can write ξ in the form

$$\xi_0 = \frac{m_0 + \sqrt{d}}{q_0},$$

where $q_0 | (d - m_0^2)$, d, m_0 and q_0 are integers, $q_0 \neq 0$, d not a perfect square. By writing ξ_0 in this form we can get a simple formulation of its continued fraction expansion $\langle a_0, a_1, a_2, \cdots \rangle$. We shall prove that the equations

$$(7.16) \qquad a_i = [\xi_i], \qquad \xi_i = \frac{m_i + \sqrt{d}}{q_i},$$

$$m_{i+1} = a_i q_i - m_i, \qquad q_{i+1} = \frac{d - m_{i+1}^2}{q_i}$$

define infinite sequences of integers m_i, q_i, a_i, and irrationals ξ_i in such a way that equations (7.7) hold, and hence we will have the continued fraction expansion of ξ_0.

In the first place, we start with ξ_0, m_0, q_0 as determined above, and we let $a_0 = [\xi_0]$. If ξ_i, m_i, q_i, a_i are known, then we take $m_{i+1} = a_i q_i - m_i$, $q_{i+1} = (d - m_{i+1}^2)/q_i$, $\xi_{i+1} = (m_{i+1} + \sqrt{d})/q_{i+1}$, $a_{i+1} = [\xi_{i+1}]$. That is, (7.16) actually does determine sequences ξ_i, m_i, q_i, a_i that are at least real.

Now we use mathematical induction to prove that the m_i and q_i are integers such that $q_i \neq 0$ and $q_i | (d - m_i^2)$. This holds for $i = 0$. If it is true at the ith stage, we observe that $m_{i+1} = a_i q_i - m_i$ is an integer. Then the equation

$$q_{i+1} = \frac{d - m_{i+1}^2}{q_i} = \frac{d - m_i^2}{q_i} + 2a_i m_i - a_i^2 q_i$$

establishes that q_{i+1} is an integer. Moreover q_{i+1} cannot be zero, since if it were, we would have $d = m_{i+1}^2$, whereas d is not a perfect square. Finally, we have $q_i = (d - m_{i+1}^2)/q_{i+1}$, so that $q_{i+1} | (d - m_{i+1}^2)$.

Next we can verify that

$$\xi_i - a_i = \frac{-a_i q_i + m_i + \sqrt{d}}{q_i} = \frac{\sqrt{d} - m_{i+1}}{q_i} = \frac{d - m_{i+1}^2}{q_i(\sqrt{d} + m_{i+1})}$$

$$= \frac{q_{i+1}}{\sqrt{d} + m_{i+1}} = \frac{1}{\xi_{i+1}},$$

which verifies (7.7) and so we have proved that $\xi_0 = \langle a_0, a_1, a_2, \cdots \rangle$, with the a_i defined by (7.16).

By ξ_i' we denote the conjugate of ξ_i, that is, $\xi_i' = (m_i - \sqrt{d})/q_i$. Since the conjugate of a quotient equals the quotient of the conjugates, we get the equation

$$\xi_0' = \frac{\xi_n' h_{n-1} + h_{n-2}}{\xi_n' k_{n-1} + k_{n-2}}$$

by taking conjugates in (7.8). Solving for ξ_n' we have

$$\xi_n' = -\frac{k_{n-2}}{k_{n-1}} \left(\frac{\xi_0' - h_{n-2}/k_{n-2}}{\xi_0' - h_{n-1}/k_{n-1}} \right).$$

As n tends to infinity, both h_{n-1}/k_{n-1} and h_{n-2}/k_{n-2} tend to ξ_0, which is different from ξ_0', and hence the fraction in parentheses tends to 1. Thus for sufficiently large n, say $n > N$ where N is fixed, the fraction in parentheses is positive, and ξ_n' is negative. But ξ_n is positive for $n \geq 1$ and hence $\xi_n - \xi_n' > 0$ for $n > N$. Applying (7.16) we see that this gives $2\sqrt{d}/q_n > 0$ and hence $q_n > 0$ for $n > N$.

It also follows from (7.16) that

$$q_n q_{n+1} = d - m_{n+1}^2 \leqq d, \qquad q_n \leqq q_n q_{n+1} \leqq d$$

$$m_{n+1}^2 < m_{n+1}^2 + q_n q_{n+1} = d, \qquad |m_{n+1}| < \sqrt{d},$$

for $n > N$. Since d is a fixed positive integer we conclude that q_n and m_{n+1} can assume only a fixed number of possible values for $n > N$. Hence the ordered pairs (m_n, q_n) can assume only a fixed number of possible pair values for $n > N$, and so there are distinct integers j and k such that $m_j = m_k$ and $q_j = q_k$. We can suppose we have chosen j and k so that $j < k$. By (7.16) this implies that $\xi_j = \xi_k$ and hence that

$$\xi_0 = \langle a_0, a_1, \cdots, a_{j-1}, \overline{a_j, a_{j+1}, \cdots, a_{k-1}} \rangle.$$

The proof of Theorem 7.19 is now complete.

Next we determine the subclass of real quadratic irrationals that have purely periodic continued fraction expansions, that is, expressions of the form $\overline{\langle a_0, a_1, \cdots, a_n \rangle}$.

Theorem 7.20 *The continued fraction expansion of the real quadratic irrational number ξ is purely periodic if and only if $\xi > 1$ and $-1 < \xi' < 0$, where ξ' denotes the conjugate of ξ.*

Proof. First we assume that $\xi > 1$ and $-1 < \xi' < 0$. As usual we write ξ_0 for ξ and take conjugates in (7.7) to obtain

$$(7.17) \qquad \frac{1}{\xi'_{i+1}} = \xi'_i - a_i.$$

Now $a_i \geq 1$ for all i, even for $i = 0$, since $\xi_0 > 1$. Hence if $\xi'_i < 0$, then $1/\xi'_{i+1} < -1$, and we have $-1 < \xi'_{i+1} < 0$. Since $-1 < \xi'_0 < 0$ we see, by mathematical induction, that $-1 < \xi'_i < 0$ holds for all $i \geq 0$. Then, since $\xi'_i = a_i + 1/\xi'_{i+1}$ by (7.17), we have

$$0 < -\frac{1}{\xi'_{i+1}} - a_i < 1, \qquad a_i = \left[-\frac{1}{\xi'_{i+1}} \right].$$

Now ξ is a quadratic irrational, so $\xi_j = \xi_k$ for some integers j and k with $0 < j < k$. Then we have $\xi'_j = \xi'_k$ and

$$a_{j-1} = \left[-\frac{1}{\xi'_j} \right] = \left[-\frac{1}{\xi'_k} \right] = a_{k-1},$$

$$\xi_{j-1} = a_{j-1} + \frac{1}{\xi_j} = a_{k-1} + \frac{1}{\xi_k} = \xi_{k-1}.$$

Thus $\xi_j = \xi_k$ implies $\xi_{j-1} = \xi_{k-1}$. A j-fold iteration of this implication gives us $\xi_0 = \xi_{k-j}$, and we have

$$\xi = \xi_0 = \overline{\langle a_0, a_1, \cdots, a_{k-j-1} \rangle}.$$

To prove the converse, let us assume that ξ is purely periodic, say $\xi = \overline{\langle a_0, a_1, \cdots, a_{n-1} \rangle}$, where $a_0, a_1, \cdots, a_{n-1}$ are positive integers. Then $\xi > a_0 \geq 1$. Also, by (7.8) we have

$$\xi = \langle a_0, a_1, \cdots, a_{n-1}, \xi \rangle = \frac{\xi h_{n-1} + h_{n-2}}{\xi k_{n-1} + k_{n-2}}.$$

Thus ξ satisfies the equation

$$f(x) = x^2 k_{n-1} + x(k_{n-2} - h_{n-1}) - h_{n-2} = 0.$$

This quadratic equation has two roots, ξ and its conjugate ξ'. Since $\xi > 1$, we need only prove that $f(x)$ has a root between -1 and 0 in order to establish that $-1 < \xi' < 0$. We will do this by showing that $f(-1)$ and $f(0)$ have opposite signs. First we observe that $f(0) =$

$-h_{n-2} < 0$ by (7.6) since $a_i > 0$ for $i \geq 0$. Next we see that for $n > 1$

$$f(-1) = k_{n-1} - k_{n-2} + h_{n-1} - h_{n-2}$$
$$= (k_{n-2} + h_{n-2})(a_{n-1} - 1) + k_{n-3} + h_{n-3}$$
$$\geq k_{n-3} + h_{n-3} > 0.$$

Finally, if $n = 1$, we have $f(-1) = k_0 - k_{-1} + h_0 - h_{-1} = a_0 > 0$, and this completes the proof.

We now turn to the continued fraction expansion of $\sqrt{d}$ for a positive integer d not a perfect square. We get at this by considering the closely related irrational number $\sqrt{d} + [\sqrt{d}]$. This number satisfies the conditions of Theorem 7.20, and so its continued fraction is purely periodic,

$$(7.18) \quad \sqrt{d} + [\sqrt{d}] = \overline{\langle a_0, a_1, \cdots, a_{r-1} \rangle} = \langle a_0, \overline{a_1, \cdots, a_{r-1}, a_0} \rangle.$$

We can suppose that we have chosen r to be the smallest integer for which $\sqrt{d} + [\sqrt{d}]$ has an expansion of the form (7.18). Now we note that $\xi_i = \langle a_i, a_{i+1}, \cdots \rangle$ is purely periodic for all values of i, and that $\xi_0 = \xi_r = \xi_{2r} = \cdots$. Furthermore $\xi_1, \xi_2, \cdots, \xi_{r-1}$ are all different from ξ_0, since otherwise there would be a shorter period. Thus $\xi_i = \xi_0$ if and only if i is of the form mr.

Now we can start with $\xi_0 = \sqrt{d} + [\sqrt{d}]$, $q_0 = 1$, $m_0 = [\sqrt{d}]$ in (7.16) because $1 | (d - [\sqrt{d}]^2)$. Then, for all $j \geq 0$,

$$(7.19) \quad \frac{m_{jr} + \sqrt{d}}{q_{jr}} = \xi_{jr} = \xi_0 = \frac{m_0 + \sqrt{d}}{q_0} = [\sqrt{d}] + \sqrt{d},$$

$$m_{jr} - q_{jr}[\sqrt{d}] = (q_{jr} - 1)\sqrt{d},$$

and hence $q_{jr} = 1$ since the left side is rational and $\sqrt{d}$ is irrational. Moreover $q_i = 1$ for no other values of the subscript i. For $q_i = 1$ implies $\xi_i = m_i + \sqrt{d}$, but ξ_i has a purely periodic expansion so that, by Theorem 7.20 we have $-1 < m_i - \sqrt{d} < 0$, $\sqrt{d} - 1 < m_i < \sqrt{d}$, and hence $m_i = [\sqrt{d}]$. Thus $\xi_i = \xi_0$ and i is a multiple of r.

We also establish that $q_i = -1$ does not hold for any i. For $q_i = -1$ implies $\xi_i = -m_i - \sqrt{d}$ by (7.16), and by Theorem 7.20 we would have $-m_i - \sqrt{d} > 1$ and $-1 < -m_i + \sqrt{d} < 0$. But this implies $\sqrt{d} < m_i < -\sqrt{d} - 1$, which is impossible.

Noting that $a_0 = [\sqrt{d} + [\sqrt{d}]] = 2[\sqrt{d}]$, we can now turn to the case $\xi = \sqrt{d}$. Using (7.18) we have

$$\sqrt{d} = -[\sqrt{d}] + (\sqrt{d} + [\sqrt{d}])$$

$$= -[\sqrt{d}] + \langle 2[\sqrt{d}], \overline{a_1, a_2, \cdots, a_{r-1}, a_0} \rangle$$

$$= \langle [\sqrt{d}], \overline{a_1, a_2, \cdots, a_{r-1}, a_0} \rangle$$

with $a_0 = 2[\sqrt{d}]$.

When we apply (7.16) to $\sqrt{d} + [\sqrt{d}]$, $q_0 = 1$, $m_0 = [\sqrt{d}]$ we have $a_0 = 2[\sqrt{d}]$, $m_1 = [\sqrt{d}]$, $q_1 = d - [\sqrt{d}]^2$. But we can also apply (7.16) to $\sqrt{d}$ with $q_0 = 1$, $m_0 = 0$, and we find $a_0 = [\sqrt{d}]$, $m_1 = [\sqrt{d}]$, $q_1 = d - [\sqrt{d}]^2$. The value of a_0 is different, but the values of m_1, and of q_1, are the same in both cases. Since $\xi_i = (m_i + \sqrt{d})/q_i$ we see that further application of (7.16) yields the same values for the a_i, for the m_i, and for the q_i, in both cases. In other words, the expansions of $\sqrt{d} + [\sqrt{d}]$ and $\sqrt{d}$ differ only in the values of a_0 and m_0. Stating our results explicitly for the case $\sqrt{d}$ we have the following theorem.

Theorem 7.21 *If the positive integer d is not a perfect square, the simple continued fraction expansion of $\sqrt{d}$ has the form $\sqrt{d} = \langle a_0, \overline{a_1, a_2, \cdots, a_{r-1}, 2a_0} \rangle$ with $a_0 = [\sqrt{d}]$. Furthermore with $\xi_0 = \sqrt{d}$, $q_0 = 1$, $m_0 = 0$, in equations (7.16), we have $q_i = 1$ if and only if $r \mid i$, and $q_i = -1$ holds for no subscript i. Here r denotes the length of the shortest period in the expansion of $\sqrt{d}$.*

Problem

1. For what positive integers c does the quadratic irrational $([\sqrt{d}] + \sqrt{d})/c$ have a purely periodic expansion?

7.8 Pell's Equation

The equation $x^2 - dy^2 = N$, with given integers d and N and unknowns x and y, is usually called Pell's equation. If d is negative, it can have only a finite number of solutions. If d is a perfect square, say $d = a^2$, the equation reduces to $(x - ay)(x + ay) = N$ and again there is only a finite number of solutions. The most interesting case of the equation arises when d is a positive integer not a perfect square. For this case, simple continued fractions are very useful.

We expand $\sqrt{d}$ into a continued fraction expansion as in Theorem 7.21, with convergents h_n/k_n, and with q_n defined by equations (7.16) with $\xi_0 = \sqrt{d}$, $q_0 = 1$, $m_0 = 0$.

Theorem 7.22 *If d is a positive integer not a perfect square, then $h_n^2 - dk_n^2 = (-1)^{n-1}q_{n+1}$ for all integers $n \geq -1$.*

Proof. From equations (7.8) and (7.16) we have

$$\sqrt{d} = \xi_0 = \frac{\xi_{n+1}h_n + h_{n-1}}{\xi_{n+1}k_n + k_{n-1}} = \frac{(m_{n+1} + \sqrt{d})h_n + q_{n+1}h_{n-1}}{(m_{n+1} + \sqrt{d})k_n + q_{n+1}k_{n-1}}.$$

We simplify this equation and separate it into a rational and a purely irrational part much as we did in (7.19). Each part must be zero so we get two equations, and we can eliminate m_{n+1} from them. The final result is

$$h_n^2 - dk_n^2 = (h_nk_{n-1} - h_{n-1}k_n)q_{n+1} = (-1)^{n-1}q_{n+1},$$

where we used Theorem 7.5 in the last step.

Corollary 7.23 *Taking r as the length of the period of the expansion of $\sqrt{d}$, as in Theorem 7.21, we have for $n \geq 0$,*

$$h_{nr-1}^2 - dk_{nr-1}^2 = (-1)^{nr}q_{nr} = (-1)^{nr}.$$

It can be seen that Theorem 7.22 gives us solutions of Pell's equation for certain values of N. In particular, Corollary 7.23 gives infinitely many solutions of $x^2 - dy^2 = 1$ by the use of even values nr. Of course if r is even, all values of nr are even. If r is odd, Corollary 7.23 gives infinitely many solutions of $x^2 - dy^2 = -1$ by the use of odd integers $n \geq 1$. The next theorem shows that every solution of $x^2 - dy^2 = \pm 1$ can be obtained from the continued fraction expansion of $\sqrt{d}$. But first we make this simple observation: apart from such trivial solutions as $x = \pm 1$, $y = 0$ of $x^2 - dy^2 = 1$, all solutions of $x^2 - dy^2 = N$ fall into sets of four by all combinations of signs $\pm x$, $\pm y$. Hence it is sufficient to discuss the positive solutions $x > 0$, $y > 0$.

Theorem 7.24 *Let d be a positive integer not a perfect square, and let the convergents to the continued fraction expansion of $\sqrt{d}$ be h_n/k_n. Let the integer N satisfy $|N| < \sqrt{d}$. Then any positive solution $x = s$, $y = t$ of $x^2 - dy^2 = N$ with $(s, t) = 1$ satisfies $s = h_n$, $t = k_n$ for some positive integer n.*

Proof. Let E and M be positive integers such that $(E, M) = 1$ and $E^2 - \rho M^2 = \sigma$, where $\sqrt{\rho}$ is irrational and $0 < \sigma < \sqrt{\rho}$. Here ρ and σ are real numbers, not necessarily integers. Then

$$\frac{E}{M} - \sqrt{\rho} = \frac{\sigma}{M(E + M\sqrt{\rho})},$$

and hence

$$0 < \frac{E}{M} - \sqrt{\rho} < \frac{\sqrt{\rho}}{M(E + M\sqrt{\rho})} = \frac{1}{M^2(E/(M\sqrt{\rho}) + 1)}.$$

Also $0 < E/M - \sqrt{\rho}$ implies $E/(M\sqrt{\rho}) > 1$, and therefore

$$\left| \frac{E}{M} - \sqrt{\rho} \right| < \frac{1}{2M^2}.$$

By Theorem 7.14, E/M is a convergent in the continued fraction expansion of $\sqrt{\rho}$.

If $N > 0$, we take $\sigma = N$, $\rho = d$, $E = s$, $M = t$, and the theorem holds in this case.

If $N < 0$, then $t^2 - (1/d)s^2 = -N/d$, and we take $\sigma = -N/d$, $\rho = 1/d$, $E = t$, $M = s$. We find that t/s is a convergent in the expansion of $1/\sqrt{d}$. Then Theorem 7.15 shows that s/t is a convergent in the expansion of $\sqrt{d}$.

Theorem 7.25 *All positive solutions of $x^2 - dy^2 = \pm 1$ are to be found among $x = h_n$, $y = k_n$, where h_n/k_n are the convergents of the expansion of $\sqrt{d}$. If r is the period of the expansion of $\sqrt{d}$, as in Theorem 7.21, and if r is even, then $x^2 - dy^2 = -1$ has no solutions, and all* *positive solutions of $x^2 - dy^2 = 1$ are given by $x = h_{nr-1}$, $y = k_{nr-1}$ for $n = 1, 2, 3, \cdots$. On the other hand if r is odd, then $x = h_{nr-1}$, $y = k_{nr-1}$ give all positive solutions of $x^2 - dy^2 = -1$ by use of $n = 1, 3, 5, \cdots$, and all positive solutions of $x^2 - dy^2 = 1$ by use of $n = 2, 4, 6, \cdots$.*

Proof. This result is a corollary of Theorems 7.21, 7.22, and 7.24.

The sequence of pairs (h_0, k_0), (h_1, k_1), $\cdots$ will include all positive solutions of $x^2 - dy^2 = 1$. Furthermore, $a_0 = [\sqrt{d}] > 0$ so the sequence $h_0, h_1, h_2, \cdots$ is strictly increasing. If we let x_1, y_1 denote the first solution that appears, then for every other solution x, y we will have $x > x_1$, and hence $y > y_1$ also. Having found this least positive solution by means of continued fractions, we can find all the remaining positive solutions by a simpler method.

Theorem 7.26 *Let x_1, y_1 be the least positive solution of $x^2 - dy^2 = 1$, d being a positive integer not a perfect square. Then all positive solutions are given by x_n, y_n for $n = 1, 2, 3, \cdots$ where x_n and y_n are the integers defined by $x_n + y_n \sqrt{d} = (x_1 + y_1 \sqrt{d})^n$.*
The values of x_n and y_n are determined by expanding the power and equating the rational parts, and the purely irrational parts. For example, $x_3 + y_3 \sqrt{d} = (x_1 + y_1\sqrt{d})^3$ so that $x_3 = x_1^3 + 3x_1y_1^2d$ and $y_3 = 3x_1^2y_1 + y_1^3d$.

Proof. First we establish that x_n, y_n is a solution. We have $x_n - y_n \sqrt{d} = (x_1 - y_1 \sqrt{d})^n$, since the conjugate of a product is the product of the conjugates. Hence we can write

$$x_n^2 - y_n^2d = (x_n - y_n \sqrt{d})(x_n + y_n \sqrt{d})$$
$$= (x_1 - y_1 \sqrt{d})^n(x_1 + y_1 \sqrt{d})^n = (x_1^2 - y_1^2d)^n = 1.$$

Next we show that every positive solution can be obtained. Suppose there is a positive solution s, t that is not in the collection $\{x_n, y_n\}$. Since both $x_1 + y_1 \sqrt{d}$ and $s + t \sqrt{d}$ are greater than 1, there must be some integer m such that $(x_1 + y_1 \sqrt{d})^m \leq s + t \sqrt{d} < (x_1 + y_1 \sqrt{d})^{m+1}$. We cannot have $(x_1 + y_1 \sqrt{d})^m = s + t \sqrt{d}$, for this would imply $x_m + y_m \sqrt{d} = s + t \sqrt{d}$, and hence $s = x_m, t = y_m$.

Now $(x_1 - y_1 \sqrt{d})^m = (x_1 + y_1 \sqrt{d})^{-m}$, and we can multiply the above inequality by $(x_1 - y_1 \sqrt{d})^m$ to obtain

$$1 < (s + t \sqrt{d})(x_1 - y_1 \sqrt{d})^m < x_1 + y_1 \sqrt{d}.$$

Defining integers a and b by $a + b \sqrt{d} = (s + t \sqrt{d})(x_1 - y_1 \sqrt{d})^m$ we have

$$a^2 - b^2 d = (s^2 - t^2 d)(x_1^2 - y_1^2 d)^m = 1$$

so a, b is a solution of $x^2 - dy^2 = 1$ such that $1 < a + b \sqrt{d} < x_1 + y_1 \sqrt{d}$. But then $0 < (a + b \sqrt{d})^{-1} < 1$, and hence $0 < a - b \sqrt{d} < 1$. Now we have

$$a = \tfrac{1}{2}(a + b \sqrt{d}) + \tfrac{1}{2}(a - b \sqrt{d}) > \tfrac{1}{2} + 0 > 0,$$

$$b \sqrt{d} = \tfrac{1}{2}(a + b \sqrt{d}) - \tfrac{1}{2}(a - b \sqrt{d}) > \tfrac{1}{2} - \tfrac{1}{2} = 0,$$

so a, b is a positive solution. Therefore $a > x_1$, $b > y_1$, but this contradicts $a + b \sqrt{d} < x_1 + y_1 \sqrt{d}$, and hence our supposition was false. All positive solutions are given by x_n, y_n, $n = 1, 2, 3, \cdots$.

It may be noted that the definition of x_n, y_n can be extended to zero and negative n. They then give nonpositive solutions.

For N different from 1 there are certain results that can be proved, but they are not as complete as what we have shown to be true in the case $N = 1$. For example, if x_1, y_1 is the smallest positive solution of $x^2 - dy^2 = 1$, and if $r_0^2 - ds_0^2 = N$, then integers r_n, s_n can be defined by $r_n + s_n \sqrt{d} = (r_0 + s_0 \sqrt{d})(x_1 + y_1 \sqrt{d})^n$, and it is easy to show that r_n, s_n are solutions of $x^2 - dy^2 = N$. However, there is no assurance that all positive solutions can be obtained in this way starting from a fixed r_0, s_0.

Problems

The symbol d denotes a positive integer, not a perfect square.

1. Assuming that $x^2 - dy^2 = -1$ is solvable, let x_1, y_1 be the smallest positive solution. Prove that x_2, y_2, defined by $x_2 + y_2 \sqrt{d} = (x_1 + y_1 \sqrt{d})^2$ is the smallest positive solution of $x^2 - dy^2 = 1$. Also prove that all solutions of

$x^2 - dy^2 = -1$ are given by x_n, y_n, where $x_n + y_n \sqrt{d} = (x_1 + y_1 \sqrt{d})^n$, with $n = 1, 3, 5, 7, \cdots$, and that all solutions of $x^2 - dy^2 = 1$ are given by x_n, y_n with $n = 2, 4, 6, 8, \cdots$.

2. Prove that if $x^2 - dy^2 = N$ has one solution, it has infinitely many. *Suggestion:* use the identity $(x_1^2 - dy_1^2)(x_2^2 - dy_2^2) = (x_1x_2 - dy_1y_2)^2 - d(x_1y_2 - x_2y_1)^2$.

3. Prove that $x^2 - dy^2 = -1$ has no solution if $d \equiv 3 \pmod 4$.

4. Let d be a positive integer, not a perfect square. If k is any positive integer, prove that there are infinitely many solutions in integers of $x^2 - dy^2 = 1$ with $k|y$.

7.9   Numerical Computation

The numerical computations involved in finding a simple continued fraction can be rather lengthy. In general the algorithm (7.7) must be used. However if ξ_0 is a quadratic irrational the work can be simplified. It is probably best to use (7.16) in a slightly altered form. From (7.16) we have

$$q_{i+1} = \frac{d - m_{i+1}^2}{q_i} = \frac{d - (a_iq_i - m_i)^2}{q_i} = \frac{d - m_i^2}{q_i} - a_i^2q_i + 2a_im_i$$

$$= q_{i-1} - a_i(a_iq_i - m_i) + a_im_i = q_{i-1} + a_i(m_i - m_{i+1}).$$

Starting with $\xi_0 = (m_0 + \sqrt{d})/q_0$, $q_0 | (d - m_0^2)$, we obtain, in turn,

$$a_0 = \left[\frac{m_0 + \sqrt{d}}{q_0} \right], \quad m_1 = a_0q_0 - m_0, \quad q_1 = \frac{d - m_1^2}{q_0},$$

$$a_1 = \left[\frac{m_1 + \sqrt{d}}{q_1} \right], \quad m_2 = a_1q_1 - m_1, \quad q_2 = q_0 + a_1(m_1 - m_2),$$

$$\cdots \cdots \cdots \cdots \cdots \cdots \cdots \cdots \cdots \cdots \cdots \cdots \cdots \cdots \cdots$$

$$a_{i-1} = \left[\frac{m_{i-1} + \sqrt{d}}{q_{i-1}} \right], \quad m_i = a_{i-1}q_{i-1} - m_{i-1},$$

$$q_i = q_{i-2} + a_{i-1}(m_{i-1} - m_i), \quad i \geq 1.$$

The formula $q_iq_{i+1} = d - m_{i+1}^2$ serves as a good check. Even for large numbers, this procedure is fairly simple to carry out.

For quite small numbers it is often easiest to obtain the expansion directly. For example for $\sqrt{3}$ we can compute as follows:

$$\xi_0 = \sqrt{3} = 1 + \frac{1}{\xi_1}, \qquad 1 + \sqrt{3} - 1 = 1 + \frac{1}{\sqrt{3} - 1}$$

$$\xi_1 = \frac{1}{\sqrt{3} - 1} = \frac{\sqrt{3} + 1}{2} = 1 + \frac{1}{\xi_2},$$

$$\xi_2 = \frac{2}{\sqrt{3} - 1} = \sqrt{3} + 1 = 2 + \frac{1}{\xi_3},$$

$$\xi_3 = \frac{1}{\sqrt{3} - 1}.$$

In this case $\xi_3 = \xi_1$ so we stop. We have

$$a_0 = 1, \quad a_1 = 1, \quad a_2 = 2, \quad a_3 = a_1 = 1, \quad \cdots, \quad \sqrt{3} = \langle 1, \overline{1, 2} \rangle.$$

When a continued fraction is known the convergents can be obtained from (7.6). The work can be systematized. The following example, for $\sqrt{3}$, demonstrates a convenient method.

	0	1	
	1	0	
1	1	1	$h_0 = 1, k_0 = 1$
1	2	1	$h_1 = 2, k_1 = 1$
2	5	3	$h_2 = 5, k_2 = 3$
1	7	4	$\cdots \cdots \cdots$
2	19	11	
.	.	.	
.	.	.	
.	.	.	

Chapter 8

Elementary Remarks on the Distribution of Primes

8.1 The Function $\pi(x)$

The discussion in Section 1.3 makes it clear that the primes are distributed among the natural numbers in a very irregular way. Theorem 1.18 shows that there are arbitrarily large gaps in the sequence of primes. The proof of Theorem 1.17 not only shows that there are infinitely many primes but also that the rth prime p_r is no greater than $\prod_{j=1}^{r-1} p_j + 1$, the product of the first $r - 1$ primes plus 1. A minor change in the proof shows that $p_r \leq \prod_{j=1}^{r-1} p_j - 1$ if $r > 2$.

In this chapter we abandon our convention that letters of the roman alphabet represent integers.

Definition 8.1 *For real x we let $\pi(x)$ denote the number of primes that do not exceed x. Thus for example*

$$\pi(-1) = \pi(1) = 0, \qquad \pi(2) = \pi(5/2) = 1.$$

Theorem 8.1 *There exist positive constants a and b such that*

$$a\,\frac{x}{\log x} < \pi(x) < b\,\frac{x}{\log x}$$

for $x \geq 2$.

Proof. For n a positive integer and p a prime let p^{μ_p} be the largest power of p that divides the binomial coefficient $\binom{2n}{n}$. According to Theorem 4.2

$$(8.1) \qquad \mu_p = \sum_{j \geq 1} \left(\left[\frac{2n}{p^j} \right] - 2 \left[\frac{n}{p^j} \right] \right).$$

We define the integer ν_p by the inequalities $p^{\nu_p} \leq 2n < p^{1+\nu_p}$. Clearly ν_p exists and is unique. Then $\left[\frac{2n}{p^j} \right] - 2 \left[\frac{n}{p^j} \right] = 0 - 0 = 0$ for $j > \nu_p$. We also have for every j,

$$\left[\frac{2n}{p^j} \right] - 2 \left[\frac{n}{p^j} \right] < \frac{2n}{p^j} - 2 \left(\frac{n}{p^j} - 1 \right) = 2$$

and hence $[2n/p^j] - 2[n/p^j] \leq 1$ for all $j \geq 1$. Using this in (8.1) we obtain

$$(8.2) \qquad \mu_p \leq \sum_{j=1}^{\nu_p} 1 = \nu_p$$

and therefore

$$(8.3) \qquad \binom{2n}{n} \Big| \prod_{p \leq 2n} p^{\nu_p}.$$

On the other hand if $n < p \leq 2n$ then $p \mid (2n)!$ and $p \nmid n!$ so we have $\prod_{n < p \leq 2n} p \Big| \binom{2n}{n}$, which, along with (8.3), gives us

$$\prod_{n < p \leq 2n} p \leq \binom{2n}{n} \leq \prod_{p \leq 2n} p^{\nu_p} \leq \prod_{p \leq 2n} 2n$$

and hence, changing each p in the first product to n,

$$(8.4) \qquad n^{\pi(2n) - \pi(n)} \leq \binom{2n}{n} \leq (2n)^{\pi(2n)}.$$

But $\binom{2n}{n} \leq (1+1)^{2n} = 2^{2n}$ and

$$\binom{2n}{n} = \frac{(2n)(2n-1) \cdots (n+1)}{n!} = \prod_{j=1}^{n} \frac{n+j}{j} \geq \prod_{j=1}^{n} 2 = 2^n.$$

Using these inequalities in (8.4) and taking logarithms, we obtain

$$(8.5) \qquad \pi(2n) - \pi(n) \leq \frac{2n \log 2}{\log n}, \qquad \pi(2n) \geq \frac{n \log 2}{\log (2n)},$$

where we must assume $n > 1$ in the first inequality.

For any real $x \geq 2$ we let $2n$ be the greatest even integer that does not exceed x. Then we have $x \geq 2n$, $n \geq 1$, $2n + 2 > x$, and hence

$$\pi(x) \geq \pi(2n) \geq \frac{n \log 2}{\log (2n)} \geq \frac{n \log 2}{\log x} \geq \frac{(2n + 2) \log 2}{4 \log x} > \frac{\log 2}{4} \frac{x}{\log x}.$$

In order to get the other half of the inequality we use the first part of (8.5). For any real $y \geq 4$ we let $2n$ be the least even integer not less than y. We have $y \leq 2n$, $\pi(y) \leq \pi(2n)$, $y + 2 > 2n$, $\frac{y}{2} > n - 1$,
$\pi\left(\frac{y}{2}\right) \geq \pi(n - 1) \geq \pi(n) - 1$, and hence

$$\pi(y) - \pi\left(\frac{y}{2}\right) \leq \pi(2n) - \pi(n) + 1 \leq \frac{2n \log 2}{\log n} + 1 \leq \frac{(y + 2) \log 2}{\log (y/2)} + 1$$

$$\leq \frac{2(y + 2) \log 2}{\log y} + 1 \leq \frac{3y \log 2}{\log y} + 1 < \frac{4y \log 2}{\log y}.$$

Therefore $\pi(y) - \pi(y/2) < (4 \log 2)y/\log y$ if $y \geq 4$. But for $2 \leq y < 4$ we have $\pi(y) - \pi(y/2) \leq \pi(4) = 2$, and it is easily seen that the function $y/\log y$ takes on its minimum value, e, when $y = e$. Therefore we have

$$\pi(y) - \pi\left(\frac{y}{2}\right) \leq \frac{(2/e)y}{\log y} \qquad \text{for } 2 \leq y < 4,$$

and hence

$$\pi(y) - \pi\left(\frac{y}{2}\right) < \frac{(4 \log 2)y}{\log y} \qquad \text{for } y \geq 2$$

since $2/e < 4 \log 2$. Now for $y \geq 2$ we have

$$(8.6) \quad \pi(y) \log y - \pi\left(\frac{y}{2}\right) \log \frac{y}{2} = \left(\pi(y) - \pi\left(\frac{y}{2}\right)\right) \log y$$

$$+ \pi\left(\frac{y}{2}\right) \log 2 < 4y \log 2 + \frac{y}{2} \log 2 = \frac{9}{2} y \log 2.$$

Now for any real $x \geq 2$ there is a non-negative integer j such that $2^{j+2} > x \geq 2^{j+1}$. We replace y in (8.6) by x, $x/2$, $x/2^2$, $\cdots$, $x/2^j$, and sum. Since $x/2^{j+1} < 2$, $\pi(x/2^{j+1}) = 0$, we get

$$\pi(x) \log x < \frac{9}{2}\left(x + \frac{x}{2} + \cdots + \frac{x}{2^j}\right) \log 2 < 9x \log 2.$$

Therefore we can take $a = (\log 2)/4$, $b = 9 \log 2$, and the theorem is proved. We have found values of a and b that suffice, but they are by no means the best possible values.

The theorem we have just proved tells us something about how numerously and how scarcely the primes are distributed. Since there are infinitely many primes, we cannot say that there are more natural numbers than there are primes. However the ratio $\pi(n)/n$ represents the proportion of primes in the first n natural numbers. Since $\pi(n)/n < b/\log n$ tends to zero as n increases, we are led to say that the primes are scarcer than the natural numbers. This is often stated as: "almost all positive integers are composite." Of course the theorem tells us a good deal more. Since

$$a < \frac{\pi(x)}{x/\log x} < b,$$

the function $\pi(x)$ is of order $x/\log x$. The primes are neither too numerous nor too scarce. Since

$$\frac{\sqrt{x}}{\pi(x)} < \frac{\log x}{a\sqrt{x}} \to 0 \qquad \text{as } x \to \infty,$$

the sequence of squares is scarcer than the sequence of primes. The prime number theorem mentioned in Section 1.3 is a refinement of the present theorem.

Problem

1. Prove that ν_p, as defined following (8.1), is equal to $\left[\dfrac{\log 2n}{\log p}\right]$.

8.2 The Sequence of Primes

Results concerning the size of the rth prime, p_r, can also be used to describe how numerous the primes are. Our first result is essentially a corollary to Theorem 8.1.

Theorem 8.2 *There exist positive constants c and d such that $cr \log r < p_r < dr \log r$ for $r \geq 2$.*

Proof. Using Theorem 8.1 and the fact that $p_r \geq r$ we have

$$r = \pi(p_r) < b \frac{p_r}{\log p_r}, \qquad p_r > \frac{r \log p_r}{b} \geq \frac{1}{b} r \log r.$$

The other way around we have $r = \pi(p_r) > a p_r / \log p_r$. If r is large so is p_r, and there is a constant k such that $\log p_r / \sqrt{p_r} < a$ if $r \geq k$. Then, for $r \geq k$,

$$r \frac{\log p_r}{p_r} > a > \frac{\log p_r}{\sqrt{p_r}},$$

hence $r > \sqrt{p_r}$, $\log p_r < 2 \log r$ and therefore $a p_r < r \log p_r < 2r \log r$. If d is larger than the largest number among

$$\frac{2}{a}, \quad \frac{p_2}{2 \log 2}, \quad \frac{p_3}{3 \log 3}, \quad \cdots, \quad \frac{p_{k-1}}{(k-1) \log (k-1)},$$

then $p_r < dr \log r$ for $r \geq 2$.

Theorem 8.3 *The series $\displaystyle\sum_{r=1}^{\infty} \frac{1}{p_r}$ diverges.*

Proof. For $r > 1$ we have

$$\frac{1}{p_r} > \frac{1}{dr \log r}$$

and the series $\displaystyle\sum_{r=2}^{\infty} 1/(r \log r)$ diverges.

If a series $\displaystyle\sum_{r=1}^{\infty} a_r^k$ of positive terms converges for all values of $k > f$ and diverges for all values of $k < f$, f being fixed, then f is called the exponent of convergence of the sequence a_r. The sequence $1/p_r$ has exponent of convergence 1. If $k > 1$, then $1/p_r^k < 1/r^k$ and $\displaystyle\sum_{r=1}^{\infty} 1/r^k$ converges. If $0 < k \leq 1$, it follows from Theorem 8.3 that $\displaystyle\sum_{r=1}^{\infty} 1/p_r^k$ diverges.

The sequence $a_r = 1/r^2$ has exponent of convergence $\frac{1}{2}$. In fact, if $a_r = 1/[r^{1+\varepsilon}]$, $\varepsilon > 0$, then $a_r < 1/(r^{1+\varepsilon} - 1) < 2/r^{1+\varepsilon}$ if $r \geq 2$ and the sequence a_r has exponent of convergence $(1 + \varepsilon)^{-1} < 1$. In a sense the primes are denser than the sequence consisting of $[r^{1+\varepsilon}]$.

Theorem 8.4 *There is a constant* k *such that*

$$\sum_{2 < p \leq x} \frac{1}{p} < k \log \log x \qquad \text{if } x \geq 3.$$

Proof. By Theorem 8.2

$$\sum_{2 < p \leq x} \frac{1}{p} < \sum_{r=2}^{\pi(x)} \frac{1}{cr \log r} \leq \frac{1}{c} \sum_{r=2}^{[x]} \frac{1}{r \log r} = \frac{1}{c} \left(\frac{1}{2 \log 2} + \sum_{r=3}^{[x]} \int_{r-1}^{r} \frac{dt}{r \log r} \right)$$

$$\leq \frac{1}{2c \log 2} + \frac{1}{c} \sum_{r=3}^{[x]} \int_{r-1}^{r} \frac{dt}{t \log t} \leq \frac{1}{2c \log 2} + \frac{1}{c} \int_{2}^{x} \frac{dt}{t \log t}$$

$$= \frac{1}{2c \log 2} + \frac{1}{c} \log \log x - \frac{1}{c} \log \log 2,$$

and this is less than $k \log \log x$ for $x \geq 3$, if k is large enough.

The method used in this proof occurs frequently in number theory. It is the method ordinarily found in proofs of the integral test in the theory of series. For a monotonic function $f(x)$, we compare $\sum_{n=M}^{N} f(n)$ with $\int_{M-1}^{N} f(x)dx$. Geometrically, $\int_{M-1}^{N} f(x)dx$ is the area under the curve $y = f(x)$, whereas $\sum_{n=M}^{N} f(n)$ represents the area covered by rectangles having unit bases and altitudes $f(n)$, $n = M, M + 1, \cdots, N$.

In contrast with Theorem 8.3, Theorem 8.4 shows that the primes are not too numerous.

Theorem 8.5 *If* $x \geq 2$ *then* $\prod_{p \leq x} p < 4^x$.

Proof. This theorem is obviously true for $2 \leq x < 3$. If it is true when x is an odd integer $n \geq 3$, then it is true for $n \leq x < n + 2$ since $\prod_{p \leq x} p = \prod_{p \leq n} p < 4^n < 4^x$. Therefore we need to consider only odd integers n with $n \geq 3$. The proof is now by induction on the odd integer n. Noting that the theorem holds for $n = 3$, we assume the result for all odd integers greater than 1 that are less than some odd integer $n \geq 5$. We define $k = (n \pm 1)/2$ where the sign is chosen so that k is odd. Then $k \geq 3$. Now

$$(8.7) \qquad\qquad \binom{n}{k} = \frac{n!}{k!(n-k)!}$$

and $n - k$ is even and $n - k = 2k \mp 1 - k \leq k + 1$. If p is a prime such that $k < p \leq n$, then p is odd and $p | n!$, $p \nmid k!$, $p \nmid (n-k)!$. Hence from (8.7) we see that the product of all such primes divides $\binom{n}{k}$, and so

$$\prod_{k < p \leq n} p \leq \binom{n}{k}.$$

But $\binom{n}{k} = \binom{n}{n-k}$ and both these binomial coefficients appear in the expansion of $(1 + 1)^n$. This implies that $\binom{n}{k} < 2^{n-1}$. Using this and the induction hypothesis we have

$$\prod_{p \leq n} p = \prod_{p \leq k} p \cdot \prod_{k < p \leq n} p < 4^k \cdot 2^{n-1} = 2^{n+2k-1} \leq 2^{2n} = 4^n$$

because $n \geq 2k - 1$.

Problems

1. Find the exponent of convergence of the sequence of the reciprocals of the increasing positive integers that lack the digit 9 when written in ordinary decimal notation.

2. Give an independent proof of Theorem 1.18 ("There are arbitrarily large gaps in the series of primes") by using Theorem 8.2.

3. Write s_r for the sum of the first r primes. Prove that there are positive constants a_1 and b_1 such that

$$a_1 r^2 \log r < s_r < b_1 r^2 \log r.$$

4. (a) Let $\{a_j\}$, $\{b_j\}$, $\{c_j\}$ be increasing sequences of real numbers, each with limit infinity. Say that a_j is asymptotic to b_j, written $a_j \sim b_j$, if and only

if $\lim a_j/b_j = 1$. Prove that $a_j \sim b_j$ implies $\log a_j \sim \log b_j$, but that the converse is false.

(b) If $a_j \sim b_j$ prove that $b_j \sim a_j$; if $a_j \sim b_j$ and $c_j \sim d_j$ prove that $a_j c_j \sim b_j d_j$.

(c) Prove that $\lim (\log a_j)/a_j = 0$.

(d) If $\lim c_j/a_j = 0$, prove that $a_j \sim b_j$ if and only if $a_j \sim b_j + c_j$.

(e) The prime number theorem states that $\pi(n) \sim n/\log n$. A sketch is now given that this is implied by $p_n \sim n \log n$. Verify the steps in this proof and prove the converse result. Note that $p_{n+1} \sim (n+1) \log (n+1) \sim n \log n \sim p_n$. For integers $k > 1$ define n by $p_n \leq k < p_{n+1}$, so that n is a function of k, and $k \sim p_n$. Also $n = \pi(k)$ and hence $k \sim n \log n = \pi(k) \log \pi(k)$ and $\log k \sim \log \pi(k) + \log \log \pi(k) \sim \log \pi(k)$. It follows that $k \sim \pi(k) \log k$ or $\pi(k) \sim k/\log k$.

8.3 Bertrand's Postulate

Theorem 8.6 *For every positive integer n there is a prime p such that $n < p \leq 2n$.*

Proof. It is a simple matter to check that the theorem is true for $n \leq 7$. Suppose that the result is false for some integer $n \geq 8$. By the definition of μ_p and (8.2), with this supposition we have

$$(8.8) \qquad \binom{2n}{n} = \prod_{p \leq 2n} p^{\mu_p} = \prod_{p \leq n} p^{\mu_p}, \qquad \mu_p \leq \nu_p.$$

For any prime p in the range $2n/3 < p \leq n$ we have

$$p \geq 3, \quad p^2 > \frac{2}{3} np \geq 2n, \quad 1 \leq \frac{n}{p} < \frac{3}{2}, \quad 2 \leq \frac{2n}{p} < 3$$

and so by (8.1)

$$\mu_p = \left[\frac{2n}{p}\right] - 2\left[\frac{n}{p}\right] = 2 - 2 = 0.$$

For any prime p in the range $\sqrt{2n} < p \leq 2n/3$ we have $p^2 > 2n$, hence $\nu_p = 1$ and $\mu_p \leq 1$. For any prime p satisfying $p \leq \sqrt{2n}$ we have $p^{\mu_p} \leq p^{\nu_p} \leq 2n$. Using these facts in (8.8) we obtain

$$\binom{2n}{n} = \prod_{p \leq \sqrt{2n}} p^{\mu_p} \prod_{\sqrt{2n} < p \leq 2n/3} p^{\mu_p} \prod_{2n/3 < p \leq n} p^{\mu_p}$$

$$\leq \prod_{p \leq \sqrt{2n}} 2n \prod_{p \leq 2n/3} p.$$

The first product in the last expression has at most $\sqrt{2n} - 2$ factors, since $\sqrt{2n} \geq 4$ and 1 and 4 are not primes. We apply Theorem 8.5 to the second product and then we have

(8.9)
$$\binom{2n}{n} \leq (2n)^{\sqrt{2n}-2} 4^{2n/3}.$$

Now $\binom{2n}{n}$ is the largest of the $2n + 1$ terms in the binomial expansion of $(1 + 1)^{2n}$ so we have

$$(2n + 1) \binom{2n}{n} > 2^{2n}.$$

But $4n^2 > 2n + 1$, and hence

$$4n^2 \binom{2n}{n} > 2^{2n}, \qquad \binom{2n}{n} > 2^{2n}(2n)^{-2}.$$

This with (8.9) implies

$$2^{2n}(2n)^{-2} < (2n)^{\sqrt{2n}-2} 4^{2n/3}, \qquad 2^{2n/3} < (2n)^{\sqrt{2n}}.$$

Taking logarithms and then dividing by $\sqrt{2n}$, we get

(8.10)
$$\frac{1}{3} \sqrt{2n} \log 2 < \log (2n).$$

But $(1/3) \sqrt{2n} \log 2 - \log (2n)$ is positive if $n = 450$ and

$$\frac{d}{dn} \left(\frac{1}{3} \sqrt{2n} \log 2 - \log (2n) \right) = \frac{\log 2}{3 \sqrt{2n}} - \frac{1}{n},$$

which is positive for $n \geq 38$. Hence (8.10) is false for $n \geq 450$, and the theorem holds for $n \geq 450$.

To complete the proof we merely exhibit suitable p for $n = 8$, $9, \cdots, 449$. We can use:

$$
\begin{array}{rll}
p = & 13 \quad \text{for} & 8 \leq n \leq 12 \\
& 23 & 13 \leq n \leq 22 \\
& 43 & 23 \leq n \leq 42 \\
& 83 & 43 \leq n \leq 82 \\
& 163 & 83 \leq n \leq 162 \\
& 317 & 163 \leq n \leq 316 \\
& 631 & 317 \leq n \leq 449
\end{array}
$$

The reader may discover that $n = 450$ is not the smallest value of n that makes (8.10) false. That particular value is an easy one to substitute in (8.10). It is much easier to extend the above table further than necessary than it is to compute further values of (8.10). In fact the table as it is will carry us to $n = 630$.

This proof is fairly typical of a great many proofs in number theory. In the proof one uses inequalities and estimates the sizes of various expressions. Often these estimates are good enough to prove the theorem for large values of n, say, but are too crude to yield the desired result for smaller n. We are then forced to take care of these smaller n by more special methods.

Problems

1. Prove that for every positive real number $x > 1$ there is a prime p such that $x < p < 2x$.
2. Prove that $n! = m^k$ is impossible in integers $m, n > 1, k > 1$.
3. Let k and r be positive integers, $k > 1, r > 1$. Prove that there is a prime whose digital representation to base r has exactly k digits.
4. For this problem include 1 as a prime. Prove that every positive integer can be represented as a sum of one or more distinct primes.
5. Prove that the following three properties of a positive integer n are equivalent: (i) all primes $\leq \sqrt{n}$ are divisors of n; (ii) all positive integers $< n$ and prime to n are primes; (iii) every composite integer $< n$ has a factor in common with n. Furthermore, prove that only a finite number of positive integers have these properties, and find them. *Suggestion:* if n is large enough there are distinct primes p_1, p_2, p_3, p_4 such that $\dfrac{\sqrt{n}}{2^j} < p_j < \dfrac{\sqrt{n}}{2^{j-1}}$ for $j = 1, 2, 3, 4$.

Chapter 9

Algebraic Numbers

9.1 Polynomials

Algebraic numbers are the roots of certain types of polynomials, so it is natural to begin our discussion with this topic. Our plan in this chapter is to proceed from the most general results about algebraic numbers to stronger specific results about special classes of algebraic numbers. In this process of proving more and more about less and less, we have selected material of a number theoretic aspect as contrasted with the more "algebraic" parts of the theory. In other words, we are concerned with such questions as divisibility, uniqueness of factorization, and prime numbers, rather than questions concerning the algebraic structure of the groups, rings, and fields arising in the theory.

The polynomials that we will consider will have rational numbers for coefficients. Such polynomials are called polynomials over R, where R denotes the field of rational numbers. This collection of polynomials is often denoted by $R[x]$, and more generally the set of all polynomials with coefficients in a field F is denoted by $F[x]$. That the set of rational numbers forms a field can be verified from the postulates in Section 2.10. In a polynomial such as

$$f(x) = a_0 x^n + a_1 x^{n-1} + \cdots + a_n, \qquad a_0 \neq 0,$$

the non-negative integer n is called the degree of the polynomial, and a_0 is called the leading coefficient. If $a_0 = 1$, the polynomial is called "monic." Since we assign no degree to the zero polynomial, we can assert without exception that the degree of the product of two polynomials is the sum of the degrees of the polynomials.

A polynomial $f(x)$ is said to be divisible by a polynomial $g(x)$, not identically zero, if there exists a polynomial $q(x)$ such that $f(x) = g(x)q(x)$ and we write

$$g(x)\,|\,f(x).$$

Also, $g(x)$ is said to be a divisor or factor of $f(x)$. The degree of $g(x)$ here does not exceed that of $f(x)$, unless $f(x)$ is identically zero, written $f(x) \equiv 0$. This concept of divisibility is not the same as the divisibility that we have considered earlier. In fact $3\,|\,7$ holds if 3 and 7 are thought of as polynomials of degree zero, whereas it is not true that the integer 3 divides the integer 7.

Theorem 9.1 *To any polynomials $f(x)$ and $g(x)$ over R with $g(x) \not\equiv 0$, there correspond unique polynomials $q(x)$ and $r(x)$ such that $f(x) = g(x)q(x) + r(x)$, where either $r(x) \equiv 0$ or $r(x)$ is of lower degree than $g(x)$.*

Proof. In case $f(x) \equiv 0$ or $f(x)$ has lower degree than $g(x)$, define $q(x) \equiv 0$ and $r(x) = f(x)$. Otherwise divide $g(x)$ into $f(x)$ to get a quotient $q(x)$ and a remainder $r(x)$. Clearly $q(x)$ and $r(x)$ are polynomials over R, and either $r(x) \equiv 0$ or the degree of $r(x)$ is less than the degree of $g(x)$ if the division has been carried to completion. If there were another pair, $q_1(x)$ and $r_1(x)$, then we would have

$$f(x) = g(x)q_1(x) + r_1(x), \qquad r(x) - r_1(x) = g(x)\{q_1(x) - q(x)\}.$$

Thus $g(x)$ would be a divisor of the polynomial $r(x) - r_1(x)$ which, unless identically zero, has lower degree than $g(x)$. Hence $r(x) - r_1(x) \equiv 0$, and it follows that $q(x) = q_1(x)$.

Theorem 9.2 *Any polynomials $f(x)$ and $g(x)$, not both identically zero, have a common divisor $h(x)$ which is a linear combination of $f(x)$ and $g(x)$. Thus $h(x)\,|\,f(x)$, $h(x)\,|\,g(x)$, and*

(9.1) $$h(x) = f(x)F(x) + g(x)G(x)$$

for some polynomials $F(x)$ and $G(x)$.

Proof. From all the polynomials of the form (9.1) that are not identically zero, choose any one of least degree and designate it by $h(x)$. If

$h(x)$ were not a divisor of $f(x)$, Theorem 9.1 would give us $f(x) = h(x)q(x) + r(x)$ with $r(x) \not\equiv 0$ and $r(x)$ of degree lower than $h(x)$. But then $r(x) = f(x) - h(x)q(x) = f(x)\{1 - F(x)q(x)\} - g(x)\{G(x)q(x)\}$ which is of the form (9.1) in contradiction with the choice of $h(x)$. Thus $h(x)\big|f(x)$ and similarly $h(x)\big|g(x)$.

Theorem 9.3 *To any polynomials $f(x)$ and $g(x)$, not both identically zero, there corresponds a unique monic polynomial $d(x)$ having the properties*

(1) $d(x)\big|f(x)$, $d(x)\big|g(x)$;
(2) $d(x)$ *is a linear combination of $f(x)$ and $g(x)$, as in (9.1)*;
(3) *any common divisor of $f(x)$ and $g(x)$ is a divisor of $d(x)$, and thus there is no common divisor having higher degree than that of $d(x)$.*

Proof. Define $d(x) = c^{-1}h(x)$, where c is the leading coefficient of $h(x)$, so that $d(x)$ is monic. Properties (1) and (2) are inherited from $h(x)$ by $d(x)$. Equation (9.1) implies $d(x) = c^{-1}f(x)F(x) + c^{-1}g(x)G(x)$, and this equation shows that if $m(x)$ is a common divisor of $f(x)$ and $g(x)$, then $m(x)\big|d(x)$. Finally, to prove that $d(x)$ is unique, suppose that $d(x)$ and $d_1(x)$ both satisfy properties (1), (2), (3). We then have $d(x)\big|d_1(x)$ and $d_1(x)\big|d(x)$, hence $d_1(x) = q(x)d(x)$ and $d(x) = q_1(x)d_1(x)$ for some polynomials $q(x)$ and $q_1(x)$. This implies $q(x)q_1(x) = 1$, from which we see that $q(x)$ and $q_1(x)$ are of degree zero. Since both $d(x)$ and $d_1(x)$ are monic, we have $q(x) = 1$, $d_1(x) = d(x)$.

Definition 9.1 *The polynomial $d(x)$ is called the greatest common divisor of $f(x)$ and $g(x)$. We write $(f(x), g(x)) = d(x)$.*

Definition 9.2 *A polynomial $f(x)$, not identically zero, is irreducible, or prime, over R if there is no factoring, $f(x) = g(x)h(x)$, of $f(x)$ into two polynomials $g(x)$ and $h(x)$ of positive degrees over R.*

For example $x^2 - 2$ is irreducible over R. It has the factoring $(x - \sqrt{2})(x + \sqrt{2})$ over the field of real numbers, but it has no factoring over R.

Theorem 9.4 *If an irreducible polynomial $p(x)$ divides a product $f(x)g(x)$, then $p(x)$ divides at least one of the polynomials $f(x)$ and $g(x)$.*

Proof. If $f(x) \equiv 0$ or $g(x) \equiv 0$ the result is obvious. If neither is identically zero, let us assume that $p(x) \nmid f(x)$ and prove that $p(x)\big|g(x)$.

The assumption that $p(x) \nmid f(x)$ implies that $(p(x), f(x)) = 1$, and hence by Theorem 9.3 there exist polynomials $F(x)$ and $G(x)$ such that $1 = p(x)F(x) + f(x)G(x)$. Multiplying by $g(x)$ we get

$$g(x) = p(x)g(x)F(x) + f(x)g(x)G(x).$$

Now $p(x)$ is a divisor of the right member of this equation because $p(x) \,|\, f(x)g(x)$, and hence $p(x) \,|\, g(x)$.

Theorem 9.5 *Any polynomial $f(x)$ over R of positive degree can be factored into a product $f(x) = cp_1(x)p_2(x) \cdots p_k(x)$ where the $p_j(x)$ are irreducible monic polynomials over R. This factoring is unique apart from order.*

Proof. Clearly $f(x)$ can be factored repeatedly until it becomes a product of irreducible polynomials, and the constant c can be adjusted to make all the factors monic. We must prove uniqueness. Let us consider another factoring, $f(x) = cq_1(x)q_2(x) \cdots q_j(x)$, into irreducible monic polynomials. According to Theorem 9.4, $p_1(x)$ divides some $q_i(x)$, and we can reorder the $q_m(x)$ to make $p_1(x) \,|\, q_1(x)$. Since $p_1(x)$ and $q_1(x)$ are irreducible and monic, we have $p_1(x) = q_1(x)$. A repetition of this argument yields

$$p_2(x) = q_2(x), \quad p_3(x) = q_3(x), \quad \cdots \quad \text{and} \quad k = j.$$

Definition 9.3 *A polynomial $f(x) = a_0 x^n + \cdots + a_n$ with integral coefficients a_j is said to be primitive if the greatest common divisor of its coefficients is 1. Obviously, here we mean the greatest common divisor of integers as defined in Definition 1.2.*

Theorem 9.6 *The product of two primitive polynomials is primitive.*

Proof. Let $a_0 x^n + \cdots + a_n$ and $b_0 x^m + \cdots + b_m$ be primitive polynomials and denote their product by $c_0 x^{n+m} + \cdots + c_{n+m}$. Suppose that this product polynomial is not primitive, so that there is a prime p which divides every coefficient c_k. Since $a_0 x^n + \cdots + a_n$ is primitive, at least one of its coefficients is not divisible by p. Let a_i denote the first such coefficient and let b_j denote the first coefficient of $b_0 x^m + \cdots + b_m$, not divisible by p. Then the coefficient of $x^{n+m-i-j}$ in the product polynomial is

(9.2)
$$c_{i+j} = \sum a_k b_{i+j-k}$$

summed over all k such that $0 \leq k \leq n$, $0 \leq i + j - k \leq m$. In this sum, any term with $k < i$ is a multiple of p. Any term with $k > i$ that appears in the sum will have the factor b_{i+j-k} with $i + j - k < j$ and will also be a multiple of p. The term $a_i b_j$, for $k = i$, appears in the sum, and we have $c_{i+j} \equiv a_i b_j \pmod{p}$. But this is in contradiction with $p | c_{i+j}$, $p \nmid a_i$, $p \nmid b_j$.

Theorem 9.7 *Gauss' Lemma. If a monic polynomial $f(x)$ with integral coefficients factors into two monic polynomials with rational coefficients, say $f(x) = g(x)h(x)$, then $g(x)$ and $h(x)$ have integral coefficients.*

Proof. If $g(x) = x^n + a_1 x^{n-1} + \cdots + a_n$, the a_i are rational. Let k be any positive common multiple of all the denominators of the a_i. Then $kg(x)$ has integral coefficients. If d is the greatest common divisor of the coefficients of $kg(x)$, then d divides the leading coefficient k of $kg(x)$. Taking $c = k/d > 0$, we see that $cg(x)$ is a primitive polynomial. Similarly there is an integer $c_1 > 0$ such that $c_1 h(x)$ is a primitive polynomial. Then by Theorem 9.6 the product $\{cg(x)\}\{c_1 h(x)\} = cc_1 f(x)$ is primitive. But, since $f(x)$ has integral coefficients, this implies that $cc_1 = 1$, hence $c = c_1 = 1$.

Problems

1. If $f(x)|g(x)$ and $g(x)|f(x)$, prove that there is a rational number c such that $g(x) = cf(x)$.
2. If $f(x)|g(x)$ and $g(x)|h(x)$, prove that $f(x)|h(x)$.
3. If $p(x)$ is irreducible and $g(x)|p(x)$, prove that either $g(x)$ is a constant or $g(x) = cp(x)$ for some rational number c.
4. If $p(x)$ is irreducible, prove that $cp(x)$ is irreducible for any rational $c \neq 0$.
5. If a polynomial $f(x)$ with integral coefficients factors into a product $g(x)h(x)$ of two polynomials with coefficients in R, prove that there is a factoring $g_1(x)h_1(x)$ with integral coefficients.
6. If $f(x)$ and $g(x)$ are primitive polynomials, and if $f(x)|g(x)$ and $g(x)|f(x)$, prove that $f(x) = \pm g(x)$.

9.2   Algebraic Numbers

Definition 9.4 *A complex number ξ is called an algebraic number if it satisfies some polynomial equation $f(x) = 0$ where $f(x)$ is a polynomial over R.*

Every rational number r is an algebraic number because $f(x)$ can be taken as $x - r$ in this case.

Theorem 9.8 *An algebraic number ξ satisfies a unique irreducible monic polynomial equation $g(x) = 0$ over R. Furthermore every polynomial equation over R satisfied by ξ is divisible by $g(x)$.*

Proof. From all polynomial equations over R satisfied by ξ, choose one of lowest degree, say $G(x) = 0$. If the leading coefficient of $G(x)$ is c, define $g(x) = c^{-1}G(x)$, so that $g(\xi) = 0$ and $g(x)$ is monic. The polynomial $g(x)$ is irreducible, for if $g(x) = h_1(x)h_2(x)$, then one at least of $h_1(\xi) = 0$ and $h_2(\xi) = 0$ would hold, contrary to the fact that $G(x) = 0$ and $g(x) = 0$ are polynomial equations over R of least degree satisfied by ξ.

Next let $f(x) = 0$ be any polynomial equation over R having ξ as a root. Applying Theorem 9.1, we get $f(x) = g(x)q(x) + r(x)$. The remainder $r(x)$ must be identically zero, for otherwise the degree of $r(x)$ would be less than that of $g(x)$, and ξ would be a root of $r(x)$ since $f(\xi) = g(\xi) = 0$. Hence $g(x)$ is a divisor of $f(x)$.

Finally to prove that $g(x)$ is unique, suppose that $g_1(x)$ is an irreducible monic polynomial such that $g_1(\xi) = 0$. Then $g(x)|g_1(x)$ by the argument above, say $g_1(x) = g(x)q(x)$. But the irreducibility of $g_1(x)$ then implies that $q(x)$ is a constant, in fact $q(x) = 1$ since $g_1(x)$ and $g(x)$ are monic. Thus we have $g_1(x) = g(x)$.

Definition 9.5 *The minimal equation of an algebraic number ξ is the equation $g(x) = 0$ described in Theorem 9.8. The minimal polynomial of ξ is $g(x)$. The degree of an algebraic number is the degree of its minimal polynomial.*

Definition 9.6 *An algebraic number ξ is an algebraic integer if it satisfies some monic polynomial equation*

$$(9.3) \qquad f(x) = x^n + b_1 x^{n-1} + \cdots + b_n = 0$$

with integral coefficients.

Theorem 9.9 *Among the rational numbers, the only ones that are algebraic integers are the integers 0, ± 1, ± 2, $\cdots$.*

Proof. Any integer m is an algebraic integer because $f(x)$ can be taken as $x - m$. On the other hand, if any rational number m/q is an algebraic integer, then we may suppose $(m, q) = 1$, and we have

$$\left(\frac{m}{q}\right)^n + b_1 \left(\frac{m}{q}\right)^{n-1} + \cdots + b_n = 0,$$

$$m^n + b_1 q m^{n-1} + \cdots + b_n q^n = 0.$$

Thus $q \mid m^n$, so that $q = \pm 1$, and m/q is an integer.

The word "integer" in Definition 9.6 is thus simply a generalization of our previous usage. In algebraic number theory, $0, \pm 1, \pm 2, \cdots$ are often referred to as "rational integers" to distinguish them from the other algebraic integers, that are not rational. For example, $\sqrt{2}$ is an algebraic integer but not a rational integer.

Theorem 9.10 *The minimal equation of an algebraic integer is monic with integral coefficients.*

Proof. The equation is monic by definition, so we need prove only that the coefficients are integers. Let the algebraic integer ξ satisfy $f(x) = 0$ as in (9.3), and let its minimal equation be $g(x) = 0$, monic and irreducible over R. By Theorem 9.8, $g(x)$ is a divisor of $f(x)$, say $f(x) = g(x)h(x)$, and the quotient $h(x)$, like $f(x)$ and $g(x)$, is monic and has coefficients in R. Applying Theorem 9.7, we see that $g(x)$ has integral coefficients.

Theorem 9.11 *Let n be a positive rational integer and ξ a complex number. Suppose that the complex numbers $\theta_1, \theta_2, \cdots, \theta_n$, not all zero, satisfy the equations*

$$(9.4) \quad \xi \theta_j = a_{j,1} \theta_1 + a_{j,2} \theta_2 + \cdots + a_{j,n} \theta_n, \qquad j = 1, 2, \cdots, n,$$

where the n^2 coefficients $a_{j,i}$ are rational. Then ξ is an algebraic number. Moreover, if the $a_{j,i}$ are rational integers, ξ is an algebraic integer.

Proof. Equations (9.4) can be thought of as a system of homogeneous linear equations in $\theta_1, \theta_2, \cdots, \theta_n$. Since the θ_i are not all zero, the determinant of coefficients must vanish:

$$\begin{vmatrix} \xi - a_{1,1} & -a_{1,2} & \cdots & -a_{1,n} \\ -a_{2,1} & \xi - a_{2,2} & \cdots & -a_{2,n} \\ \cdots & \cdots & \cdots & \cdots \\ -a_{n,1} & -a_{n,2} & \cdots & \xi - a_{n,n} \end{vmatrix} = 0.$$

Expansion of this determinant gives an equation $\xi^n + b_1\xi^{n-1} + \cdots + b_n = 0$, where the b_i are polynomials in the $a_{j,k}$. Thus the b_i are rational, and they are rational integers if the $a_{j,k}$ are.

Theorem 9.12 *If α and β are algebraic numbers, so are $\alpha + \beta$ and $\alpha\beta$. If α and β are algebraic integers, so are $\alpha + \beta$ and $\alpha\beta$.*

Proof. Suppose that α and β satisfy

$$\alpha^m + a_1\alpha^{m-1} + \cdots + a_m = 0,$$

$$\beta^r + b_1\beta^{r-1} + \cdots + b_r = 0$$

with rational coefficients a_i and b_j. Let $n = mr$, and define the complex numbers $\theta_1, \cdots, \theta_n$ as the numbers

$$1, \qquad \alpha, \qquad \alpha^2, \quad \cdots, \qquad \alpha^{m-1},$$

$$\beta, \qquad \alpha\beta, \qquad \alpha^2\beta, \quad \cdots, \qquad \alpha^{m-1}\beta,$$

$$\cdots \cdots \cdots \cdots \cdots \cdots \cdots \cdots$$

$$\beta^{r-1}, \quad \alpha\beta^{r-1}, \quad \alpha^2\beta^{r-1}, \quad \cdots, \quad \alpha^{m-1}\beta^{r-1},$$

in any order. Thus $\theta_1, \cdots, \theta_n$ are the numbers $\alpha^s\beta^t$ with $s = 0, 1, \cdots, m - 1$ and $t = 0, 1, \cdots, r - 1$. Hence for any θ_j,

$$\alpha\theta_j = \alpha^{s+1}\beta^t = \begin{cases} \text{some } \theta_k & \text{if } s + 1 \leq m - 1 \\ (-a_1\alpha^{m-1} - a_2\alpha^{m-2} - \cdots - a_m)\beta^t & \text{if } s + 1 = m. \end{cases}$$

In either case we see that there are rational constants $h_{j,1}, \cdots, h_{j,n}$ such that $\alpha\theta_j = h_{j,1}\theta_1 + \cdots + h_{j,n}\theta_n$. Similarly there are rational constants $k_{j,1}, \cdots, k_{j,n}$ such that $\beta\theta_j = k_{j,1}\theta_1 + \cdots + k_{j,n}\theta_n$, and hence $(\alpha + \beta)\theta_j = (h_{j,1} + k_{j,1})\theta_1 + \cdots + (h_{j,n} + k_{j,n})\theta_n$. These equations are of the form (9.4), and so we conclude that $\alpha + \beta$ is algebraic. Furthermore, if α and β are algebraic integers, then the a_j, b_j, $h_{j,i}$, $k_{j,i}$ are all rational integers, and $\alpha + \beta$ is an algebraic integer.

We also have $\alpha\beta\theta_j = \alpha(k_{j,1}\theta_1 + \cdots + k_{j,n}\theta_n) = k_{j,1}\alpha\theta_1 + \cdots + k_{j,n}\alpha\theta_n$ from which we find $\alpha\beta\theta_j = c_{j,1}\theta_1 + \cdots + c_{j,n}\theta_n$ where $c_{j,i} = k_{j,1}h_{1,i} + k_{j,2}h_{2,i} + \cdots + k_{j,n}h_{n,i}$. Again we apply Theorem 9.11 to conclude that $\alpha\beta$ is algebraic, and that it is an algebraic integer if α and β are.

This theorem states that the set of algebraic numbers is closed under addition and multiplication, and likewise for the set of algebraic integers. The following result states a little more.

Theorem 9.13 *The set of all algebraic numbers forms a field. The class of all algebraic integers forms a ring.*

Proof. Rings and fields are defined in Definition 2.12. The rational numbers 0 and 1 serve as the zero and unit for the system. Most of the postulates are easily seen to be satisfied if we remember that algebraic numbers are complex numbers whose properties we are familiar with. The only place where any difficulty arises is in proving the existence of additive and multiplicative inverses. If $\alpha \neq 0$ is a solution of

$$a_0 x^n + a_1 x^{n-1} + \cdots + a_n = 0$$

then $-\alpha$ and α^{-1} are solutions of

$$a_0 x^n - a_1 x^{n-1} + a_2 x^{n-2} - \cdots + (-1)^n a_n = 0$$

and

$$a_0 + a_1 x + a_2 x^2 + \cdots + a_n x^n = 0,$$

respectively. Therefore if α is an algebraic number, then so are $-\alpha$ and α^{-1}. If α is an algebraic integer, then so is $-\alpha$, but not necessarily α^{-1}. Therefore the algebraic numbers form a field, the algebraic integers a ring.

Problems

1. Find the minimal polynomial of each of the following algebraic numbers: 7, $\sqrt[3]{7}$, $(1 + \sqrt[3]{7})/2$, $1 + \sqrt{2} + \sqrt{3}$. Which of these are algebraic integers?
2. Prove that if α is algebraic of degree n, then $-\alpha$, α^{-1}, and $\alpha - 1$ are also of degree n.
3. Prove that if α is algebraic of degree n, and β is algebraic of degree m, then $\alpha + \beta$ is of degree $\leq mn$. Prove a similar result for $\alpha\beta$.
4. Prove that the set of all real algebraic numbers (i.e. algebraic numbers that are real) forms a field, and the set of all real algebraic integers forms a ring.

9.3   Algebraic Number Fields

The field discussed in Theorem 9.13 contains the totality of algebraic numbers. In general, an algebraic number field is any subset of this total collection that is a field itself. For example, if ξ is an algebraic number, then it can be readily verified that the collection of all numbers of the form $f(\xi)/h(\xi)$, $h(\xi) \neq 0$, f and h polynomials over R, constitutes a field. This field is denoted by $R(\xi)$, and it is called the extension of R by ξ.

Theorem 9.14 *If ξ is an algebraic number of degree n, then every number in $R(\xi)$ can be written uniquely in the form*

$$(9.5) \qquad a_0 + a_1\xi + \cdots + a_{n-1}\xi^{n-1}$$

where the a_i are rational numbers.

Proof. Consider any number $f(\xi)/h(\xi)$ of $R(\xi)$. If the minimal polynomial of ξ is $g(x)$, then $g(x) \nmid h(x)$, by Theorem 9.8, since $h(\xi) \neq 0$. But $g(x)$ is irreducible, so the greatest common polynomial divisor of $g(x)$ and $h(x)$ is 1, and so by Theorem 9.3 there exist polynomials $G(x)$ and $H(x)$ such that $1 = g(x)G(x) + h(x)H(x)$. Replacing x by ξ and using the fact that $g(\xi) = 0$, we get $1/h(\xi) = H(\xi)$ and $f(\xi)/h(\xi) = f(\xi)H(\xi)$. Let $k(x) = f(x)H(x)$ so that $f(\xi)/h(\xi) = k(\xi)$. Dividing $k(x)$ by $g(x)$, we get $k(x) = g(x)q(x) + r(x)$, and hence $f(\xi)/h(\xi) = k(\xi) = r(\xi)$ where $r(\xi)$ is of the form (9.5).

To prove that the form (9.5) is unique, suppose $r(\xi)$ and $r_1(\xi)$ are expressions of the form (9.5). If $r(x) - r_1(x)$ is not identically zero, then it is a polynomial of degree less than n. Since the minimal polynomial of ξ has degree n, we have $r(\xi) - r_1(\xi) \neq 0$, $r(\xi) \neq r_1(\xi)$, unless $r(x)$ and $r_1(x)$ are the same polynomial.

The field $R(\xi)$ can be looked at in a different way, by consideration of congruences modulo the polynomial $g(x)$. That is, in analogy with Definition 2.1, for any polynomial $G(x)$ of degree at least one we will write

$$f_1(x) \equiv f_2(x) \pmod{G(x)}$$

if $G(x) | (f_1(x) - f_2(x))$. Ultimately, in order to get back to $R(\xi)$ we will take the minimal polynomial $g(x)$ of ξ for $G(x)$. However, the theory of congruences is more general, and we start with the polynomial $G(x)$ over R, irreducible or not. The properties of congruences in Theorem 2.1 can be extended at once to the polynomial case. For example, part (c) of the theorem has the analogue: If $f_1(x) \equiv f_2(x) \pmod{G(x)}$ and $h_1(x) \equiv h_2(x) \pmod{G(x)}$, then $f_1(x)h_1(x) \equiv f_2(x)h_2(x) \pmod{G(x)}$.

By the division algorithm Theorem 9.1, any polynomial $f(x)$ over R is mapped by division by $G(x)$ onto a unique polynomial $r(x)$ modulo $G(x)$;

$$f(x) = G(x)q(x) + r(x), \qquad f(x) \equiv r(x) \pmod{G(x)}.$$

Thus the set of polynomials $r(x)$ consisting of 0 and all polynomials over R of degree less than n constitute a "complete residue system modulo $G(x)$" in the sense of Definition 2.2. Of course the present residue system has infinitely many members, whereas the residue system modulo m contained precisely m elements.

Theorem 9.15 *Let $G(x)$ be a polynomial over R of degree $n \geq 1$. The totality of polynomials*

$$(9.6) \qquad\qquad r(x) = a_0 + a_1 x + \cdots + a_{n-1} x^{n-1}$$

with coefficients in R, and with addition and multiplication modulo $G(x)$, forms a ring.

Proof. This theorem is the analogue of the first part of Theorem 2.33, and its proof is virtually the same. First we note that the polynomials (9.6) form a group under addition, with identity element 0, the additive inverse of $r(x)$ being $-r(x)$. Next, the polynomials (9.6) are closed under multiplication modulo $G(x)$, and the associative property of multiplication comes from the corresponding property for polynomials over R with ordinary multiplication, that is

$$\{r_1(x)r_2(x)\}r_3(x) = r_1(x)\{r_2(x)r_3(x)\}$$

implies

$$\{r_1(x)r_2(x)\}r_3(x) \equiv r_1(x)\{r_2(x)r_3(x)\} \pmod{G(x)}.$$

Similarly, the distributive property modulo $G(x)$ is inherited from the distributive property of polynomials over R.

Before stating the next theorem, we extend Definition 2.10 to the concept of isomorphism between fields. Two fields F and F' are isomorphic if there is a one-to-one correspondence between the elements of F and the elements of F' such that if a and b in F correspond respectively to a' and b' in F', then $a + b$ and ab in F correspond respectively to $a' + b'$ and $a'b'$ in F'. A virtually identical definition is used for the concept of isomorphism between rings. The following result is a direct analogue of the second part of Theorem 2.33.

Theorem 9.16 *The ring of polynomials modulo $G(x)$ described in Theorem 9.15 is a field if and only if $G(x)$ is an irreducible polynomial. If $G(x)$ is the minimal polynomial of the algebraic number ξ, then this field is isomorphic to $R(\xi)$.*

Proof. If the polynomial $G(x)$ is reducible over R, say $G(x) = G_1(x)G_2(x)$ where $G_1(x)$ and $G_2(x)$ have degrees between 1 and $n - 1$, then $G_1(x)$ and $G_2(x)$ are of the form (9.6). But then $G_1(x)$ has no multiplicative inverse modulo $G(x)$ since $G_1(x)f(x) \equiv 1 \pmod{G(x)}$ implies

$$G(x)\big|\{G_1(x)f(x) - 1\}, \quad G_1(x)\big|\{G_1(x)f(x) - 1\}, \quad G_1(x)\big|1.$$

Hence the ring of polynomials modulo $G(x)$ is not a field.

On the other hand, if $G(x)$ is irreducible over R, then every polynomial $r(x)$ of the form (9.6) has a unique multiplicative inverse $r_1(x)$ modulo $G(x)$, of the form (9.6). To show this we note that the greatest common divisor of $G(x)$ and $r(x)$ is 1, and so by Theorem 9.3 there exist polynomials $f(x)$ and $h(x)$ such that

$$(9.7) \qquad\qquad 1 = r(x)f(x) + G(x)h(x).$$

Applying Theorem 9.1 to $f(x)$ and $G(x)$ we get $f(x) = G(x)q(x) + r_1(x)$ where $r_1(x)$ is of the form (9.6). Thus (9.7) can be written

$$1 = r(x)r_1(x) + G(x)\{h(x) + r(x)q(x)\}, \qquad r(x)r_1(x) \equiv 1 \pmod{G(x)},$$

so $r_1(x)$ is a multiplicative inverse of $r(x)$ of the form (9.6). This inverse is unique because if $r(x)r_2(x) \equiv 1 \pmod{G(x)}$ then

$$r(x)r_1(x) \equiv r(x)r_2(x) \pmod{G(x)}, \qquad G(x)\big|r(x)\{r_1(x) - r_2(x)\}.$$

Since $G(x) \nmid r(x)$ we have $G(x)\big|\{r_1(x) - r_2(x)\}$ by Theorem 9.4. But the polynomial $r_1(x) - r_2(x)$ is either identically zero or is of degree less than n, the degree of $G(x)$. Hence $r_1(x) - r_2(x) = 0$, $r_1(x) = r_2(x)$.

Finally, if $G(x)$ is the minimal polynomial $g(x)$ of the algebraic number ξ, we must show that the field is isomorphic to $R(\xi)$. To each $r(x)$ of the form (9.6) we let correspond the number $r(\xi)$ of $R(\xi)$. Theorem 9.15 shows that this correspondence is one-to-one. If

$$r_1(x)r_2(x) \equiv r_3(x), \quad r_1(x) + r_2(x) \equiv r_4(x) \pmod{G(x)}$$

then

$$r_1(x)r_2(x) = r_3(x) + q_1(x)G(x), \qquad r_1(x) + r_2(x) = r_4(x) + q_2(x)G(x),$$

and hence

$$r_1(\xi)r_2(\xi) = r_3(\xi), \qquad r_1(\xi) + r_3(\xi) = r_4(\xi),$$

since $G(\xi) = 0$. Therefore the correspondence preserves multiplication and addition.

The theorem we have just proved is significant in that it makes possible the development of the theory of algebraic numbers from the consideration of polynomials without any reference to the roots of the polynomials. The fundamental theorem of algebra states that every polynomial of positive degree over R has a root that is a complex number. Therefore the algebraic number fields obtained by means of Theorem 9.16 are essentially the same—isomorphic to—the fields $R(\xi)$ of Theorem 9.14, but one does not need a knowledge of the fundamental theorem of algebra to use the method of Theorem 9.16.

The fundamental theorem of algebra implies, and is sometimes stated in the form, that every polynomial $f(x)$ of degree n over R has n complex roots. If $f(x)$ is irreducible over R, then the n roots, say $\xi_1, \cdots,$ ξ_n, are called conjugate algebraic numbers, and the conjugates of any one of them are simply all the others. Now Theorem 9.16 does not make any distinction between conjugates, whereas Theorem 9.14 allows for such a distinction. For example, let $g(x)$ be the irreducible polynomial $x^3 - 2$. In Theorem 9.14 we can take ξ to be any one of the three algebraic numbers which are solutions of $x^3 - 2 = 0$, namely $\sqrt[3]{2}, \omega \sqrt[3]{2}, \omega^2 \sqrt[3]{2}$ where $\omega = (-1 + i\sqrt{3})/2$. Thus there are three fields

$$(9.8) \qquad R(\sqrt[3]{2}), \quad R(\omega \sqrt[3]{2}), \quad R(\omega^2 \sqrt[3]{2}).$$

The first of these consists of real numbers, whereas the other two contain nonreal elements. Therefore, the first is certainly a different field from the others. It is not so apparent, but can be proved, that the last two differ from each other. On the other hand, if we apply Theorem 9.16 to the polynomial $x^3 - 2$, we obtain a single field consisting of all polynomials $a_0 + a_1x + a_2x^2$ over R modulo $x^3 - 2$. According to Theorem 9.16, this field is isomorphic to each of the fields (9.8). Since isomorphism is a transitive property, the fields (9.8) are isomorphic to each other. They differ in that they contain different elements, but they are essentially the same except for the names of their elements.

Problems

1. Prove that the fields of (9.8), although isomorphic, are distinct. *Suggestion:* to prove that $R(\omega^2 \sqrt[3]{2})$ is different from $R(\omega \sqrt[3]{2})$, assume that $\omega^2 \sqrt[3]{2}$ is an element of the latter field, that is, assume that there are rationals a, b, c such that $\omega^2 \sqrt[3]{2} = a + b\omega \sqrt[3]{2} + c(\omega \sqrt[3]{2})^2$. Prove that no such rationals exist.

2. Prove that the field $R(i)$, where $i^2 = -1$, is isomorphic to the field of all polynomials $a + bx$ with a and b in R, taken modulo $x^2 + 1$.

3. Prove that any algebraic number field contains R as a subfield.

4. Assuming the fundamental theorem of algebra, prove Theorem 9.10 by the following procedure. Let the algebraic integer ξ satisfy some monic polynomial equation $f(x) = 0$ with integral coefficients. Then we can factor $f(x)$ in the field of complex numbers, say

$$f(x) = (x - \xi)(x - \xi_2)(x - \xi_3) \cdots (x - \xi_n).$$

If $g(x)$ is the minimal polynomial of ξ, then $g(x)|f(x)$ by Theorem 9.8, and so

$$g(x) = (x - \xi)(x - \theta_2) \cdots (x - \theta_r)$$

where $\theta_2, \cdots, \theta_r$ are a subset of $\xi_2, \cdots, \xi_n$. Thus $\xi, \theta_2, \cdots, \theta_r$ are algebraic integers, and by Theorem 9.12 the coefficients of $g(x)$ are algebraic integers. Then apply Theorem 9.9.

9.4 Algebraic Integers

Any algebraic number field contains the elements 0 and 1, and so, by the postulates for a field, must contain all the rational numbers. Thus any algebraic number field contains at least some algebraic integers, the rational integers 0, ± 1, ± 2, $\cdots$. The following result shows that, in general, an algebraic number field also contains other algebraic integers.

Theorem 9.17 *If α is any algebraic number, there is a rational integer b such that $b\alpha$ is an algebraic integer.*

Proof. Let $f(x)$ be a polynomial over R such that $f(\alpha) = 0$. We may presume that the coefficients of $f(x)$ are rational integers, since we can multiply by the least common multiple of the denominators of the coefficients. Thus we can take $f(x)$ in the form

$$f(x) = bx^n + a_1x^{n-1} + \cdots + a_n = bx^n + \sum_{j=1}^{n} a_jx^{n-j}$$

with rational integers b and a_j. Then $b\alpha$ is a zero of

$$b^{n-1}f\left(\frac{x}{b}\right) = x^n + \sum_{j=1}^{n} a_jb^{j-1}x^{n-j},$$

and hence $b\alpha$ is an algebraic integer.

Theorem 9.18 *The integers of any algebraic number field form a ring.*

Proof. If α and β are integers in such a field F, then $\alpha + \beta$ and $\alpha\beta$ are in F since F is a field. But by Theorems 9.12 and 9.13, $\alpha + \beta$, $\alpha\beta$, and $-\alpha$ are algebraic integers. Thus the integers of F form a ring with 0 and 1 as the identity elements of addition and multiplication.

Definition 9.7 *In any algebraic number field F an integer $\alpha \neq 0$ is said to be a divisor of an integer β if there exists an integer γ such that $\beta = \alpha\gamma$. In this case we write $\alpha|\beta$. Any divisor of the integer 1 is called a unit of F. Non-zero integers α and β are called associates if α/β is a unit.*

This definition of associates does not appear to be symmetrical in α and β, but we shall establish that the property really is symmetric.

Theorem 9.19 *The reciprocal of a unit is a unit. The units of an algebraic number field form a multiplicative group.*

Proof. If ε_1 is a unit, then there exists an integer ε_2 such that $\varepsilon_1\varepsilon_2 = 1$. Hence ε_2 is also a unit, and it is the reciprocal of ε_1. If, similarly, ε_3 is any unit with reciprocal ε_4, then the product $\varepsilon_1\varepsilon_3$ is a unit because $(\varepsilon_1\varepsilon_3)(\varepsilon_2\varepsilon_4) = 1$. Hence the units of an algebraic number field form a multiplicative group where the identity element is 1, and the inverse of ε is the reciprocal of ε.

If α and β are associates, then α/β is a unit by definition, and by the above theorem β/α is also a unit. Hence the definition of associates is symmetric: if α and β are associates, then so are β and α.

Problems

1. Prove that the units of the rational number field R are ± 1, and that integers α and β are associates in this field if and only if $\alpha = \pm \beta$.
2. For any algebraic number α, define m as the smallest positive rational integer such that $m\alpha$ is an algebraic integer. Prove that if $b\alpha$ is an algebraic integer, where b is a rational integer, then $m|b$.
3. Let $\alpha = \alpha_1 + \alpha_2 i$ be an algebraic number, where α_1 and α_2 are real. Does it follow that α_1 and α_2 are algebraic numbers? If α is an algebraic integer, would α_1 and α_2 necessarily be algebraic integers?

9.5 Quadratic Fields

A quadratic field is one of the form $R(\xi)$ where ξ is a root of an irreducible quadratic polynomial over R. By Theorem 9.14 the elements of such a field are the totality of numbers of the form $a_0 + a_1 \xi$, where a_0 and a_1 are rational numbers. Since ξ is of the form $(a + b\sqrt{m})/c$ where a, b, c, m are integers, we see that

$$R(\xi) = R\left(\frac{a + b\sqrt{m}}{c}\right) = R(a + b\sqrt{m}) = R(b\sqrt{m}) = R(\sqrt{m})$$

Here we have presumed that $c \neq 0$ and that m is square-free, $m \neq 1$. On the other hand, if m and n are two different square-free rational integers, neither of which is 1, then $R(\sqrt{m}) \neq R(\sqrt{n})$ since $\sqrt{m}$ is not in $R(\sqrt{n})$. That is, it is impossible to find rational numbers a and b such that $\sqrt{m} = a + b\sqrt{n}$.

Theorem 9.20 *Every quadratic field is of the form $R(\sqrt{m})$ where m is a square-free rational integer, positive or negative but not equal to 1. Numbers of the form $a + b\sqrt{m}$ with rational integers a and b are integers of $R(\sqrt{m})$. These are the only integers of $R(\sqrt{m})$ if $m \equiv 2$ or 3 (mod 4). If $m \equiv 1$ (mod 4), the numbers $(a + b\sqrt{m})/2$, with odd rational integers a and b, are also integers of $R(\sqrt{m})$, and there are no further integers.*

Proof. We have already proved the first part of the theorem. All that remains is to identify the algebraic integers. Any number in $R(\sqrt{m})$ is of the form $\alpha = (a + b\sqrt{m})/c$ where a, b, c are rational integers with

$c > 0$. There is no loss in generality in assuming that $(a, b, c) = 1$ so that α is in its lowest terms. If $b = 0$, then α is rational and, by Theorem 9.9, is an algebraic integer if and only if it is a rational integer, that is $c = 1$. If $b \neq 0$, then α is not rational, and its minimal equation is quadratic,

$$\left(x - \frac{a + b\sqrt{m}}{c}\right)\left(x - \frac{a - b\sqrt{m}}{c}\right) = x^2 - \frac{2a}{c}x + \frac{a^2 - b^2 m}{c^2} = 0.$$

According to Theorem 9.10, α will then be an algebraic integer if and only if this equation is monic with integral coefficients. Thus α is an algebraic integer if and only if

$$(9.9) \qquad\qquad c \mid 2a \quad \text{and} \quad c^2 \mid (a^2 - b^2 m),$$

and this includes the case $b = 0$, since $(a, b, c) = 1$. If $(a, c) > 1$ and $c \mid 2a$, then a and c have some common prime factor, say p, and $p \nmid b$ since $(a, b, c) = 1$. Then $p^2 \mid a^2$ and $p^2 \mid c^2$, and if $c^2 \mid (a^2 - b^2 m)$, we would have $p^2 \mid b^2 m$, $p^2 \mid m$, which is impossible since m is square-free. Therefore (9.9) can hold only if $(a, c) = 1$. If $c \mid 2a$ and $c > 2$ then $(a, c) > 1$, so that (9.9) can hold only if $c = 1$ or $c = 2$. It is obvious that (9.9) holds for $c = 1$. For $c = 2$ condition (9.9) becomes $a^2 \equiv b^2 m \pmod 4$ and we also have a odd since $(a, c) = 1$. Then (9.9) becomes $b^2 m \equiv a^2 \equiv 1 \pmod 4$, which requires that b be odd, and then reduces to $m \equiv b^2 m \equiv 1 \pmod 4$. To sum up: (9.9) is satisfied if and only if either $c = 1$ or $c = 2$, a odd, b odd, $m \equiv 1 \pmod 4$, and this completes the proof.

Definition 9.8 *The norm $N(\alpha)$ of a number $\alpha = (a + b\sqrt{m})/c$ in $R(\sqrt{m})$ is the product of α and its conjugate, $\bar{\alpha} = (a - b\sqrt{m})/c$,*

$$N(\alpha) = \alpha\bar{\alpha} = \frac{a + b\sqrt{m}}{c}\frac{a - b\sqrt{m}}{c} = \frac{a^2 - b^2 m}{c^2}.$$

Note that if α is a rational number in $R(\sqrt{m})$, then $\bar{\alpha} = \alpha$.

Theorem 9.21 *The norm of a product equals the product of the norms, $N(\alpha\beta) = N(\alpha)N(\beta)$. $N(\alpha) = 0$ if and only if $\alpha = 0$. The norm of an integer in $R(\sqrt{m})$ is a rational integer. If γ is an integer in $R(\sqrt{m})$, then $N(\gamma) = \pm 1$ if and only if γ is a unit.*

Proof. For α and β in $R(\sqrt{m})$ it is easy to verify that $\overline{(\alpha\beta)} = \bar{\alpha}\bar{\beta}$. Then we have $N(\alpha\beta) = \alpha\beta\bar{\alpha}\bar{\beta} = \alpha\bar{\alpha}\beta\bar{\beta} = N(\alpha)N(\beta)$. If $\alpha = 0$, then

$\bar{\alpha} = 0$ and $N(\alpha) = 0$. Conversely if $N(\alpha) = 0$, then $\alpha\bar{\alpha} = 0$ so that $\alpha = 0$ or $\bar{\alpha} = 0$; but $\bar{\alpha} = 0$ implies $\alpha = 0$.

Next, if γ is an algebraic integer in $R(\sqrt{m})$, it has degree either 1 or 2. If it has degree 1, then γ is a rational integer by Theorem 9.9, and $N(\gamma) = \gamma\bar{\gamma} = \gamma^2$ so that $N(\gamma)$ is a rational integer. If γ is of degree 2, then the minimal equation of γ, $x^2 - (\gamma + \bar{\gamma})x + \gamma\bar{\gamma} = 0$, has rational integer coefficients, and again $N(\gamma) = \gamma\bar{\gamma}$ is a rational integer.

If $N(\gamma) = \pm 1$ and γ is an integer, then $\gamma\bar{\gamma} = \pm 1$, $\gamma \mid 1$, so that γ is a unit. To prove the converse, let γ be a unit. Then there is an integer ε such that $\gamma\varepsilon = 1$. This implies $N(\gamma)N(\varepsilon) = N(1) = 1$, so that $N(\gamma) = \pm 1$ since $N(\gamma)$ and $N(\varepsilon)$ are rational integers.

Remark. The integers of $R(i)$ are often called Gaussian integers.

Problems

1. If an integer α in $R(\sqrt{m})$ is neither zero nor a unit, prove that $|N(\alpha)| > 1$.
2. If $m \equiv 1 \pmod 4$, prove that the integers of $R(\sqrt{m})$ are all numbers of the form

$$a + b\frac{1 + \sqrt{m}}{2},$$

   where a and b are rational integers.
3. If α is any integer, and ε any unit, in $R(\sqrt{m})$, prove that $\varepsilon \mid \alpha$.
4. If α and $\beta \neq 0$ are integers in $R(\sqrt{m})$, and if $\alpha \mid \beta$, prove that $\bar{\alpha} \mid \bar{\beta}$ and $N(\alpha) \mid N(\beta)$.
5. If α is an algebraic number in $R(\sqrt{m})$ with $m < 0$, prove that $N(\alpha) \geqq 0$. Show that this is false if $m > 0$.
6. Prove that the following assertion is false in $R(i)$: If $N(\alpha)$ is a rational integer, then α is an algebraic integer.
7. Prove that the assertion of the preceding problem is false in every quadratic field. *Suggestion:* Define $\alpha = (x - 2\sqrt{m})/y$, so that $N(\alpha)$ is certainly an integer if x and y satisfy $x^2 - y^2 = 4m$. Choose $x = m + 1$, $y = m - 1$ so that α is not an integer if $|m - 1| > 4$. The cases $|m - 1| \leqq 4$ can be treated specially.

9.6   Units in Quadratic Fields

A quadratic field $R(\sqrt{m})$ is called imaginary if $m < 0$, and it is called real if $m > 1$. There are striking differences between these two sorts of quadratic fields. We shall see that an imaginary quadratic field has only a finite number of units; in fact for most of these fields ± 1 are the only units. On the other hand, every real quadratic field has infinitely many units.

Theorem 9.22 *Let m be a negative square-free rational integer. The field $R(\sqrt{m})$ has units ± 1, and these are the only units except in the cases $m = -1$, and $m = -3$. The units for $R(i)$ are ± 1 and $\pm i$. The units for $R(\sqrt{-3})$ are ± 1, $(1 \pm \sqrt{-3})/2$, and $(-1 \pm \sqrt{-3})/2$.*

Proof. Taking note of Theorem 9.21, we look for all integers α in $R(\sqrt{m})$ such that $N(\alpha) = \pm 1$. According to Theorem 9.20 we can write α in one of the two forms $x + y\sqrt{m}$ and $(x + y\sqrt{m})/2$ where x and y are rational integers and where, in the second form, x and y are odd and $m \equiv 1 \pmod 4$. Then $N(\alpha) = x^2 - my^2$ or $N(\alpha) = (x^2 - my^2)/4$ respectively. Since m is negative we have $x^2 - my^2 \geq 0$ so there are no α with $N(\alpha) = -1$. For $m < -1$ we have $x^2 - my^2 \geq -my^2 \geq 2y^2$ and the only solutions of $x^2 - my^2 = 1$ are $y = 0$, $x = \pm 1$ in this case. For $m = -1$, the equation $x^2 - my^2 = 1$ has the solutions $x = 0$, $y = \pm 1$, and $x = \pm 1$, $y = 0$ and no others. For $m \equiv 1 \pmod 4$, $m < -3$ there are no solutions of $(x^2 - my^2)/4 = 1$ with odd x and y since $x^2 - my^2 \geq 1 - m > 4$. Finally, for $m = -3$, we see that the solutions of the equation $(x^2 + 3y^2)/4 = 1$ with odd x and y are just $x = 1$, $y = \pm 1$ and $x = -1$, $y = \pm 1$. These solutions give exactly the units described in the theorem.

Theorem 9.23 *There are infinitely many units in any real quadratic field.*

Proof. The numbers $\alpha = x + y\sqrt{m}$ with integers x, y are integers in $R(\sqrt{m})$ with norms $N(\alpha) = x^2 - my^2$. If $x^2 - my^2 = 1$, then α is a unit. But the equation $x^2 - my^2 = 1$, $m > 1$, was treated in Theorems 7.25 and 7.26 where it was proved that it has infinitely many solutions.

Problem

1. Prove that the units of $R(\sqrt{2})$ are $\pm(1 + \sqrt{2})^n$ where n ranges over all integers.

9.7   Primes in Quadratic Fields

Definition 9.9 *An algebraic integer α, not a unit, in a quadratic field $R(\sqrt{m})$ is called a prime if it is divisible only by its associates and the units of the field.*

This definition is almost the same as the definition of primes among the rational integers. There is this difference, however. In R all primes are positive, whereas in $R(\sqrt{m})$ no such property is required. Thus if π is a prime and ε is a unit in $R(\sqrt{m})$, then $\varepsilon\pi$ is an associated prime in $R(\sqrt{m})$. For example, $-\pi$ is an associated prime of π.

Theorem 9.24 *If the norm of an integer α in $R(\sqrt{m})$ is $\pm p$, where p is a rational prime, then α is a prime.*

Proof. Suppose that $\alpha = \beta\gamma$ where β and γ are integers in $R(\sqrt{m})$. By Theorem 9.21 we have $N(\alpha) = N(\beta)N(\gamma) = \pm p$. Then since $N(\beta)$ and $N(\gamma)$ are rational integers, one of them must be ± 1, so that either β or γ is a unit and the other an associate of α. Thus α is a prime.

Theorem 9.25 *Every integer in $R(\sqrt{m})$, not zero or a unit, can be factored into a product of primes.*

Proof. If α is not a prime, it can be factored into a product $\beta\gamma$ where neither β nor γ is a unit. Repeating the procedure, we factor β and γ if they are not primes. The process of factoring must stop since otherwise we could get α in the form $\beta_1\beta_2 \cdots \beta_n$ with n arbitrarily large, and no factor β_j a unit. But this would imply that

$$N(\alpha) = \prod_{j=1}^{n} N(\beta_j), \quad |N(\alpha)| = \prod_{j=1}^{n} |N(\beta_j)| \geq 2^n, \quad n \text{ arbitrary,}$$

since $|N(\beta_j)|$ is an integer > 1.

Although we have established that there is factorization into primes, this factorization may not be unique. In fact, we showed in Section 1.3 that factorization in the field $R(\sqrt{-6})$ is not unique. In the next section we prove that factorization is unique in the field $R(i)$. The general question of the values of m for which $R(\sqrt{m})$ has the unique factorization property, is an unsolved problem. There is, however, a close connection between unique factorization and the Euclidean algorithm, as we now show.

Just as in the case of the rational field, a unique factorization theorem will have to disregard the order in which the various prime factors appear. But now a new ambiguity arises due to the existence of associated primes. The two factorings

$$\alpha = \pi_1\pi_2 \cdots \pi_r = (\varepsilon_1\pi_1)(\varepsilon_2\pi_2) \cdots (\varepsilon_r\pi_r)$$

where the ε_j are units with product 1, will have to be considered as being the same.

Definition 9.10 *A quadratic field $R(\sqrt{m})$ is said to have the unique factorization property if every integer α in $R(\sqrt{m})$, not zero or a unit, can be factored into primes uniquely, apart from the order of the primes and ambiguities between associated primes.*

Definition 9.11 *A quadratic field $R(\sqrt{m})$ is said to be Euclidean if the integers of $R(\sqrt{m})$ satisfy a Euclidean algorithm, that is, if α and β are integers of $R(\sqrt{m})$ with $\beta \neq 0$, there exist integers γ and δ of $R(\sqrt{m})$ such that $\alpha = \beta\gamma + \delta$, $|N(\delta)| < |N(\beta)|$.*

Theorem 9.26 *Every Euclidean quadratic field has the unique factorization property.*

Proof. The proof of this theorem is similar to the procedure used in establishing the fundamental theorem of arithmetic, Theorem 1.16. First we establish that if α and β are any two integers of $R(\sqrt{m})$ having no common factors except units, then there exist integers λ_0 and μ_0 in $R(\sqrt{m})$ such that $\alpha\lambda_0 + \beta\mu_0 = 1$. Let S denote the set of integers of the form $\alpha\lambda + \beta\mu$ where λ and μ range over all integers of $R(\sqrt{m})$. The norm $N(\alpha\lambda + \beta\mu)$ of any integer in S is a rational integer, so we can choose an integer, $\alpha\lambda_1 + \beta\mu_1 = \varepsilon$ say, such that $|N(\varepsilon)|$ is the least positive value taken on by $|N(\alpha\lambda + \beta\mu)|$. Applying the Euclidean algorithm to α and ε we get

$$\alpha = \varepsilon\gamma + \delta, \quad |N(\delta)| < |N(\varepsilon)|.$$

Then we have

$$\delta = \alpha - \varepsilon\gamma = \alpha - \gamma(\alpha\lambda_1 + \beta\mu_1) = \alpha(1 - \gamma\lambda_1) + \beta(-\gamma\mu_1)$$

so that δ is an integer in S. Now this requires $|N(\delta)| = 0$ by the definition of ε, and we have $\delta = 0$ by Theorem 9.21. Thus $\alpha = \varepsilon\gamma$ and hence $\varepsilon|\alpha$. Similarly we find $\varepsilon|\beta$, and therefore ε is a unit. Then ε^{-1} is also a unit by Theorem 9.19, and we have

$$1 = \varepsilon^{-1}\varepsilon = \varepsilon^{-1}(\alpha\lambda_1 + \beta\mu_1) = \alpha(\varepsilon^{-1}\lambda_1) + \beta(\varepsilon^{-1}\mu_1) = \alpha\lambda_0 + \beta\mu_0,$$

say.

Next we prove that if π is a prime in $R(\sqrt{m})$ and if $\pi|\alpha\beta$, then $\pi|\alpha$ or $\pi|\beta$. For if $\pi \nmid \alpha$, then π and α have no common factors except units, and hence there exist integers λ_0 and μ_0 such that $1 = \pi\lambda_0 + \alpha\mu_0$. Then $\beta = \pi\beta\lambda_0 + \alpha\beta\mu_0$ and $\pi|\beta$ because $\pi|\alpha\beta$. This can be extended by mathematical induction to prove that if $\pi|(\alpha_1\alpha_2 \cdots \alpha_n)$, then π divides at least one factor α_j of the product.

From this point on the proof is identical with the first proof of Theorem 1.16, and there is no need to repeat the details.

Problems

1. If π is a prime and ε a unit in $R(\sqrt{m})$, prove that $\varepsilon\pi$ is a prime.
2. Prove that $1 + i$ is a prime in $R(i)$.
3. Prove that $11 + 2\sqrt{6}$ is a prime in $R(\sqrt{6})$.
4. Prove that 3 is a prime in $R(i)$, but not a prime in $R(\sqrt{6})$.
5. Prove that there are infinitely many primes in any quadratic field $R(\sqrt{m})$.

9.8   Unique Factorization

In this section we shall apply Theorem 9.26 to various quadratic fields, namely $R(i)$, $R(\sqrt{-2})$, $R(\sqrt{-3})$, $R(\sqrt{-7})$, $R(\sqrt{2})$, $R(\sqrt{3})$. We shall show that these fields have the unique factorization property by proving that they are Euclidean fields. There are other Euclidean quadratic fields, but we focus our attention on these few for which the Euclidean algorithm is easily established.

Theorem 9.27 *The fields $R(\sqrt{m})$ for $m = -1, -2, -3, -7, 2, 3$, are Euclidean and so have the unique factorization property.*

Proof. Consider any integers α and β of $R(\sqrt{m})$ with $\beta \neq 0$. Then $\alpha/\beta = u + v\sqrt{m}$ where u and v are rational numbers, and we choose rational integers x and y that are closest to u and v, that is, so that

(9.10) $$0 \leq |u - x| \leq \tfrac{1}{2}, \qquad 0 \leq |v - y| \leq \tfrac{1}{2}.$$

If we denote $x + y\sqrt{m}$ by γ and $\alpha - \beta\gamma$ by δ, then γ and δ are integers in $R(\sqrt{m})$ and $N(\delta) = N(\alpha - \beta\gamma) = N(\beta)N(\alpha/\beta - \gamma) = N(\beta)N((u - x) + (v - y)\sqrt{m}) = N(\beta)\{(u - x)^2 - m(v - y)^2\}$,

(9.11) $$|N(\delta)| = |N(\beta)|\,|(u - x)^2 - m(v - y)^2|.$$

By Equations (9.10) we have

$$-\frac{m}{4} \leq (u - x)^2 - m(v - y)^2 \leq \frac{1}{4} \quad \text{if} \quad m > 0,$$

$$0 \leq (u - x)^2 - m(v - y)^2 \leq \frac{1}{4} + \frac{1}{4}(-m) \quad \text{if} \quad m < 0,$$

and hence, by (9.11), $|N(\delta)| < |N(\beta)|$ if $m = 2, 3, -1, -2$. Therefore $R(\sqrt{m})$ is Euclidean for these values of m.

For the cases $m = -3$ and $m = -7$ we must choose γ in a different way. With u and v defined as above, we choose a rational integer s as close to $2v$ as possible and then choose a rational integer r, such that $r \equiv s \pmod{2}$, as close to $2u$ as possible. Then we have $|2v - s| \leq \tfrac{1}{2}$ and $|2u - r| \leq 1$, and the number $\gamma = (r + s\sqrt{m})/2$ is an integer of $R(\sqrt{m})$ by Theorem 9.20, since $m \equiv 1 \pmod{4}$ in the cases under discussion. As before, $\delta = \alpha - \beta\gamma$ is an integer in $R(\sqrt{m})$ and

$$N(\delta) = N(\beta)N\left(\frac{\alpha}{\beta} - \gamma\right) = N(\beta)\left\{\left(u - \frac{r}{2}\right)^2 - m\left(v - \frac{s}{2}\right)^2\right\},$$

$$|N(\delta)| \leq |N(\beta)|\left\{\frac{1}{4} + \frac{1}{16}(-m)\right\} < |N(\beta)|,$$

for $m = -3$ and $m = -7$.

Problems

1. Prove that $R(\sqrt{-11})$ has the unique factorization property.
2. Prove that $R(\sqrt{5})$ has the unique factorization property.
3. Prove that in $R(i)$ the quotient γ and remainder δ obtained in the proof of Theorem 9.27 are not necessarily unique. That is, prove that in $R(i)$ there

exist integers α, β, γ, δ, γ_1, δ_1 such that

$$\alpha = \beta\gamma + \delta = \beta\gamma_1 + \delta_1, \quad N(\delta) < N(\beta), \quad N(\delta_1) < N(\beta),$$
$$\gamma \neq \gamma_1, \quad \delta \neq \delta_1.$$

4. If α and β are integers of $R(i)$, not both zero, say that γ is a greatest common divisor of α and β if $N(\gamma)$ is greatest among norms of all common divisors of α and β. Prove that there are exactly four greatest common divisors of any fixed pair α, β, and that each of the four is divisible by any common divisor.

9.9 Primes in Quadratic Fields Having the Unique Factorization Property

If a field $R(\sqrt{m})$ has the unique factorization property, we can say much more about the primes of the field than we did in Section 9.7.

Theorem 9.28 *Let $R(\sqrt{m})$ have the unique factorization property. Then to any prime π in $R(\sqrt{m})$ there corresponds one and only one rational prime p such that $\pi|p$.*

Proof. The prime π is a divisor of the rational integer $N(\pi)$, and hence there exist positive rational integers divisible by π. Let n be the least of these. Then n is a rational prime. For otherwise $n = n_1 n_2$, and we have, by the unique factorization property, $\pi|n$, $\pi|(n_1 n_2)$, $\pi|n_1$ or $\pi|n_2$, a contradiction since $0 < n_1 < n$, $0 < n_2 < n$. Hence n is a rational prime, call it p. And, if π were a divisor of another rational prime q, we could find rational integers by Theorem 1.3 such that $1 = px + qy$. Since $\pi|(px + qy)$ this implies $\pi|1$, which is false, and hence the prime p is unique.

Theorem 9.29 *Let $R(\sqrt{m})$ have the unique factorization property. Then:*

(1) *Any rational prime p is either a prime π of the field or a product $\pi_1 \pi_2$ of two primes, not necessarily distinct, of $R(\sqrt{m})$.*

(2) *The totality of primes π, π_1, π_2 obtained by applying part 1 to all rational primes, together with their associates, constitute the set of all primes of $R(\sqrt{m})$.*

(3) *An odd rational prime p satisfying $(p, m) = 1$ is a product $\pi_1 \pi_2$ of two primes in $R(\sqrt{m})$ if and only if $\left(\dfrac{m}{p}\right) = 1$.*

(4) *If* $(2, m) = 1$, *then 2 is the associate of a square of a prime if* $m \equiv 3 \pmod 4$; *2 is a prime if* $m \equiv 5 \pmod 8$; *and 2 is the product of two distinct primes if* $m \equiv 1 \pmod 8$.

(5) *Any rational prime p that divides m is the associate of the square of a prime in* $R(\sqrt m)$.

Proof. (1) If the rational prime p is not a prime in $R(\sqrt m)$, then $p = \pi\beta$ for some prime π and some integer β of $R(\sqrt m)$. Then we have $N(\pi)N(\beta) = N(p) = p^2$. Since $N(\pi) \neq \pm 1$, we must have either $N(\beta) = \pm 1$ or $N(\beta) = \pm p$. If $N(\beta) = \pm 1$, then β is a unit by Theorem 9.21, and π is an associate of p, which then must be a prime in $R(\sqrt m)$. If $N(\beta) = \pm p$, we must show that β is a prime. If $\beta = \beta_1\beta_2$, then $N(\beta_1)N(\beta_2) = \pm p$ and one of $N(\beta_1)$ and $N(\beta_2)$ must have the value ± 1, so that either β_1 or β_2 is a unit. Thus β is a prime and p is a product $\pi\beta$ of two primes in $R(\sqrt m)$.

(2) The statement (2) now follows directly from Theorem 9.28 and statement (1).

(3) If p is an odd rational prime such that $(p, m) = 1$ and $\left(\dfrac{m}{p}\right) = 1$, there exists a rational integer x satisfying

$$x^2 \equiv m \pmod p, \quad p|(x^2 - m), \quad p|(x - \sqrt m)(x + \sqrt m).$$

If p were a prime of $R(\sqrt m)$, it would divide one of the factors $x - \sqrt m$ and $x + \sqrt m$, so that one of

$$\frac{x}{p} - \frac{\sqrt m}{p}, \quad \frac{x}{p} + \frac{\sqrt m}{p}$$

would be an integer in $R(\sqrt m)$. But this is impossible by Theorem 9.20, and hence p is not a prime in $R(\sqrt m)$. Therefore, by statement (1), $p = \pi_1\pi_2$ if $\left(\dfrac{m}{p}\right) = 1$.

Now suppose that p is an odd rational prime, that $(p, m) = 1$, and that p is not a prime in $R(\sqrt m)$. Then from the proof of statement (1) we see that $p = \pi\beta$, $N(\beta) = \pm p$, and $N(\pi) = \pm p$. We can write $\pi = a + b\sqrt m$ where a and b are rational integers or, if $m \equiv 1 \pmod 4$, halves of odd rational integers. Then $a^2 - mb^2 = N(\pi) = \pm p$, and we have $(2a)^2 - m(2b)^2 = \pm 4p$, $(2a)^2 \equiv m(2b)^2$ (mod p). Here $2a$ and $2b$ are rational integers and neither is a multiple of p, for if p divided either one it would divide the other and we would have $p^2|4a^2$, $p^2|4b^2$, $p^2|(4a^2 - 4mb^2)$, $p^2|4p$. Therefore $(2b, p) = 1$, and there is a rational integer w such that $2bw \equiv 1$ (mod p), $(2aw)^2 \equiv m(2bw)^2 \equiv m$ (mod p), and we have $\left(\dfrac{m}{p}\right) = 1$.

(4) If $m \equiv 3$ (mod 4), then

$$m^2 - m = 2\,\frac{m^2 - m}{2} = (m + \sqrt{m})(m - \sqrt{m}),$$

and $2 \nmid (m \pm \sqrt{m})$, so 2 cannot be a prime of $R(\sqrt{m})$. Hence 2 is divisible by a prime $x + y\sqrt{m}$ and this prime must have norm ± 2. Therefore $x^2 - my^2 = \pm 2$. But this implies that

$$\pm \frac{x - y\sqrt{m}}{x + y\sqrt{m}} = \pm \frac{x^2 + my^2 - 2xy\sqrt{m}}{x^2 - my^2} = \frac{x^2 + my^2}{2} - xy\sqrt{m},$$

and, similarly,

$$\pm \frac{x + y\sqrt{m}}{x - y\sqrt{m}} = \frac{x^2 + my^2}{2} + xy\sqrt{m},$$

and therefore $(x - y\sqrt{m})(x + y\sqrt{m})^{-1}$ and its inverse are integers of $R(\sqrt{m})$. Hence $(x - y\sqrt{m})(x + y\sqrt{m})^{-1}$ is a unit, and $x - y\sqrt{m}$ and $x + y\sqrt{m}$ are associates.

If $m \equiv 1$ (mod 4) and if 2 is not a prime in $R(\sqrt{m})$ then 2 is divisible by a prime $\frac{1}{2}(x + y\sqrt{m})$ having norm ± 2. This would mean that there are rational integers x and y, both even or both odd such that

(9.12) $$x^2 - my^2 = \pm 8.$$

If x and y are even, say $x = 2x_0$, $y = 2y_0$, then (9.12) would require $x_0^2 - my_0^2 = \pm 2$. But, since $m \equiv 1$ (mod 4), $x_0^2 - my_0^2$ is either odd or a multiple of 4. Thus (9.12) can have solutions only with odd x and y. Then $x^2 \equiv y^2 \equiv 1$ (mod 8), and (9.12) implies

$$x^2 - my^2 \equiv 1 - m \equiv 0, \qquad m \equiv 1 \text{ (mod 8).}$$

It follows that 2 is a prime in $R(\sqrt{m})$ if $m \equiv 5$ (mod 8).

Now if $m \equiv 1 \pmod 8$ we observe that

$$\frac{1-m}{4} = 2\frac{1-m}{8} = \frac{1-\sqrt{m}}{2}\frac{1+\sqrt{m}}{2},$$

and $2 \nmid (1 \pm \sqrt{m})/2$, so 2 cannot be a prime in $R(\sqrt{m})$. Hence (9.12) has solutions in odd integers x and y. Now the primes $\frac{1}{2}(x + y\sqrt{m})$ and $\frac{1}{2}(x - y\sqrt{m})$ are not associates in $R(\sqrt{m})$ because their quotient is not a unit. In fact their quotient is

$$\frac{x + y\sqrt{m}}{x - y\sqrt{m}} = \pm\frac{x^2 + my^2}{8} \pm \frac{xy\sqrt{m}}{4}$$

which is not even an integer in $R(\sqrt{m})$.

(5) Let p be a rational prime divisor of m. If $p = |m|$ then $p = \pm\sqrt{m} \cdot \sqrt{m}$ and hence p is the associate of the square of a prime in $R(\sqrt{m})$. If $p < |m|$, we note that

(9.13) $m = p\dfrac{m}{p} = \sqrt{m} \cdot \sqrt{m}.$

But p is not a divisor of $\sqrt{m}$ in $R(\sqrt{m})$ and hence p is not a prime in $R(\sqrt{m})$. Therefore p is divisible by a prime π, with $N(\pi) = \pm p$, and hence π is not a divisor of m/p. But, by (9.13), π is also a divisor of $\sqrt{m}$, π^2 is a divisor of m, and hence π^2 is a divisor of p.

The theorem we have just proved provides a method for determining the primes of a quadratic field having the unique factorization property. For such $R(\sqrt{m})$ we look at all the rational primes p. Those p for which $(p, 2m) = 1$ and $\left(\dfrac{m}{p}\right) = -1$, together with all their associates in $R(\sqrt{m})$, are primes in $R(\sqrt{m})$. Those p for which $(p, 2m) = 1$ and $\left(\dfrac{m}{p}\right) = +1$ will factor into $p = \pi_1\pi_2$, a product of two primes of $R(\sqrt{m})$, with $N(\pi_1) = N(\pi_2) = \pm p$. Any other factoring of p will merely replace π_1 and π_2 by associates. The primes p for which $(p, 2m) > 1$ will either be primes of $R(\sqrt{m})$ or products of two primes of $R(\sqrt{m})$.

Suppose that α is an integer in $R(\sqrt{m})$ and that $N(\alpha) = \pm p$, p a rational prime. Then $\bar{\alpha}$ is also an integer in $R(\sqrt{m})$ and $\alpha\bar{\alpha} = N(\alpha) = \pm p$, and this necessitates that α be a prime in $R(\sqrt{m})$. If $m \not\equiv 1 \pmod 4$, we can write $\alpha = x + y\sqrt{m}$, $N(\alpha) = x^2 - my^2$, with integers x and y. If $m \equiv 1 \pmod 4$, we can write $\alpha = (x + y\sqrt{m})/2$, $4N(\alpha) = x^2 - my^2$, with x and y integers, both odd or both even.

Combining these facts we have the following. Let $R(\sqrt{m})$ have the unique factorization property, and let p be a rational prime such that $(p, 2m) = 1$, $\left(\dfrac{m}{p}\right) = +1$. Then if $m \not\equiv 1 \pmod 4$, one at least of the two equations $x^2 - my^2 = \pm p$ has a solution. Let $x = a$, $y = b$ be such a solution. Then the numbers $\alpha = a + b\sqrt{m}$, $\bar{\alpha} = a - b\sqrt{m}$, and the associates of α and $\bar{\alpha}$ are primes in $R(\sqrt{m})$, and these are the only primes in $R(\sqrt{m})$ that divide p. On the other hand, if $m \equiv 1 \pmod 4$, one at least of the two equations $x^2 - my^2 = \pm 4p$ has a solution with x and y both odd or both even. Again denoting such a solution by $x = a$, $y = b$, we can say that the numbers $\alpha = (a + b\sqrt{m})/2$, $\bar{\alpha} = (a - b\sqrt{m})/2$, and their associates are primes in $R(\sqrt{m})$, and these are the only primes in $R(\sqrt{m})$ that divide p. It is worth noting that our consideration of algebraic number fields has thus given us information concerning diophantine equations.

It must be remembered that these results apply only to those $R(\sqrt{m})$ that have the unique factorization property.

Example. $m = -1$. Gaussian primes. The field is $R(i)$ and we have

$$2m = -2, \quad 1^2 + 1^2 = 2, \quad \overline{1 + i} = 1 - i,$$
$$\left(\frac{m}{p}\right) = \begin{cases} +1 \text{ if } p = 4k + 1 \\ -1 \text{ if } p = 4k + 3. \end{cases}$$

For each rational prime p of the form $4k + 1$ the equation $x^2 + y^2 = p$ has a solution since $x^2 + y^2 = -p$ is clearly impossible. For each such p choose a solution $x = a_p$, $y = b_p$.

The primes in $R(i)$ are $1 + i$, all rational primes $p = 4k + 3$, all $a_p + ib_p$, all $a_p - ib_p$, together with all their associates. Note that $1 - i = \overline{1 + i}$ has not been included since $1 - i = -i(1 + i)$, i is a unit of $R(i)$, and hence $1 - i$ is an associate of $1 + i$.

Example. $m = -3$. The field is $R(\sqrt{-3})$ and we have

$$2m = -6, \quad x^2 + 3y^2 = \pm 4 \cdot 2 \text{ has no solution,}$$

$$3^2 + 3 \cdot 1^2 = 4 \cdot 3, \quad \frac{3 + \sqrt{-3}}{2} = \frac{3 - \sqrt{-3}}{2},$$

$$\left(\frac{m}{p}\right) = \begin{cases} +1 \text{ if } p = 3k + 1, \ (p, 6) = 1 \\ -1 \text{ if } p = 3k + 2, \ (p, 6) = 1. \end{cases}$$

For each odd $p = 3k + 1$, choose a_p, b_p such that $a_p^2 + 3b_p^2 = 4p$.

The primes in $R(\sqrt{-3})$ are 2, $(3 + \sqrt{-3})/2$, all odd rational primes $p = 3k + 2$, all $(a_p + b_p \sqrt{-3})/2$, all $(a_p - b_p \sqrt{-3})/2$, together with all their associates. Here, again, we omit $(3 - \sqrt{-3})/2$ because it can be shown to be an associate of $(3 + \sqrt{-3})/2$. We could have included 2 among the $p = 3k + 2$ by just omitting the word "odd".

It can be noted that after Sections 9.1–9.4 on algebraic numbers in general, we turned our attention to quadratic fields. Many of our theorems can be extended to fields of algebraic numbers of higher degree, but of course it is not possible to obtain results as detailed as those for quadratic fields. Our brief survey of algebraic numbers has omitted not only these generalizations but also many other aspects of algebraic number theory that have been investigated.

Problems

1. In the second example, where $m = -3$, we know from the theory that if p is any prime of the form $3k + 1$, then there are integers x and y such that $x^2 + 3y^2 = 4p$. Let $x = 2u - y$ and establish that any such prime can be expressed in the form $u^2 - uy + y^2$.

2. The rational prime 13 can be factored in two ways in $R(\sqrt{-3})$,

$$13 = \frac{7 + \sqrt{-3}}{2} \cdot \frac{7 - \sqrt{-3}}{2} = (1 + 2\sqrt{-3})(1 - 2\sqrt{-3}).$$

Prove that this is not in conflict with the fact that $R(\sqrt{-3})$ has the unique factorization property.

3. Prove that $\sqrt{3} - 1$ and $\sqrt{3} + 1$ are associates in $R(\sqrt{3})$.

4. Prove that the primes of $R(\sqrt{3})$ are $\sqrt{3} - 1$, $\sqrt{3}$, all rational primes $p \equiv \pm 5 \pmod{12}$, all factors $a + b\sqrt{3}$ of rational primes $p \equiv \pm 1 \pmod{12}$, and all associates of these primes.

5. Prove that the primes of $R(\sqrt{2})$ are $\sqrt{2}$, all rational primes of the form $8k \pm 3$, and all factors $a + b\sqrt{2}$ of rational primes of the form $8k \pm 1$, and all associates of these primes.

6. Prove that if m is square-free, $m < 0$, $|m|$ not a prime, then $R(\sqrt{m})$ does not have the unique factorization property. *Suggestion:* use part (5) of Theorem 9.29.

Chapter 10

The Partition Function

10.1 Partitions

Definition 10.1 *The partition function $p(n)$ is defined as the number of ways that the positive integer n can be written as a sum of positive integers. Two partitions are not considered to be different if they differ only in the order of their summands. It is convenient to define $p(0) = 1$.*

For example $5 = 5 = 4 + 1 = 3 + 2 = 3 + 1 + 1 = 2 + 2 + 1 = 2 + 1 + 1 + 1 = 1 + 1 + 1 + 1 + 1$, and $p(5) = 7$. Similarly, $p(1) = 1$, $p(2) = 2$, $p(3) = 3$, $p(4) = 5$.

Other partition functions can be defined for which the summands must satisfy certain restrictions. We will make use of some of these.

Definition 10.2

$p_m(n) = $ *the number of partitions of n into summands less than or equal to m.*

$p^o(n) = $ *the number of partitions of n into odd summands.*

$p^d(n) = $ *the number of partitions of n into distinct summands.*

$q^e(n) = $ *the number of partitions of n into an even number of distinct summands.*

$q^o(n) = $ *the number of partitions of n into an odd number of distinct summands.*

We make the convention $p_m(0) = p^o(0) = p^d(0) = q^e(0) = 1$, $q^o(0) = 0$.

Since $5 = 2 + 2 + 1 = 2 + 1 + 1 + 1 = 1 + 1 + 1 + 1 + 1$ we have $p_2(5) = 3$. Also $5 = 5 = 3 + 1 + 1 = 1 + 1 + 1 + 1 + 1$, and $5 = 5 = 4 + 1 = 3 + 2$, and $5 = 4 + 1 = 3 + 2$, and $5 = 5$, so that $p^o(5) = 3$, $p^d(5) = 3$, $q^e(5) = 2$, $q^o(5) = 1$.

Theorem 10.1 *We have*

(a) $p_m(n) = p(n)$ *if* $n \leq m$,

(b) $p_m(n) \leq p(n)$ *for all* $n \geq 0$,

(c) $p_m(n) = p_{m-1}(n) + p_m(n - m)$ *if* $n \geq m > 1$,

(d) $p^d(n) = q^e(n) + q^o(n)$.

Proof. With the possible exception of (c), these are all obvious from the definitions. To prove (c) we note that each partition of n counted by $p_m(n)$ either has or does not have a summand equal to m. The partitions of the second sort are counted by $p_{m-1}(n)$. The partitions of the first sort are obtained by adding a summand m to each partition of $n - m$ into summands less than or equal to m, and hence are $p_m(n - m)$ in number. If $n = m$, the term $p_m(n - m) = 1$ counts the single partition $n = m$.

Theorem 10.2 *For* $n \geq 1$ *we have* $p^d(n) = p^o(n)$.

Proof. Consider any partition counted by $p^o(n)$. It will consist of, say, r_1 summands a_1, r_2 summands a_2, $\cdots$, r_s summands a_s, where the a_i are distinct odd integers and $\sum_{i=1}^{s} r_i a_i = n$. Now we can write each r_i in the form $r_i = \sum_j b_j^{(i)} 2^j$, $b_j^{(i)} = 0$ or 1. Then $n = \sum_{i=1}^{s} \sum_j b_j^{(i)} 2^j a_i$ gives us a partition of n whose summands are all the integers $2^j a_i$ for which $b_j^{(i)} = 1$. Also, since the a_i are distinct and odd, the summands $2^j a_i$ are distinct, and this new partition is counted by $p^d(n)$.

We can reverse the process. If $n = \sum_{k=1}^{t} c_k$ and the c_k are distinct, we write each c_k as $2^{e_k} d_k$, d_k odd. Then we let $a_1, a_2, \cdots, a_s$ be all the different integers to be found among the $d_1, d_2, \cdots, d_t$, and we let $b_j^{(i)} = 1$ if $2^j a_i$ is some c_k, $b_j^{(i)} = 0$ otherwise. Then $\sum_{i=1}^{s} \sum_j b_j^{(i)} 2^j a_i = \sum_{k=1}^{t} c_k = n$, and we get back the partition of n into r_1 summands a_1, r_2 summands a_2, $\cdots$, r_s summands a_s where $r_i = \sum_j b_j^{(i)} 2^j$. We have found a one-to-one correspondence between the partitions counted by $p^o(n)$ and those counted by $p^d(n)$ and hence we have $p^o(n) = p^d(n)$.

10.2   Graphs

A partition of n can be represented geometrically. If $n = a_1 + a_2 + \cdots + a_r$ is a partition, we can arrange the summands a_i in such a way that $a_1 \geqq a_2 \geqq \cdots \geqq a_r$. Then the graph of this partition is the array of points having a_1 points in the top row, a_2 in the next row, and so on down to a_r in the bottom row.

```
·  ·  ·  ·  ·
·  ·  ·  ·
·  ·  ·  ·
·  ·
·
```

$$19 = 6 + 5 + 5 + 2 + 1.$$

If we read the graph vertically instead of horizontally, we obtain a possibly different partition. For example, from $19 = 6 + 5 + 5 + 2 + 1$ we get $19 = 5 + 4 + 3 + 3 + 3 + 1$. From a partition $n = a_1 + a_2 + \cdots + a_r$ consisting of r summands with largest summand a_1, we obtain a partition of n into a_1 summands with largest summand r. Since this correspondence is reversible we have the following theorem.

Theorem 10.3 *The number of partitions of n into m summands is the same as the number of partitions of n having largest summand m. The number of partitions of n into at most m summands is $p_m(n)$.*

Theorem 10.4 *If $n \geqq 0$ then*

$$q^e(n) - q^o(n) = \begin{cases} (-1)^j & \text{if } n = (3j^2 \pm j)/2 \text{ for some } j = 0, 1, 2, \cdots \\ 0 & \text{otherwise.} \end{cases}$$

Proof. For $n = 0$ we have $j = 0$ and $q^e(0) - q^o(0) = 1$. We now suppose $n \geqq 1$ and consider a partition $n = a_1 + a_2 + \cdots + a_r$ into distinct summands. In the graph of this partition we let A_1 denote the point farthest to the right in the first row. Since the summands are distinct there will be no point directly below A_1. If $a_2 = a_1 - 1$, there will be a point A_2 directly below the point that is immediately to the left of A_1. If $a_2 < a_1 - 1$, there will be no such point A_2. If $a_3 = a_1 - 2$, then $a_2 = a_1 - 1$ and there will be a point A_3 directly below the point that is immediately to the left of A_2. If $a_2 = a_1 - 1$ and $a_3 < a_2 - 1$, there will be no point A_3. We continue this process as far as possible, thus obtaining a set of points $A_1, A_2, \cdots, A_s$, $s \geqq 1$, lying on a line through A_1 with slope 1. We also label the points of the bottom row $B_1, B_2, \cdots, B_t$, $t = a_r$. Notice that B_t and A_s may be the same point.

```
 •    •    •    •    •    •    •   A₁
 •    •    •    •    •    •   A₂
 •    •    •    •    •   A₃
 •    •    •
 •    •
B₁   B₂
```

Now we wish to change the graph into the graph of another partition of n into distinct summands. First, we try taking the points $B_1, B_2, \cdots, B_t$ and placing them to the right of $A_1, A_2, \cdots, A_t$; B_1 to the right of A_1, B_2 to the right of A_2, etc. It is obvious that we cannot do this if $t > s$ or if $t = s$ and $B_t = A_s$. However we can do it if $t < s$ or if $t = s$ and $B_t \neq A_s$, and we obtain a graph of a partition into distinct summands. Second, we try the reverse process, putting $A_1, A_2, \cdots, A_s$ underneath $B_1, B_2, \cdots, B_s$. This will give a proper graph if and only if $s < t - 1$ or $s = t - 1$ and $B_t \neq A_s$.

In other words, we can move the B_i if $t < s$ or if $t = s$ and $B_t \neq A_s$. We can move the A_i if $s < t - 1$ or if $s = t - 1$ and $B_t \neq A_s$. There is no graph in which both the A_i and the B_i can be moved. The graphs in which neither is possible are those for which $t = s$ and $B_t = A_s$ and those for which $s = t - 1$ and $B_t = A_s$. Starting with a partition P for which the A_i can be moved, we obtain a partition P' having the s points that were just moved in the bottom row. These points are in the B_i position and, of course, can be moved back to return to the partition P. A similar situation arises if the partition P is such that the B_i can be moved. In both cases the number of summands in P' differs from that in P by 1. This pairs off all the partitions of n for which either the A_i or the B_i can be moved, and in any pair P, P', one has an even number of summands, the other an odd number.

Let us consider the exceptional partitions for which neither the A_i nor the B_i can be moved, those for which $B_t = A_s$, $s = t$ or $t - 1$.

Since $B_t = A_s$ the graph consists of s rows. The bottom row has t points and the partition is $n = a_1 + a_2 + \cdots + a_s$, $a_s = t$, $a_{s-1} = t + 1$, $a_1 = t + s - 1$. Therefore $n = st + (s - 1)s/2$. If $s = t$, this is $n = (3s^2 - s)/2$; and if $s = t - 1$, it is $n = (3s^2 + s)/2$. It is easy to verify that the integers $(3s^2 \pm s)/2$, $s = 1, 2, \cdots$, are all distinct. Therefore we have paired off the partitions counted by $q^e(n)$ with those counted by $q^o(n)$ except for a single partition into s summands if $n = (3s^2 \pm s)/2$. This means

$$q^e(n) - q^o(n) = \begin{cases} (-1)^s & \text{if } n = (3s^2 \pm s)/2 \text{ for some } s = 1, 2, \cdots \\ 0 & \text{otherwise.} \end{cases}$$

Problem

1. Let $p'(n)$ denote the number of partitions, $n = a_1 + a_2 + \cdots + a_r$, of n into summands $a_1 \geq a_2 \geq a_3 \geq \cdots \geq a_r = 1$ such that consecutive a_i differ by at most 1. Read the graphs of such partitions vertically in order to prove that $p'(n) = \mu^d(n)$.

10.3   Generating Functions

Many results concerning the partition function depend on the theory of analytic functions and are beyond the scope of this book. However in the following sections we will obtain some interesting results without the use of very much analysis. In this section we discuss the main ideas heuristically without regard for careful proofs. Nothing will really be proved. The purpose of this section is just to make clear the ideas behind the proofs in the later sections.

The function $(1 - x^n)^{-1}$ has the expansion $\sum\limits_{j=0}^{\infty} x^{jn}$. Taking $n = 1$, $2, \cdots, m$ and multiplying we find

$$\prod_{n=1}^{m} (1 - x^n)^{-1} = (1 + x^{1 \cdot 1} + x^{2 \cdot 1} + \cdots)(1 + x^{1 \cdot 2} + x^{2 \cdot 2} + \cdots)$$

$$\times (1 + x^{1 \cdot 3} + x^{2 \cdot 3} + \cdots) \cdots$$

$$(1 + x^{1 \cdot m} + x^{2 \cdot m} + \cdots)$$

$$= \sum_{j_1=0}^{\infty} \sum_{j_2=0}^{\infty} \cdots \sum_{j_m=0}^{\infty} x^{j_1 \cdot 1 + j_2 \cdot 2 + \ldots + j_m \cdot m}$$

$$= \sum_{j=0}^{\infty} c_j x^j$$

where c_j is the number of solutions of $j_1 \cdot 1 + j_2 \cdot 2 + \cdots + j_m \cdot m = n$ in non-negative integers $j_1, j_2, \cdots, j_m$. That is $c_j = p_m(j)$, and we have

$$\sum_{n=0}^{\infty} p_m(n) x^n = \prod_{n=1}^{m} (1 - x^n)^{-1}.$$

This argument, like the rest in this section, is purely formal. We have said nothing about the convergence of the series involved and have not questioned the matter of multiplying series.

In a similar way we find

$$\sum_{n=0}^{\infty} p(n) x^n = \prod_{n=1}^{\infty} (1 - x^n)^{-1}.$$

The function $\prod_{n=1}^{\infty} (1 - x^n)^{-1}$ is called the generating function for $p(n)$, and application of analytic methods to this function leads to results about $p(n)$.

The generating function for $p_m(n)$ is $\prod_{n=1}^{m} (1 - x^n)^{-1}$. Similarly the generating function for $p^o(n)$ is found to be

$$\sum_{n=0}^{\infty} p^o(n) x^n = \prod_{n=1}^{\infty} (1 - x^{2n-1})^{-1},$$

and the generating function for $p^d(n)$ is

$$\sum_{n=0}^{\infty} p^d(n) x^n = \prod_{n=1}^{\infty} (1 + x^n).$$

Theorem 10.2 is equivalent to $\prod\limits_{n=1}^{\infty} (1 + x^n) = \prod\limits_{n=1}^{\infty} (1 - x^{2n-1})^{-1}$. This formula can be proved directly and then used to give another proof of Theorem 10.2. Formally, at least, we have

$$(1 - x^{2n-1})(1 + x^{2n-1})(1 + x^{2(2n-1)})(1 + x^{2^2(2n-1)}) \cdots$$
$$= (1 - x^{2(2n-1)})(1 + x^{2(2n-1)})(1 + x^{2^2(2n-1)}) \cdots$$
$$= (1 - x^{2^2(2n-1)})(1 + x^{2^2(2n-1)}) \cdots$$

$$= \cdots$$

$$= 1.$$

Taking $n = 1, 2, 3, \cdots$ and multiplying we find

$$\prod_{n=1}^{\infty} (1 - x^{2n-1}) \prod_{j=1}^{\infty} (1 + x^j) = 1$$

and

$$\prod_{j=1}^{\infty} (1 + x^j) = \prod_{n=1}^{\infty} (1 - x^{2n-1})^{-1}.$$

In a similar way we can multiply out $\prod\limits_{n=1}^{\infty} (1 - x^n)$ formally to get

$$\prod_{n=1}^{\infty} (1 - x^n) = \sum_{n=0}^{\infty} (q^e(n) - q^o(n))x^n.$$

Then Theorem 10.4 implies

$$\prod_{n=1}^{\infty} (1 - x^n) = 1 + \sum_{j=1}^{\infty} (-1)^j (x^{(3j^2+j)/2} + x^{(3j^2-j)/2}).$$

This is known as Euler's formula. It is proved in Theorem 10.8.

Problem

1. Show that the infinite product

$$(1 + x_1)(1 + x_1x_2)(1 + x_1x_2x_3) \cdots = 1 + \sum x_1^{a_1}x_2^{a_2} \cdots x_k^{a_k}$$

where $a_i - a_{i+1}$ is 0 or 1, and $a_k = 1$. Count the number of terms in the expansion that are of degree n. Set $x_1 = x_2 = x_3 = \cdots = x$ to show that $(1 + x)(1 + x^2)(1 + x^3) \cdots$ is the generating function for $p'(n)$ of Problem 1, Section 10.2.

10.4 Euler's Formula

In this section we will prove some of the things developed in Section 10.3. In doing this we will use only rudimentary facts concerning infinite series and limits. A reader familiar with the theory of analytic functions will recognize that our functions are analytic in $|x| < 1$ and will be able to shorten our proofs.

Theorem 10.5 *Suppose $0 \leqq x < 1$ and let $\varphi_m(x) = \prod\limits_{n=1}^{m} (1 - x^n)$.*

Then $\sum\limits_{n=0}^{\infty} p_m(n)x^n$ converges and

$$\sum_{n=0}^{\infty} p_m(n)x^n = \frac{1}{\varphi_m(x)}.$$

Proof. By Theorem 10.3, $p_m(n)$ is equal to the number of partitions of n into at most m summands. This is the same as the number of partitions into exactly m summands if we allow zero summands. Then each summand is 0 or 1 or 2 or $\cdots$ or n, and we have $p_m(n) \leqq (n + 1)^m$. The series $\sum\limits_{n=0}^{\infty} (n + 1)^m x^n$ converges, by the ratio test, and hence so does $\sum\limits_{n=0}^{\infty} p_m(n)x^n$, by the comparison test.

Now

$$(1 - x^{m!k})^m \varphi_m(x)^{-1} = \prod_{n=1}^{m} \frac{1 - x^{m!k}}{1 - x^n} = \prod_{n=1}^{m} \frac{1 - (x^n)^{(m!/n)k}}{1 - x^n}$$

$$= \prod_{n=1}^{m} \sum_{j=0}^{(m!/n)k-1} x^{jn} = \sum_{h} c_h x^h$$

where the last sum is a finite sum and $0 \leqq c_h \leqq p_m(h)$ for all $h = 0$,

$1, 2, \cdots$, and $c_h = p_m(h)$ if $h < m!k$. Therefore we have

$$\sum_{h=0}^{m!k-1} p_m(h)x^h \leqq (1 - x^{m!k})^m \varphi_m(x)^{-1} \leqq \sum_{h=0}^{\infty} p_m(h)x^h.$$

As $k \to \infty$ we have

$$\sum_{h=0}^{m!k-1} p_m(h)x^h \to \sum_{h=0}^{\infty} p_m(h)x^h, \qquad (1 - x^{m!k})^m \to 1,$$

and hence

$$\varphi_m(x)^{-1} = \sum_{h=0}^{\infty} p_m(h)x^h.$$

Theorem 10.6 *For $0 \leqq x < 1$,* $\lim\limits_{m \to \infty} \varphi_m(x)$ *exists and is different from zero. We let $\varphi(x) = \lim\limits_{m \to \infty} \varphi_m(x)$ and define $\prod\limits_{n=1}^{\infty} (1 - x^n)$ to be $\varphi(x)$.*

Proof. Since $\varphi_m(0) = 1$ the result is obvious for $x = 0$. For $x > 0$ we apply the mean value theorem to the function $\log z$ to obtain a y such that $1 - x^n < y < 1$ and

$$\frac{\log 1 - \log (1 - x^n)}{1 - (1 - x^n)} = \frac{1}{y}.$$

Therefore

$$-\log (1 - x^n) = \frac{x^n}{y}, \qquad -\log (1 - x^n) \leqq \frac{x^n}{1 - x^n} \leqq \frac{x^n}{1 - x}$$

and hence

$$-\log \varphi_m(x) = \sum_{n=1}^{m} -\log (1 - x^n) \leqq \sum_{n=1}^{m} \frac{x^n}{1 - x} \leqq \frac{1 - x^{m+1}}{(1 - x)^2} < \frac{1}{(1 - x)^2}.$$

This shows that $-\log \varphi_m(x)$, and hence $\varphi_m(x)^{-1}$, is bounded for x fixed as $m \to \infty$.
But

$$\varphi_m(x)^{-1} = \prod_{n=1}^{m} \frac{1}{1 - x^n}$$

increases monotonically for x fixed as $m \to \infty$. Since $\varphi_1(x)^{-1} = 1/(1 - x) > 0$ this shows that $\lim_{m \to \infty} \varphi_m(x)^{-1}$ exists and is different from zero. Therefore $\lim_{m \to \infty} \varphi_m(x)$ exists and is also different from zero.

Theorem 10.7 *For* $0 \leqq x < 1$ *the series* $\sum_{n=0}^{\infty} p(n)x^n$ *converges, and*

$$\sum_{n=0}^{\infty} p(n)x^n = \varphi(x)^{-1}.$$

Proof. We have, using Theorem 10.5,

$$\sum_{n=0}^{m} p(n)x^n = \sum_{n=0}^{m} p_m(n)x^n \leqq \sum_{n=0}^{\infty} p_m(n)x^n = \varphi_m(x)^{-1} \leqq \varphi(x)^{-1}.$$

For x fixed, $\sum_{n=0}^{m} p(n)x^n$ increases as $m \to \infty$. Therefore $\sum_{n=0}^{\infty} p(n)x^n = \lim_{m \to \infty} \sum_{n=0}^{m} p(n)x^n$ exists and is $\leqq \varphi(x)^{-1}$.

But now

$$\sum_{n=0}^{\infty} p(n)x^n \geqq \sum_{n=0}^{\infty} p_m(n)x^n = \varphi_m(x)^{-1}.$$

Letting $m \to \infty$ we have $\sum_{n=0}^{\infty} p(n)x^n \geqq \varphi(x)^{-1}$, and hence

$$\sum_{n=0}^{\infty} p(n)x^n = \varphi(x)^{-1}.$$

Theorem 10.8 *Euler's formula. For* $0 \leqq x < 1$ *we have*

$$\varphi(x) = 1 + \sum_{j=1}^{\infty} (-1)^j (x^{(3j^2+j)/2} + x^{(3j^2-j)/2}).$$

Proof. The ratio test shows that $\sum_{j=1}^{\infty} x^{(3j^2 \pm j)/2}$ converges; therefore so does the above series. Let $q_m^e(n)$ be the number of partitions of n into an even number of distinct summands no greater than m, and let $q_m^o(n)$ be the number of partitions of n into an odd number of distinct summands no greater than m. As in Definition 10.2 we will take $q_m^e(0) = 1$,

$q_m^o(0) = 0$. Then

(10.1) $\varphi_m(x) = (1 - x)(1 - x^2)(1 - x^3) \cdots (1 - x^m)$

$$= \sum_n (q_m^e(n) - q_m^o(n))x^n,$$

a finite sum. But for $n \leq m$ we have $q_m^e(n) = q^e(n)$, $q_m^o(n) = q^o(n)$, and we also have $q_m^e(n) + q_m^o(n) \leq p(n)$ for all n. Therefore

$$\left| \varphi_m(x) - \sum_{n=0}^{m} (q^e(n) - q^o(n))x^n \right|$$

$$\leq \sum_{n > m} |q_m^e(n) - q_m^o(n)| x^n \leq \sum_{n=m+1}^{\infty} p(n)x^n.$$

Since $\sum\limits_{n=m+1}^{\infty} p(n)x^n \to 0$ as $m \to \infty$, we get $\sum\limits_{n=0}^{\infty} (q^e(n) - q^o(n))x^n = \varphi(x)$ by letting $m \to \infty$. Using Theorem 10.4, we have the present theorem.

We will have occasion to multiply power series. For this we need the following lemma.

Lemma 10.9 *Let* $\sum\limits_{j=0}^{\infty} a_j x^j$ *and* $\sum\limits_{k=0}^{\infty} b_k x^k$ *be absolutely convergent for* $0 \leq x < 1$. *Then* $\sum\limits_{h=0}^{\infty} \left(\sum\limits_{j=0}^{h} a_j b_{h-j} \right) x^h$ *converges and has the value* $\sum\limits_{j=0}^{\infty} a_j x_j \sum\limits_{k=0}^{\infty} b_k x^k$ *for* $0 \leq x < 1$.

Proof. The condition $0 \leq x < 1$ could be replaced by $|x| < 1$; we take $0 \leq x < 1$ just to keep the lemma in agreement with our other theorems. The sums $\sum\limits_{j=0}^{m} a_j x^j$ and $\sum\limits_{k=0}^{m} b_k x^k$ are polynomials and can be multiplied by the usual rules of algebra. The terms of degree m or less in the product of the polynomials are precisely the terms in

$$\sum_{h=0}^{m} \left(\sum_{j=0}^{h} a_j b_{h-j} \right) x^h.$$

All other terms in the product are of the form $a_j b_k x^{j+k}$ with $j + k > m$.

Since $j + k > m$ implies that at least one of j and k exceeds $[m/2]$, we see that

$$\sum_{j=0}^{m} a_j x^j \sum_{k=[m/2]}^{m} b_k x^k + \sum_{j=[m/2]}^{m} a_j x^j \sum_{k=0}^{m} b_k x^k,$$

when multiplied out, will be a sum of terms including all the terms $a_j b_k x^{j+k}$, $j + k > m$, and possibly others. This implies that

$$\left| \sum_{j=0}^{m} a_j x^j \sum_{k=0}^{m} b_k x^k - \sum_{h=0}^{m} \left(\sum_{j=0}^{m} a_j b_{h-j} \right) x^h \right|$$

$$\leq \sum_{j=0}^{m} |a_j x^j| \sum_{k=[m/2]}^{m} |b_k x^k| + \sum_{j=[m/2]}^{m} |a_j x^j| \sum_{k=0}^{m} |b_k x^k|$$

$$\leq \sum_{j=0}^{\infty} |a_j x^j| \sum_{k=[m/2]}^{\infty} |b_k x^k| + \sum_{j=[m/2]}^{\infty} |a_j x^j| \sum_{k=0}^{\infty} |b_k x^k|,$$

since all four infinite series in this last expression are convergent. Letting $m \to \infty$ we see that $\sum_{h=0}^{\infty} \left(\sum_{j=0}^{h} a_j b_{h-j} \right) x^h$ converges and is equal to $\sum_{j=0}^{\infty} a_j x^j \sum_{k=0}^{\infty} b_k x^k$.

This lemma implies that if $\sum_{j=0}^{\infty} a_j x^j$ and $\sum_{k=0}^{\infty} b_k x^k$ converge absolutely for $0 \leq x < 1$, then so does $\sum_{h=0}^{\infty} \left(\sum_{j=0}^{h} a_j b_{h-j} \right) x^h$. Applying it to $\sum_{j=0}^{\infty} |a_j| x^j$ and $\sum_{k=0}^{\infty} |b_k| x^k$, we find that $\sum_{h=0}^{\infty} \left(\sum_{j=0}^{h} |a_j b_{h-j}| \right) x^h$ converges for $0 \leq x < 1$. Since $\left| \sum_{j=0}^{h} a_j b_{h-j} \right| \leq \sum_{j=0}^{\infty} |a_j b_{h-j}|$, we see that $\sum_{h=0}^{\infty} \left(\sum_{j=0}^{h} a_j b_{h-j} \right) x^h$ converges absolutely for $0 \leq x < 1$. Then the lemma can be extended to the product of any finite number of power series $\sum_{j=0}^{\infty} a_j^{(i)} x^j$ that are absolutely convergent for $0 \leq x < 1$.

Another fact that we will use is the following:

Lemma 10.10 *If* $\sum_{j=0}^{\infty} a_j x^j$ *and* $\sum_{j=0}^{\infty} b_j x^j$ *converge absolutely and*

$\sum_{j=0}^{\infty} a_j x^j = \sum_{j=0}^{\infty} b_j x^j$ *for* $0 \leqq x < 1$, *then* $a_j = b_j$ *for all* $j = 0, 1, 2, \cdots$.

Proof. If $c_j = a_j - b_j$, then $|c_j x^j| \leqq |a_j x^j| + |b_j x^j|$, and hence $\sum_{j=0}^{\infty} c_j x^j$ converges absolutely for $0 \leqq x < 1$ and we need only show that $\sum_{j=0}^{\infty} c_j x^j = 0$ implies $c_j = 0$. Setting $x = 0$ we have $c_0 = 0$. Suppose the lemma is false. Then there is some $c_j \neq 0$, and we can let k be the smallest positive integer for which $c_k \neq 0$. Then $\sum_{j=0}^{\infty} c_j x^j = \sum_{j=k}^{\infty} c_j x^j$ and, because this series converges absolutely for $x = \frac{1}{2}$, there is an integer $m > k$ such that $\sum_{j=m+1}^{\infty} |c_j 2^{-j}| < 2^{-k-1}|c_k|$. Now for $0 < x < 1$ we have $\sum_{j=k}^{\infty} c_j x^j = 0$ and, dividing by x^k, we get

$$c_k + \sum_{j=k+1}^{m} c_j x^{j-k} + \sum_{j=m+1}^{\infty} c_j x^{j-k} = 0.$$

Then for $0 < x \leqq \frac{1}{2}$ we can write

$$|c_k| \leqq \left| \sum_{j=k+1}^{m} c_j x^{j-k} \right| + \left| \sum_{j=m+1}^{\infty} c_j x^{j-k} \right|$$

$$\leqq \left| \sum_{j=k+1}^{m} c_j x^{j-k} \right| + \sum_{j=m+1}^{\infty} |c_j| x^{j-k}$$

$$\leqq \left| \sum_{j=k+1}^{m} c_j x^{j-k} \right| + \sum_{j=m+1}^{\infty} |c_j| 2^{-j+k}$$

$$< \left| c_{k+1} x + c_{k+2} x^2 + \cdots + c_m x^{m-k} \right| + 2^k \cdot 2^{-k-1} |c_k|,$$

and finally

$$\tfrac{1}{2}|c_k| < |c_{k+1}x + c_{k+2}x^2 + \cdots + c_m x^{m-k}|.$$

But $c_{k+1}x + c_{k+2}x^2 + \cdots + c_m x^{m-k}$ is a polynomial, and we can make its value less than the positive number $|c_k|/2$ by choosing x close enough to zero, $0 < x \leq \tfrac{1}{2}$. This is a contradiction and therefore the lemma is proved.

Now we can return to the partition function.

Theorem 10.11 *If $n \geq 1$ then*

$$p(n) = p(n-1) + p(n-2) - p(n-5) - p(n-7)$$

$$+ p(n-12) + p(n-15) - \cdots = \sum_j (-1)^{j+1} p(n - \tfrac{1}{2}(3j^2 \pm j))$$

where the sum extends over all positive integers for which the arguments of the partition function are non-negative.

Proof. From Theorems 10.7 and 10.8 we have

$$\left(1 + \sum_{j=1}^\infty (-1)^j (x^{(3j^2+j)/2} + x^{(3j^2-j)/2})\right) \sum_{k=0}^\infty p(k)x^k = \varphi(x)\varphi(x)^{-1} = 1$$

if $0 \leq x < 1$; that is

$$(1 - x - x^2 + x^5 + x^7 - x^{12} - x^{15} + \cdots) \sum_{k=0}^\infty p(k)x^k = 1.$$

Applying Lemma 10.9 we find

$$\sum_{h=0}^\infty (p(h) - p(h-1) - p(h-2)$$

$$+ p(h-5) + p(h-7) - \cdots)x^h = 1,$$

which implies $p(h) - p(h-1) - p(h-2) + \cdots = 0$ by Lemma 10.10.

The theorem we have just proved can be used to construct a table of $p(n)$. There is a similar formula for the function $\sigma(n)$, the sum of the divisors of n.

Theorem 10.12 *For $n \geq 1$ we have*

$$\sigma(n) - \sigma(n-1) - \sigma(n-2) + \sigma(n-5) + \sigma(n-7)$$

$$- \sigma(n-12) - \sigma(n-15) + \cdots = \begin{cases} (-1)^{j+1}n & \text{if } n = \dfrac{3j^2 \pm j}{2} \\ 0 & \text{otherwise} \end{cases}$$

where the sum extends as far as the arguments are positive.

Proof. Taking the derivative of $\log \varphi_m(x) = \log \prod\limits_{n=1}^{m} (1 - x^n)$ we get

$$\frac{\varphi'_m(x)}{\varphi_m(x)} = \sum_{n=1}^{m} \frac{-nx^{n-1}}{1 - x^n} = \sum_{n=1}^{m} \sum_{j=1}^{\infty} -nx^{jn-1} = \sum_{n=1}^{m} \sum_{k=1}^{\infty} c_{n,k} x^{k-1}$$

for $0 \leq x < 1$, where

$$c_{n,k} = \begin{cases} -n & \text{if } n \mid k \\ 0 & \text{otherwise.} \end{cases}$$

There are m series $\sum\limits_{k=1}^{\infty} c_{n,k} x^{k-1}$ each of which converges absolutely. They can be added term by term to give

$$(10.2) \qquad \frac{\varphi'_m(x)}{\varphi_m(x)} = \sum_{k=1}^{\infty} \left(\sum_{n=1}^{m} c_{n,k} \right) x^{k-1}$$

Using (10.1) we have $\varphi'_m(x) = \sum\limits_{n} n(q^e_m(n) - q^o_m(n))x^{n-1}$ since $\varphi_m(x)$ is a finite sum, a polynomial in x. But we can also write (10.1) in the form of an infinite series,

$$\varphi_m(x) = \sum_{n=0}^{\infty} (q^e_m(n) - q^o_m(n))x^n$$

in which all the terms from a certain n on are zero. Then equation

(10.2) can be put in the form

$$\sum_{n} n(q_m^e(n) - q_m^o(n))x^{n-1} = \sum_{n=0}^{\infty} (q_m^e(n) - q_m^o(n))x^n \sum_{j=0}^{\infty} \left(\sum_{i=1}^{m} c_{i,j+1}\right) x^j$$

$$= \sum_{h=0}^{\infty} \left(\sum_{n=0}^{h} (q_m^e(n) - q_m^o(n)) \sum_{i=1}^{m} c_{i,h-n+1}\right) x^h$$

by Lemma 10.9. Then Lemma 10.10 gives us

$$k(q_m^e(k) - q_m^o(k)) = \sum_{n=0}^{k-1} (q_m^e(n) - q_m^o(n)) \sum_{i=1}^{m} c_{i,k-n}.$$

For any given k we can choose $m > k$. Then $q_m^e(k) = q^e(k)$, $q_m^o(k) = q^o(k)$, $q_m^e(n) = q^e(n)$, $q_m^o(n) = q^o(n)$, and $\sum_{i=1}^{m} c_{i,k-n} = -\sum_{d|k-n} d = -\sigma(k-n)$ for $n \leq k - 1$. This with Theorem 10.4 gives us

$$-\sigma(k) + \sigma(k-1) + \sigma(k-2) - \sigma(k-5) - \sigma(k-7) + \cdots$$

$$= \begin{cases} (-1)^j k & \text{if } k = \dfrac{3j^2 \pm j}{2} \\ 0 & \text{otherwise} \end{cases}$$

and the theorem is proved.

Problems

1. Compute a short table of the values of $p(n)$, from $n = 1$ to $n = 20$, by use of Theorem 10.11.
2. Compute a short table of the values of $\sigma(n)$, from $n = 1$ to $n = 20$, by means of Theorem 10.12. Verify the entries by computing $\sigma(n) = \sum_{d|n} d$ directly.

10.5   Jacobi's Formula

Theorem 10.13 *Jacobi's formula. For* $0 \leq x < 1$,

$$\varphi(x)^3 = \sum_{j=0}^{\infty} (-1)^j (2j + 1) x^{(j^2+j)/2}.$$

Proof. The formula is obvious for $x = 0$, so we can suppose $0 < x < 1$. For $0 < q < 1$, $0 < z < 1$, we define

$$(10.3) \quad f_n(z) = \prod_{k=1}^{n} \{(1 - q^{2k-1}z^2)(1 - q^{2k-1}z^{-2})\} = \sum_{j=-n}^{n} a_j z^{2j}$$

where the a_j are polynomials in q. Since $f_n(1/z) = f_n(z)$ we have $a_{-j} = a_j$, and it is easy to see that

$$(10.4) \qquad a_n = (-1)^n q^{1+3+5+\cdots+(2n-1)} = (-1)^n q^{n^2}.$$

In order to obtain the other a_j we replace z by qz in (10.3) and find

$$f_n(qz) = \prod_{k=1}^{n} \{(1 - q^{2k+1}z^2)(1 - q^{2k-3}z^{-2})\}$$

$$= \prod_{k=2}^{n+1} (1 - q^{2k-1}z^2) \prod_{j=0}^{n-1} (1 - q^{2j-1}z^{-2})$$

and hence

$$qz^2(1 - q^{2n-1}z^{-2})f_n(qz)$$

$$= (1 - q^{2n+1}z^2) \left\{ \prod_{k=2}^{n} (1 - q^{2k-1}z^2) \right\} qz^2(1 - q^{-1}z^{-2}) \prod_{j=1}^{n} (1 - q^{2j-1}z^{-2})$$

$$= -(1 - q^{2n+1}z^2) \prod_{k=1}^{n} (1 - q^{2k-1}z^2) \prod_{j=1}^{n} (1 - q^{2j-1}z^{-2})$$

$$= (q^{2n+1}z^2 - 1)f_n(z).$$

If we write the functions f_n in terms of the a_j, using (10.3), and equate the coefficients of z^{2k}, we find

$$qa_{k-1}q^{2k-2} - q^{2n}a_k q^{2k} = q^{2n+1}a_{k-1} - a_k$$

and then

$$a_{k-1} = \frac{-(1 - q^{2n+2k})}{q^{2k-1}(1 - q^{2n-2k+2})} a_k.$$

This, along with (10.4) allows us to find $a_{n-1}, a_{n-2}, \cdots$, in turn. In fact, for $0 < j \leq n$ we find

$$a_{n-j} = \frac{(-1)^j(1 - q^{4n})(1 - q^{4n-2}) \cdots (1 - q^{4n-2j+2})}{(1 - q^2)(1 - q^4) \cdots (1 - q^{2j})} (-1)^n q^{(n-j)^2}$$

and hence

$$(10.5) \quad a_k = \frac{\displaystyle\prod_{h=n+k+1}^{2n}(1-q^{2h})}{\displaystyle\prod_{h=1}^{n-k}(1-q^{2h})}(-1)^k q^{k^2} = \frac{\varphi_{2n}(q^2)}{\varphi_{n+k}(q^2)\varphi_{n-k}(q^2)}(-1)^k q^{k^2}.$$

This formula is valid for $0 \leq k \leq n$ if we agree to take $\varphi_0(q^2) = 1$.

Returning to (10.3), we see that $f_n(z)$ is a product of $2n$ factors, one of which is $(1 - qz^{-2})$, which has the value 0 at $z = q^{\frac{1}{2}}$. Therefore taking the derivative and then setting $z = q^{\frac{1}{2}}$ we have

$$f_n'(q^{\frac{1}{2}}) = \prod_{k=1}^{n}(1-q^{2k-1}q)\left\{\prod_{j=2}^{n}(1-q^{2j-1}q^{-1})\right\}2qq^{-\frac{3}{2}}$$

$$= \frac{2q^{-\frac{1}{2}}}{1-q^{2n}}\varphi_n(q^2)^2.$$

On the other hand, we also have, from (10.3),

$$f_n'(q^{\frac{1}{2}}) = \sum_{j=-n}^{n} 2ja_j q^{j-\frac{1}{2}} - \sum_{j=1}^{n} 2ja_j q^{-\frac{1}{2}}(q^j - q^{-j}).$$

Thus we find

$$\varphi_n(q^2)^2 = (1-q^{2n})\sum_{j=1}^{n} ja_j(q^j - q^{-j}),$$

and hence, by (10.5),

$$\varphi_n(q^2)^3 = (1-q^{2n})\sum_{j=1}^{n}(-1)^j jq^{j^2}(q^j - q^{-j})\frac{\varphi_{2n}(q^2)\varphi_n(q^2)}{\varphi_{n+j}(q^2)\varphi_{n-j}(q^2)}.$$

Now

$$0 \leq \frac{\varphi_{2n}(q^2)\varphi_n(q^2)}{\varphi_{n+j}(q^2)\varphi_{n-j}(q^2)} = \prod_{h=n+j+1}^{2n}(1-q^{2h})\prod_{k=n-j+1}^{n}(1-q^{2k}) \leq 1,$$

and $\sum\limits_{j=1}^{\infty} jq^{j^2}\left|q^j - q^{-j}\right|$ converges, so we have for $n > m$

$$\left| \varphi_n(q^2)^3 - (1 - q^{2n}) \sum_{j=1}^{m} (-1)^j jq^{j^2}(q^j - q^{-j}) \frac{\varphi_{2n}(q^2)\varphi_n(q^2)}{\varphi_{n+j}(q^2)\varphi_{n-j}(q^2)} \right|$$

$$\leqq \sum_{j=m+1}^{n} jq^{j^2}\left|q^j - q^{-j}\right| \leqq \sum_{j=m+1}^{\infty} jq^{j^2}\left|q^j - q^{-j}\right|.$$

We keep m fixed but arbitrary and let $n \to \infty$. By Theorem 10.6 we have

$$\lim_{n \to \infty} \frac{\varphi_{2n}(q^2)\varphi_n(q^2)}{\varphi_{n+j}(q^2)\varphi_{n-j}(q^2)} = \frac{\varphi(q^2)^2}{\varphi(q^2)^2} = 1$$

and $\lim\limits_{n \to \infty} \varphi_n(q^2)^3 = \varphi(q^2)^3$ so that we get

$$\left| \varphi(q^2)^3 - \sum_{j=1}^{m} (-1)^j jq^{j^2}(q^j - q^{-j}) \right| \leqq \sum_{j=m+1}^{\infty} jq^{j^2}\left|q^j - q^{-j}\right|.$$

Now letting $m \to \infty$ we find

$$\varphi(q^2)^3 = \sum_{j=1}^{\infty} (-1)^j jq^{j^2}(q^j - q^{-j}) = \sum_{j=1}^{\infty} (-1)^j jq^{j^2+j} + \sum_{j=1}^{\infty} (-1)^{j-1} jq^{j^2-j}$$

where we can make the last step because both series converge. Changing j to $j + 1$, we write the last series as $\sum\limits_{j=0}^{\infty} (-1)^j(j + 1)q^{j^2+j}$ and can then add it to the first series to obtain

$$\varphi(q^2)^3 = \sum_{j=0}^{\infty} (-1)^j(2j + 1)q^{j^2+j}.$$

This is our theorem with x replaced by q^2.

Problem

1. Replace z by $q^{1/6}$ in (10.3), multiply by $\varphi_n(q^2)$, and use (10.5) to obtain a proof of Euler's formula.

10.6   A Divisibility Property

Theorem 10.14 *If p is a prime and $0 \leq x < 1$ then*

$$\frac{\varphi(x^p)}{\varphi(x)^p} = 1 + p \sum_{j=1}^{\infty} a_j x^j$$

where the a_j are integers.

Proof. For $0 \leq u < 1$ we have the expansion

$$(1 - u)^{-p} = 1 + \sum_{j=1}^{\infty} (-1)^j \frac{(-p)(-p-1) \cdots (-p-j+1)}{j!} u^j$$

$$= 1 + \sum_{j=1}^{\infty} \frac{(p+j-1)!}{j!(p-1)!} u^j = \sum_{j=0}^{\infty} b_j u^j,$$

say, and therefore

$$\frac{1-u^p}{(1-u)^p} = (1-u)^{-p} - u^p(1-u)^{-p} = \sum_{j=0}^{\infty} b_j u^j - \sum_{j=0}^{\infty} b_j u^{j+p}$$

$$= \sum_{j=0}^{p-1} b_j u^j + \sum_{j=p}^{\infty} (b_j - b_{j-p}) u^j = \sum_{j=0}^{\infty} c_j u^j,$$

say. But

$$b_j = \frac{(j+1)(j+2) \cdots (j+p-1)}{(p-1)!}$$

$$\equiv \begin{cases} 1 \ (\text{mod } p) \text{ if } j \equiv 0 \ (\text{mod } p) \\ 0 \ (\text{mod } p) \text{ if } j \not\equiv 0 \ (\text{mod } p), \end{cases}$$

and $b_0 < b_1 < b_2 < \cdots$, so that we have $c_0 = b_0 = 1$, $c_j > 0$, $c_j \equiv 0 \ (\text{mod } p)$ for $j > 0$.

Now, for $0 \leq x < 1$,

$$\frac{\varphi_m(x^p)}{\varphi_m(x)^p} = \prod_{n=1}^{m} \frac{1 - x^{pn}}{(1 - x^n)^p} = \sum_{j=0}^{\infty} a_j^{(m)} x^j$$

where $a_j^{(1)} = c_j$ and, by Lemma 10.9,

$$\sum_{h=0}^{\infty} a_h^{(m)} x^h = \sum_{j=0}^{\infty} c_j x^{mj} \sum_{k=0}^{\infty} a_k^{(m-1)} x^k = \sum_{h=0}^{\infty} \sum_{j=0}^{[h/m]} c_j a_{h-mj}^{(m-1)} x^h.$$

By Lemma 10.10 we then have

$$a_h^{(m)} = \sum_{j=0}^{[h/m]} c_j a_{h-mj}^{(m-1)},$$

and hence

$$a_h^{(m)} \equiv a_h^{(m-1)} \equiv a_h^{(1)} \equiv c_h \pmod{p},$$

$$a_h^{(m)} \geq a_h^{(m-1)} \geq a_h^{(1)} = c_h > 0,$$

$$a_h^{(m)} = a_h^{(m-1)} \text{ if } h \leq m - 1.$$

Therefore

$$\sum_{h=0}^{m} a_h^{(h)} x^h = \sum_{h=0}^{m} a_h^{(m)} x^h \leq \sum_{h=0}^{\infty} a_h^{(m)} x^h = \frac{\varphi_m(x^p)}{\varphi_m(x)^p}.$$

Since the sum on the left increases as $m \to \infty$ we see that $\sum_{h=0}^{\infty} a_h^{(h)} x^h$ converges and

$$\sum_{h=0}^{\infty} a_h^{(h)} x^h \leq \frac{\varphi(x^p)}{\varphi(x)^p}.$$

But we also have

$$\sum_{h=0}^{\infty} a_h^{(h)} x^h = \sum_{h=0}^{m} a_h^{(m)} x^h + \sum_{h=m+1}^{\infty} a_h^{(h)} x^h$$

$$\geq \sum_{h=0}^{m} a_h^{(m)} x^h + \sum_{h=m+1}^{\infty} a_h^{(m)} x^h = \frac{\varphi_m(x^p)}{\varphi_m(x)^p},$$

$$\sum_{h=0}^{\infty} a_h^{(h)} x^h \geq \frac{\varphi(x^p)}{\varphi(x)^p},$$

and finally

$$\sum_{h=0}^{\infty} a_h^{(h)} x^h = \frac{\varphi(x^p)}{\varphi(x)^p}.$$

Since $a_0^{(0)} = c_0 = 1$ and $a_h^{(h)} \equiv c_h \equiv 0 \pmod{p}$ for $h \geq 1$, the theorem is proved.

Theorem 10.15 *For $0 \leq x < 1$ we have $x\varphi(x)^4 = \sum\limits_{m=1}^{\infty} b_m x^m$ where the b_m are integers and $b_m \equiv 0 \pmod 5$ if $m \equiv 0 \pmod 5$.*

Proof. We can write Theorem 10.8 in the form

$$\varphi(x) = \sum_{k=0}^{\infty} c_k x^k, \qquad c^k = \begin{cases} (-1)^j & \text{if } k = (3j^2 \pm j)/2 \\ 0 & \text{otherwise} \end{cases}$$

and Theorem 10.13 as

$$\varphi(x)^3 = \sum_{n=0}^{\infty} d_n x^n, \qquad d_n = \begin{cases} (-1)^j(2j+1) & \text{if } n = (j^2 + j)/2 \\ 0 & \text{otherwise,} \end{cases}$$

and then apply Lemma 10.9 to obtain

$$x\varphi(x)^4 = x\varphi(x)\varphi(x)^3$$

$$= x \sum_{h=0}^{\infty} \left(\sum_{k=0}^{h} c_k d_{h-k} \right) x^h = \sum_{m=1}^{\infty} b_m x^m.$$

Then $b_m = \sum\limits_{k=0}^{m-1} c_k d_{m-1-k}$ can be written as $\sum c_k d_n$ summed over all $k \geq 0$, $n \geq 0$, such that $k + n = m - 1$. But d_n is 0 unless $n = (j^2 + j)/2$, $j = 0, 1, 2, \cdots$, in which case it is $(-1)^j(2j+1)$. Furthermore we can describe c_k by saying that it is 0 unless $k = (3i^2 + i)/2$, $i = 0, \pm 1, \pm 2, \cdots$, in which case it is $(-1)^i$. Then we can write

$$(10.6) \quad b_m = \sum (-1)^i(-1)^j(2j+1) = \sum (-1)^{i+j}(2j+1)$$

summed over all i and j such that $j \geq 0$ and $(3i^2 + i)/2 + (j^2 + j)/2 = m - 1$. But

$$2(i+1)^2 + (2j+1)^2 = 8\left(1 + \frac{3i^2 + i}{2} + \frac{j^2 + j}{2}\right) - 10i^2 - 5$$

so that if $m \equiv 0 \pmod 5$, the terms in (10.6) will have to be such that $2(i+1)^2 + (2j+1)^2 \equiv 0 \pmod 5$. That is $(2j+1)^2 \equiv -2(i+1)^2 \pmod 5$. However, -2 is a quadratic nonresidue modulo 5, so this condition implies $2j + 1 \equiv 0 \pmod 5$, and hence $b_m \equiv 0 \pmod 5$ if $m \equiv 0 \pmod 5$.

Theorem 10.16 *We have* $p(5m + 4) \equiv 0 \pmod 5$.

Proof. By Theorems 10.15, 10.14, and 10.7 we have

$$\sum_{n=0}^{\infty} p(n)x^{n+1} = \frac{x}{\varphi(x)} = x\varphi(x)^4 \frac{\varphi(x^5)}{\varphi(x)^5} \frac{1}{\varphi(x^5)}$$

$$= \sum_{m=1}^{\infty} b_m x^m \left(1 + 5\sum_{j=1}^{\infty} a_j x^j\right) \sum_{k=0}^{\infty} p(k)x^{5k}$$

where the a_j and b_m are integers and $b_m \equiv 0 \pmod 5$ for $m \equiv 0 \pmod 5$. Using Lemmas 10.9 and 10.10 we find that

$$p(n - 1) \equiv \sum_{k=0}^{[n/5]} p(k)b_{n-5k} \pmod 5$$

and hence $p(5m + 4) \equiv 0 \pmod 5$ since $b_{5m+5-5k} \equiv 0 \pmod 5$.

This theorem is only one of several divisibility properties of the partition function. The methods of this section can be used to prove that $p(7n + 5) \equiv 0 \pmod 7$. With the aid of more extensive analysis, it can be shown that $p(5^k n + r) \equiv 0 \pmod{5^k}$ if $24r \equiv 1 \pmod{5^k}$, $k = 2, 3, 4, \cdots$, and there are still other congruences related to powers of 5. There are somewhat similar congruences related to powers of 7, but it is an interesting fact that $p(7^k n + r) \equiv 0 \pmod{7^k}$ if $24r \equiv 1 \pmod{7^k}$ is valid for $k = 1, 2$ but is false for $k = 3$. There are also divisibility properties related to the number 11. An identity typical of several connected with the divisibility properties is

$$\sum_{n=0}^{\infty} p(5n + 4)x^n = 5 \frac{\varphi(x^5)^5}{\varphi(x)^6}, \qquad |x| < 1.$$

Problems

1. Write Euler's formula as

$$\varphi(x) = \sum_{j=-\infty}^{\infty} (-1)^j x^{(3j^2+j)/2}.$$

   Use Jacobi's formula as in Theorem 10.13, multiply $x\varphi(x)\varphi(x)^3$ out formally and verify (10.6).

2. Obtain a congruence similar to that in Theorem 10.16 but for the modulus 35, using Theorem 10.16 and $p(7n + 5) \equiv 0 \pmod 7$.

Chapter 11

The Density of Sequences of Integers

In order even to define what is meant by the density of a sequence of integers it is necessary to use certain concepts from analysis. In this chapter it is assumed that the reader is familiar with the ideas of the limit inferior of a sequence of real numbers and the greatest lower bound, or infimum, of a set of real numbers. Also, in Section 11.2 we make use of the fact that $\sum_{n=1}^{\infty} 1/n^2 = \pi^2/6$. These are discussed in many texts, for example in *Mathematical Analysis*, by Apostol.*

Two common types of density are considered in this chapter, asymptotic density and Schnirelman density. The first is discussed in Sections 11.1 to 11.3, and the second in Section 11.4. Density will be defined for a set A of distinct positive integers. We will think of the elements of A as being arranged in a sequence according to size,

$$(11.1) \qquad a_1 < a_2 < a_3 < \cdots ,$$

and we will also denote A by $\{a_i\}$. Furthermore we will use both the terms set and sequence to describe A. The set A may be infinite or finite. That is, it may contain infinitely many elements or only a finite number of elements. It may even be empty, in which case it will be denoted by 0. If an integer m is an element of A we write $m \in A$, if not we write $m \notin A$. The set A is contained in B, $A \subset B$ or $B \supset A$, if every element of A is an element of B. We write $A = B$ if $A \subset B$

---

* Tom M. Apostol, *Mathematical Analysis*, Addison-Wesley, 1957.

and $B \subset A$, that is if A and B have precisely the same elements. The union $A \cup B$ of two sets A and B is the set of all elements m such that $m \in A$ or $m \in B$. The intersection $A \cap B$ of A and B is the set of all m such that $m \in A$ and $m \in B$. Thus, for example, $A \cup A = A \cap A = A$, $A \cup 0 = A$, $A \cap 0 = 0$. If A and B have no element in common, $A \cap B = 0$, A and B are said to be disjoint. By the complement $\bar{A}$ of A we mean the set of all positive integers that are not elements of A. Thus $A \cap \bar{A} = 0$ and $\bar{0}$ is the set of all positive integers.

11.1 Asymptotic Density

The number of positive integers in a set A that are less than or equal to x is denoted by $A(x)$. For example, if A consists of the even integers 2, 4, 6, $\cdots$, then $A(1) = 0$, $A(2) = 1$, $A(6) = 3$, $A(7) = 3$, $A(15/2) = 3$; in fact $A(x) = [x/2]$ if $x \geq 0$. On the other hand, for any set $A = \{a_i\}$ we have $A(a_j) = j$.

Definition 11.1 *The asymptotic density of a set A is*

$$\delta_1(A) = \lim_{n \to \infty} \inf \frac{A(n)}{n}.$$

In case the sequence $A(n)/n$ has a limit, we say that A has a natural density, $\delta(A)$. Thus

$$\delta(A) = \delta_1(A) = \lim_{n \to \infty} \frac{A(n)}{n}$$

if A has a natural density. If A is a finite sequence, it is clear that $\delta(A) = 0$.

Theorem 11.1 *If A is an infinite sequence, then*

$$\delta_1(A) = \lim_{n \to \infty} \inf \frac{n}{a_n}.$$

If $\delta(A)$ exists, then $\delta(A) = \lim_{n \to \infty} n/a_n$.

Proof. The sequence k/a_k is a subsequence of $A(n)/n$ and hence

$$\lim_{n \to \infty} \inf \frac{A(n)}{n} \leq \lim_{k \to \infty} \inf \frac{k}{a_k}.$$

If n is any integer $\geqq a_1$ and a_k is the smallest integer in A that exceeds n, then $a_{k-1} \leqq n < a_k$ and

$$\frac{k}{a_k} - \frac{A(n)}{n} = \frac{k}{a_k} - \frac{k-1}{n} < \frac{k}{n} - \frac{k-1}{n} = \frac{1}{n}.$$

Thus $k/a_k - A(n)/n$ tends to zero as n increases, and the theorem follows.

Problems

1. Prove that each of the following sets has a natural density, and find its value:
   - (a) the set of even positive integers;
   - (b) the set of odd positive integers;
   - (c) the positive multiples of 3;
   - (d) the positive integers of the form $4k + 2$;
   - (e) all positive integers a satisfying $a \equiv b$ (mod m), where b and $m > 1$ are fixed;
   - (f) the set of primes;
   - (g) the set $\{ar^n\}$ with $n = 1, 2, 3, \cdots$ and fixed $a \geqq 1$, fixed $r > 1$;
   - (h) the set of all perfect squares;
   - (i) the set of all positive cubes;
   - (j) the set of all positive powers, that is, all numbers of the form a^n with $a \geqq 1$, $n \geqq 2$.
2. If the natural density $\delta(A)$ exists, prove that $\delta(\bar{A})$ also exists and that $\delta(A) + \delta(\bar{A}) = 1$.
3. Prove that $\delta(A)$ exists if and only if $\delta_1(A) + \delta_1(\bar{A}) = 1$.
4. For any set A, prove that $\delta_1(A) + \delta_1(\bar{A}) \leqq 1$.
5. Define A_n as the set of all a such that $(2n)! \leqq a < (2n + 1)!$ and let A be the union of all sets A_n, $n = 1, 2, 3, \cdots$. Prove that $\delta_1(A) + \delta_1(\bar{A}) = 0$.
6. Let A^* be the set remaining after a finite number of integers are deleted from a set A. Prove that $\delta_1(A) = \delta_1(A^*)$, and that $\delta(A)$ exists if and only if $\delta(A^*)$ exists.
7. If two sets A and B are identical beyond a fixed integer n, prove that $\delta_1(A) = \delta_1(B)$.
8. Given any set $A = \{a_j\}$ and any integer $b \geqq 0$, define $B = \{b + a_j\}$. Prove that $\delta_1(A) = \delta_1(B)$.
9. Let A be the set of all even positive integers, B_1 the set of all even positive integers with an even number of digits to base ten, and B_2 the set of all odd positive integers with an odd number of digits. Define $B = B_1 \cup B_2$,

and prove that $\delta(A)$ and $\delta(B)$ exist, but that $\delta(A \cup B)$ and $\delta(A \cap B)$ do not exist.

10. If $A \cap B = 0$, prove that $\delta_1(A \cup B) \geq \delta_1(A) + \delta_1(B)$.

11. Let S denote any finite set of positive integers $a_1, a_2, \cdots , a_m$. Prove that the set A of all positive integers not divisible by any member of S has natural density

$$1 - \sum_{i=1}^{m} \frac{1}{a_i} + \sum_{i<j} \frac{1}{[a_i, a_j]} - \sum_{i<j<k} \frac{1}{[a_i, a_j, a_k]} + \cdots + \frac{(-1)^m}{[a_1, a_2, \cdots , a_m]}.$$

12. Let A be a set of positive integers such that for every integer m, the equation $x + y = m$ has at most one solution not counting order with x and y in A. Prove that A has density zero. Even more, prove that $A(n) \leq 2\sqrt{n}$.

13. Define $A = \{a_j\}$ as follows. With $a_1 = 1$, define a_{k+1} as the least positive integer that is different from all the numbers $a_h + a_i - a_j$, with $1 \leq h \leq k$, $1 \leq i \leq k$, $1 \leq j \leq k$. Prove that A satisfies the inequality of the preceding problem, and that $A(n) \geq \sqrt[3]{n} - 1$.

14. Let P be the set of integers $\{m^k\}$ with $m = 1, 2, 3, \cdots$ and $k = 2, 3, 4, \cdots$. Let P_1 be the subset with $k = 3, 4, \cdots$. Prove that

$$\lim_{n \to \infty} \frac{P_1(n)}{P(n)} = 0.$$

15. Find the asymptotic density of the set of positive integers having an odd number of digits in the base ten representation.

11.2 Square-Free Integers

An integer is square-free if it is divisible by no perfect square $a^2 > 1$. We will prove that the set of square-free integers has natural density $6/\pi^2$.

Lemma 11.2 *The function $\tau(n)$, representing the number of positive divisors of n, satisfies the inequality $\tau(n) \leq 2\sqrt{n}$ for $n \geq 1$.*

Proof. Consider the positive divisors, d, of n. Corresponding to each $d \geq \sqrt{n}$ is the distinct divisor $d' = n/d$, and $1 \leq d' \leq \sqrt{n}$. Therefore $\tau(n)$ cannot exceed twice the number of divisors d such that $1 \leq d \leq \sqrt{n}$. Clearly the number of these d cannot exceed $\sqrt{n}$, and we have $\tau(n) \leq 2\sqrt{n}$.

Theorem 11.3 *We have*

$$\sum_{n=1}^{\infty} \frac{\mu(n)}{n^2} \sum_{n=1}^{\infty} \frac{1}{n^2} = 1.$$

Proof. Writing

(11.4) $$P_m = \sum_{n=1}^{m} \frac{\mu(n)}{n^2} \sum_{n=1}^{m} \frac{1}{n^2} = R_m S_m,$$

we consider first a fixed integer $j \leqq m$. If d is any divisor of j, say $j = dq$, then $\mu(d)/d^2$ is a term of R_m and $1/q^2$ is a term of S_m and $\mu(d)/(dq)^2 = \mu(d)/j^2$ occurs in P_m. Then $1/j^2$ occurs in P_m with coefficient

$$\sum_{d|j} \mu(d) = \begin{cases} 1 \text{ if } j = 1 \\ 0 \text{ if } j > 1 \end{cases}$$

by Theorem 4.6. In case $j > m$ the product $\mu(d)/(dq)^2$ may appear in P_m for some divisors d of j. Therefore we can write

$$P_m = \sum_{j=1}^{m} \left(\sum_{d|j} \mu(d) \right) \frac{1}{j^2} + \sum_{j=m+1}^{m^2} \left({\sum_{d|j}}' \mu(d) \right) \frac{1}{j^2}$$

where $\sum'$ denotes a sum over the appropriate divisors d of j. Thus we have

$$P_m - 1 = \sum_{j=m+1}^{m^2} {\sum_{d|j}}' \frac{\mu(d)}{j^2} = \sum_{j=m+1}^{m^2} \frac{c_j}{j^2}, \qquad c_j = {\sum_{d|j}}' \mu(d),$$

and, using Lemma 11.2, we observe that

$$|c_j| \leqq {\sum_{d|j}}' |\mu(d)| \leqq \sum_{d|j} |\mu(d)| \leqq \sum_{d|j} 1 = \tau(j) \leqq 2\sqrt{j}.$$

Now we have

$$|P_m - 1| \leqq \sum_{j=m+1}^{m^2} \frac{|c_j|}{j^2} \leqq \sum_{j=m+1}^{m^2} \frac{2\sqrt{j}}{j^2} = \sum_{j=m+1}^{m^2} \frac{2}{j^{3/2}}.$$

Applying Cauchy's condition to the convergent series $\sum 2/j^{3/2}$ we see that $|P_m - 1|$ tends to zero as m tends to infinity. In view of (11.4) this establishes the theorem.

Corollary 11.4 *We have*

$$\sum_{d=1}^{\infty} \frac{\mu(d)}{d^2} = \frac{6}{\pi^2}.$$

Proof. It is well known from elementary results in the theory of Fourier series that $\sum_{n=1}^{\infty} 1/n^2 = \pi^2/6$. For instance, it follows by setting $x = 0$ in the result

$$\frac{x^2}{2} = \pi x - \frac{\pi^2}{3} + 2 \sum_{n=1}^{\infty} \frac{\cos nx}{n^2},$$

which is valid for x in the range $0 \leq x \leq 2\pi$. This result is to be found in Apostol's *Mathematical Analysis.** This with Theorem 11.3 proves the corollary.

Theorem 11.5 *The set of square-free integers has natural density* $6/\pi^2$.

Proof. Let S denote the sequence $1, 2, 3, 5, 6, 7, 10, \cdots$ of square-free integers. For any positive integer n let $p_1, p_2, \cdots, p_r$ denote all the primes such that $p_j^2 \leq n$. We first wish to prove

$$(11.5) \qquad S(n) = \sum (-1)^{\alpha_1 + \alpha_2 + \cdots + \alpha_r} \left[\frac{n}{(p_1^{\alpha_1} p_2^{\alpha_2} \cdots p_r^{\alpha_r})^2} \right]$$

where the sum ranges over the 2^r terms obtained by setting each $\alpha_j = 0$ or 1. Now $[n/t^2]$ is the number of integers $\leq n$ that are divisible by t^2, and we can interpret each term on the right side of (11.5) as a count of those integers $m \leq n$ that are divisible by $(p_1^{\alpha_1} p_2^{\alpha_2} \cdots p_r^{\alpha_r})^2$.

If m is square-free, $1 \leq m \leq n$, then m is counted by the term $[n]$ and by no other terms. If $1 \leq m \leq n$ and m is divisible by p_1^2 but by no other p_j^2, then m is counted by the terms $[n]$ and $-[n/p_1^2]$, once positively and once negatively, a net count of $1 - 1 = 0$. To take the general case, consider an integer m, $1 \leq m \leq n$, that is divisible by

* Tom M. Apostol, *Mathematical Analysis*, Addison-Wesley, 1957, p. 501.

$p_{j_1}^2, \ p_{j_2}^2, \ \cdots \ , \ p_{j_s}^2, \ s \geq 1$, but not by any of the other p_j^2. Then m is counted by the terms

$$(-1)^{\alpha_{j_1}+\alpha_{j_2}+\cdots+\alpha_{j_s}} \left[\frac{n}{(p_{j_1}^{\alpha_{j_1}} p_{j_2}^{\alpha_{j_2}} \cdots p_{j_s}^{\alpha_{j_s}})^2} \right].$$

The net count for this m is thus

$$\sum (-1)^{\alpha_{j_1}+\alpha_{j_2}+\cdots+\alpha_{j_s}} = \sum (-1)^{\alpha_{j_1}} \sum (-1)^{\alpha_{j_2}} \cdots \sum (-1)^{\alpha_{j_s}} = 0$$

since

$$\sum (-1)^{\alpha_i} = 1 + (-1) = 0.$$

This establishes (11.5).

Next we note that (11.5) can be written as

$$(11.6) \qquad\qquad S(n) = \sum_{d \mid p_1 p_2 \cdots p_r} \mu(d) \left[\frac{n}{d^2} \right].$$

In this sum any term for which $d^2 > n$ has the factor $[n/d^2] = 0$, and we can restrict d in (11.6) to be such that $d^2 \leq n$. In fact, we have

$$(11.7) \qquad\qquad S(n) = \sum_{d^2 \leq n} \mu(d) \left[\frac{n}{d^2} \right],$$

where d ranges over all positive integers such that $d^2 \leq n$, since any term in (11.7) that is not in (11.6) will belong to a value of d that is not square-free. In this case the term has the factor $\mu(d) = 0$.

Using Corollary 11.4 and (11.7) we find

$$S(n) - \frac{6n}{\pi^2} = \sum_{d^2 \leq n} \mu(d) \left(\left[\frac{n}{d^2} \right] - \frac{n}{d^2} \right) - \sum_{d^2 > n} \mu(d) \frac{n}{d^2},$$

and hence

$$(11.8) \qquad\qquad \left| \frac{S(n)}{n} - \frac{6}{n^2} \right| \leq \frac{1}{n} \sum_{d^2 \leq n} \left| \left[\frac{n}{d^2} \right] - \frac{n}{d^2} \right| + \sum_{d^2 > n} \frac{1}{d^2}.$$

But

$$\frac{1}{n} \sum_{d^2 \leq n} \left| \left[\frac{n}{d^2} \right] - \frac{n}{d^2} \right| \leq \frac{1}{n} \sum_{d^2 \leq n} 1 \leq \frac{1}{\sqrt{n}} \to 0 \qquad \text{as } n \to \infty$$

and

$$\sum_{d^2 > n} \frac{1}{d^2} \to 0 \qquad \text{as } n \to \infty$$

since $\sum 1/d^2$ converges. Therefore the right side of (11.8) tends to zero, and we have $S(n)/n \to 6/\pi^2$ as $n \to \infty$.

Problems

1. Find the density of the set of integers divisible by no square > 4.
2. Find the density of the set of integers divisible by no square > 100.
3. Find the density of the set of integers divisible by no odd square > 1.

11.3   Sets of Density Zero

We shall need the following well-known result from the theory of infinite products. For convenience we prove it here.

Lemma 11.6 *Let $\sum c_j$ be a divergent series with $0 < c_j < 1$ for $j = 1, 2, \cdots$. Then, given any real number $\varepsilon > 0$, there is an integer N such that $\prod_{j=1}^{n} (1 - c_j) < \varepsilon$ for every integer $n \geqq N$.*

Proof. We note that

$$e^{-c_j} = (1 - c_j) + \left(\frac{c_j^2}{2!} - \frac{c_j^3}{3!}\right) + \left(\frac{c_j^4}{4!} - \frac{c_j^5}{5!}\right) \cdots > 1 - c_j$$

and hence that

$$\prod_{j=1}^{n} (1 - c_j) < \prod_{j=1}^{n} e^{-c_j} = e^{-\sum_{j=1}^{n} c_j}.$$

Since $\sum c_j$ diverges we can choose N so that

$$e^{-\sum_{j=1}^{N} c_j} < \varepsilon,$$

and the lemma follows.

In this section we shall use one item of special notation. For any set of integers A and any prime p, A_p will denote the set of those elements of A such that $p|a$ but $p^2 \nmid a$.

Theorem 11.7 *If there is a set of primes $\{p_i\}$ such that $\sum p_i^{-1}$ diverges and A_{p_i} has natural density zero for $i = 1, 2, 3, \cdots,$ then A has natural density zero.*

Proof. Let I denote the set of all positive integers, let $C^{(r)} = I_{p_1} \cup I_{p_2} \cup \cdots \cup I_{p_r}$, and let $B^{(r)} = \overline{C^{(r)}}$. Then $A \cap I_{p_i} = A_{p_i}$, $A \cap C^{(r)} = A_{p_1} \cup A_{p_2} \cup \cdots \cup A_{p_r}$, and hence

$$(11.9) \qquad A \subset B^{(r)} \cup A_{p_1} \cup A_{p_2} \cup \cdots \cup A_{p_r}.$$

Now $B^{(r)}$ consists of all positive integers except those such that $p_j|n$, $p_j^2 \nmid n$ for at least one $j = 1, 2, \cdots, r$, and we will prove that

$$(11.10) \qquad B^{(r)}(n) = \sum (-1)^{\alpha_1 + \alpha_2 + \cdots + \alpha_r} \left[\frac{n}{p_1^{\alpha_1} p_2^{\alpha_2} \cdots p_r^{\alpha_r}} \right]$$

where the sum extends over the 3^r terms obtained by taking each $\alpha_i = 0, 1,$ or 2. The proof is similar to that of (11.5). Any positive integer $m \leq n$ can be written as

$$m = p_1^{\beta_1} p_2^{\beta_2} \cdots p_r^{\beta_r} k, \qquad (k, p_1 p_2 \cdots p_r) = 1, \quad \beta_i \geq 0.$$

Let $\gamma_i = \beta_i$ if $\beta_i = 0$ or 1, and $\gamma_i = 2$ if $\beta_i \geq 2$. Then m is counted by the terms on the right side of (11.10) for which $0 \leq \alpha_i \leq \gamma_i$, $i = 1, 2, \cdots, r$, and it is counted with the sign $(-1)^{\alpha_1 + \alpha_2 + \cdots + \alpha_r}$. The net count for m is then

$$\sum_{a_1=0}^{\gamma_1} \sum_{a_2=0}^{\gamma_2} \cdots \sum_{a_r=0}^{\gamma_r} (-1)^{\alpha_1 + \alpha_2 + \cdots + \alpha_r} = \prod_{i=1}^{r} \left(\sum_{a_i=0}^{\gamma_i} (-1)^{\alpha_i} \right).$$

But

$$\sum_{\alpha_i=0}^{\gamma_i} (-1)^{\alpha_i} = \begin{cases} 1 & = 1 \text{ if } \gamma_i = 0 \\ 1 - 1 & = 0 \text{ if } \gamma_i = 1 \\ 1 - 1 + 1 & = 1 \text{ if } \gamma_i = 2 \end{cases}$$

and we see that m has a count of 0 if any $\gamma_i = 1$ and otherwise has a count of 1. Since $\gamma_i = 1$ if and only if $\beta_i = 1$, the right side of (11.10) counts the $m \leq n$ that are in $B^{(r)}$, and (11.10) is established.

Removing the greatest integer symbol in (11.10) we get the inequality

$$B^{(r)}(n) \leqq \sum (-1)^{\alpha_1 + \alpha_2 + \cdots + \alpha_r} \frac{n}{p_1^{\alpha_1} p_2^{\alpha_2} \cdots p_r^{\alpha_r}} + 3^r,$$

hence

(11.11) $$\frac{B^{(r)}(n)}{n} \leqq \prod_{i=1}^{r} \left(1 - \frac{1}{p_i} + \frac{1}{p_i^2}\right) + \frac{3^r}{n}.$$

To prove the theorem we must show that for any real $\varepsilon > 0$ there is an N such that $A(n)/n < \varepsilon$ for $n \geqq N$. First we choose r so that

(11.12) $$\prod_{i=1}^{r} \left(1 - \frac{1}{p_i} + \frac{1}{p_i^2}\right) < \frac{\varepsilon}{4},$$

which can be done by Lemma 11.6 since $\sum p_i^{-1}$, and hence also $\sum (p_i^{-1} - p_i^{-2})$, diverge. The sets A_{p_i} have natural density zero so we can find an integer N_1 such that

(11.13) $$\frac{A_{p_i}(n)}{n} < \frac{\varepsilon}{2r}, \qquad i = 1, 2, \cdots, r$$

if $n \geqq N_1$. Taking $N \geqq N_1$, $N \geqq 3^r \cdot 4/\varepsilon$, and using (11.9), (11.11), (11.12), and (11.13) we see that

$$\frac{A(n)}{n} \leqq \frac{B^{(r)}(n)}{n} + \prod_{i=1}^{r} \frac{A_{p_i}(n)}{n} < \frac{\varepsilon}{4} + \frac{\varepsilon}{4} + r\left(\frac{\varepsilon}{2r}\right) = \varepsilon$$

if $n \geqq N$.

Theorem 11.8 *Let k be a fixed positive integer. If each integer in a set A is divisible by k or fewer distinct prime factors, then $\delta(A) = 0$.*

Proof. We let $D^{(k)}$ denote the set of all positive integers having k or fewer distinct prime factors. Then $A \subset D^{(k)}$, $A(n) \leqq D^{(k)}(n)$, and we need only prove the theorem for $D^{(k)}$. The proof is by induction on k. For $k = 1$ the set $D^{(1)}$ consists of all prime powers, $D^{(1)} = \{p^s\}$. We apply Theorem 11.7, taking the p_i to be all primes. The series $\sum p_i^{-1}$ diverges by Theorem 8.2, and $\delta(D_{p_i}^{(1)}) = 0$ since $D_{p_i}^{(1)}$ consists of the single element p_i. Thus $\delta(D^{(1)}) = 0$.

Turning to general k, we assume that the theorem holds in the case $k - 1$. The elements of $D_p^{(k)}$ are the positive integers that are divisible by p, but not by p^2, and that have k or fewer distinct prime factors. If $a \in D_p^{(k)}$, then $a/p \in D^{(k-1)}$. Therefore $D_p^{(k)}(n) \leq D^{(k-1)}(n/p)$, and hence $\delta(D^{(k-1)}) = 0$ implies $\delta(D_p^{(k)}) = 0$. Now we can apply Theorem 11.7 as before, and it follows that $\delta(D^{(k)}) = 0$.

As another application of Theorem 11.7 we prove the following:

Theorem 11.9 *The set of integers* $\{\phi(m)\}$, $m = 1, 2, 3, \cdots$, *has natural density zero.*

Proof. Denote the set under consideration by A. Given $\varepsilon > 0$, we choose k so that $2^{-k} < \varepsilon/2$ and separate A into two disjoint sets B and C where B consists of those members of A that are divisible by 2^k. Hence $B(n) \leq 2^{-k}n$ for all n.

Now C consists of the numbers $\phi(m)$ of A that are not divisible by 2^k. We let C^* denote the set of m for which $\phi(m) \in C$. If $q_1, q_2, \cdots,$ q_r are the distinct prime factors of m, then

$$\phi(m) = \frac{m}{q_1 q_2 \cdots q_r} (q_1 - 1)(q_2 - 1) \cdots (q_r - 1),$$

which shows that $2^{r-1} | \phi(m)$ since all but one of the q_i must be odd. Therefore, if $m \in C^*$ then $r \leq k$ and

$$\phi(m) = m \prod_{i=1}^{r} \left(1 - \frac{1}{q_i}\right) \geq m\left(1 - \frac{1}{2}\right)\left(1 - \frac{1}{3}\right) \cdots \left(1 - \frac{1}{p_k}\right) = mc_k,$$

say. Hence if $\phi(m) \in C$ and $\phi(m) \leq n$, then $m \leq n/c_k$ and hence $C(n) \leq C^*(n/c_k)$. But now the elements of the set C^* have k or fewer distinct prime factors, and so by Theorem 11.8 we see that there is an integer N such that $C^*(m)/m < \varepsilon c_k/2$ for $m \geq N$. Therefore $C(n) \leq C^*(n/c_k) < \varepsilon n/2$ if $n \geq c_k N$, and $B(n) \leq 2^{-k}n < \varepsilon n/2$. Finally we have $A(n) = B(n) + C(n) < n\varepsilon$ if $n \geq c_k N$, and this implies $\delta(A) = 0$.

Problems

1. Let k be a fixed integer. Prove that $\delta(A) = 0$ if every integer in A has the form

$$p_1 p_2 \cdots p_r p_{r+1}^{\alpha_1} p_{r+2}^{\alpha_2} \cdots p_{r+s}^{\alpha_s}$$

where the p_i are any primes, $0 \leq r \leq k$, s is arbitrary, and $\alpha_i \geq 2$ for
$i = 1, 2, \cdots, s$.

2. If a sequence of integers $A = \{a_i\}$ has the property that $\sum a_i^{-1}$ converges,
   prove that $\delta(A) = 0$. Prove that the converse is false.

3. Assuming the proposition that the set of primes $\{q_i\}$ of the form $4n + 3$ has
   the property that $\sum q_i^{-1}$ diverges, prove that the set of integers each of
   which is representable as a sum of two squares has density zero.

11.4   Schnirelmann Density and the $\alpha\beta$ Theorem

Definition 11.2 *The Schnirelmann density $d(A)$ of a set A of non-
negative integers is*

$$d(A) = \inf_{n \geq 1} \frac{A(n)}{n},$$

where $A(n)$ is the number of positive integers $\leq n$ in the set A.

Comparing this with Definition 11.1 we immediately see that
$0 \leq d(A) \leq \delta_1(A) \leq 1$. Schnirelmann density differs from asymptotic density in that it is sensitive to the first terms in the sequence.
Indeed if $1 \notin A$ then $d(A) = 0$, if $2 \notin A$ then $d(A) \leq \frac{1}{2}$, whereas it is
easy to see that $\delta_1(A)$ is unchanged if the numbers 1 or 2 are removed
from or adjoined to A. Also, $d(A) = 1$ if and only if A contains all
the positive integers.

Until now we have been considering sets A consisting only of positive integers. However, Definition 11.2 is worded in such a way that
A can contain 0, but it should be noted that the number 0 is not
counted by $A(n)$.

Definition 11.3 *Assume that $0 \in A$ and $0 \in B$. The sum $A + B$ of
the sets A and B is the collection of all integers of the form $a + b$ where
$a \in A$ and $b \in B$.*

Note that $A \subset A + B$, $B \subset A + B$. As an example let us take S
to be the set of squares 0, 1, 4, 9, $\cdots$ and I the set of all non-negative
integers. Then by Theorem 5.6 we see that $S + S + S + S = I$.

The sum $A + B$ has not been defined unless $0 \in A$ and $0 \in B$. We
will assume that 0 is in both A and B in the rest of this chapter. However, the sum could be defined for all A and B as the sum of the sets

obtained from A and B by adjoining the number 0 to each. This is equivalent to defining the sum as the collection $\{a, b, a + b\}$ with $a \in A$, $b \in B$.

The result that is proved in the remainder of this section is the $\alpha\beta$ theorem of H. B. Mann, which was conjectured about 1931, with proofs attempted subsequently by many mathematicians. The theorem states that if A and B are sets of non-negative integers, each containing 0, and if α, β, γ are the Schnirelmann densities of A, B, $A + B$, then $\gamma \geqq \min (1, \alpha + \beta)$. In other words $\gamma \geqq \alpha + \beta$ unless $\alpha + \beta > 1$, in which case $\gamma = 1$.

Actually we will prove a somewhat stronger result, Theorem 11.15, from which we will deduce the $\alpha\beta$ theorem. We start by considering any positive integer g and two sets A_1 and B_1 of non-negative integers not exceeding g. We assume throughout that A_1 and B_1 are such sets and that 0 belongs to both A_1 and B_1. Denoting $A_1 + B_1$ by C_1, we observe that C_1 may have elements $> g$ even though A_1 and B_1 do not. We also assume that for some θ, $0 < \theta \leqq 1$,

$$(11.14) \qquad A_1(m) + B_1(m) \geqq \theta m, \qquad m = 1, 2, \cdots, g.$$

Our idea is to first replace A_1 and B_1 by two new sets, A_2 and B_2, in such a way that (11.14) holds for A_2 and B_2, that $C_2 = A_2 + B_2 \subset C_1$, and that $B_2(g) < B_1(g)$.

Lemma 11.10 *Let A_1 and B_1 satisfy (11.14). If $B_1 \not\subset A_1$, then there exist sets A_2 and B_2 with $C_2 = A_2 + B_2$ such that $C_2 \subset C_1$, $B_2(g) < B_1(g)$ and $A_2(m) + B_2(m) \geqq \theta m$ for $m = 1, 2, \cdots, g$.*

Proof. We merely shift to A_1 all elements of B_1 that are not already in A_1. Define $B' = B_1 \cap \bar{A}_1$, $A_2 = A_1 \cup B'$, $B_2 = B_1 \cap \overline{B'}$, where by $\bar{A}_1$ we mean the complement of A_1, now the set of all non-negative integers not in A_1. Thus 0 belongs to both A_2 and B_2. Then $A_2(m) = A_1(m) + B'(m)$ and $B_2(m) = B_1(m) - B'(m)$ so we have $A_2(m) + B_2(m) = A_1(m) + B_1(m) \geqq \theta m$ for $m = 1, 2, \cdots, g$. Now consider any $h \in C_2$. Then $h = a + b$ with $a \in A_2$ and $b \in B_2$. Noting that B_2 is contained in both A_1 and B_1 and that $A_2 = A_1 \cup B'$, we have either $a \in A_1$ or $a \in B' \subset B_1$. In the first case we can write $h = a + b$, $a \in A_1$, $b \in B_1$; in the second case $h = b + a$, $b \in A_1$, $a \in B_1$; hence in both cases we have $h \in C_1$. Thus we have $C_2 \subset C_1$. Since it is obvious that $B_2(g) < B_1(g)$, the lemma is proved.

We will get a similar result for the case $B_1 \subset A_1$, but it is a little more complicated. We assume $B_1(g) > 0$, which implies that there is some integer $b > 0$ in B_1. Then if a is the largest integer in A_1, the sum $a + b$ is certainly not in A_1. There may be other pairs $a \in A_1$, $b \in B_1$ such that $a + b \notin A_1$. We let a_0 denote the smallest $a \in A_1$ such that there is a $b \in B_1$ for which $a + b \notin A_1$. Since $B_1 \subset A_1$ we see that $a_0 \neq 0$. Before defining A_2 and B_2 we will obtain two preliminary results.

Lemma 11.11 *Let A_1 and B_1 satisfy $B_1 \subset A_1$ and $B_1(g) > 0$. Let a_0 be defined as above. Suppose that there are integers b and z such that $b \in B_1$ and $z - a_0 < b \leqq z \leqq g$. Then for each $a \in A_1$ such that $a \leqq z - b$, we have $a + b \in A_1$, and*

$$(11.15) \qquad A_1(z) \geqq A_1(b) + A_1(z - b).$$

Proof. We have $a \leqq z - b < a_0$ and $a + b \leqq z \leqq g$, hence $a + b \in A_1$ because a_0 is minimal. Now there are $A_1(z - b)$ positive integers a belonging to A_1 with $a \leqq z - b$, and to each such a the corresponding $a + b$ also belongs to A_1. Furthermore each such $a + b$ satisfies $b < a + b \leqq z$, and hence $A_1(z) - A_1(b) \geqq A_1(z - b)$, and we have (11.15).

Lemma 11.12 *Let A_1 and B_1 satisfy (11.14), $B_1 \subset A_1$, and $B_1(g) > 0$. Define a_0 as before. If there is an integer $y \leqq g$ such that $A_1(y) < \theta y$, then $y > a_0$.*

Proof. Let z be the least integer such that $A_1(z) < \theta z$. Then $y \geqq z \geqq 1$. Since $A_1(z) + B_1(z) \geqq \theta z$ we have $B_1(z) > 0$, and hence there is a $b \in B_1$ such that $0 < b \leqq z \leqq g$. If $z \leqq a_0$, we would have $z - a_0 < b \leqq z \leqq g$, and we could apply Lemma 11.11 to get $A_1(z) \geqq A_1(b) + A_1(z - b)$. Now $b \in B_1 \subset A_1$, so we have $A_1(b) = A_1(b - 1) + 1 \geqq \theta(b - 1) + 1$ since $b - 1 < z$. Also, $A_1(z - b) \geqq \theta(z - b)$, and we are led to the contradiction $A_1(z) \geqq \theta(b - 1) + 1 + \theta(z - b) = \theta(z - 1) + 1 \geqq \theta z$. Therefore we have $z > a_0$, and hence $y > a_0$.

Lemma 11.13 *Let A_1 and B_1 satisfy $B_1 \subset A_1$ and $B_1(g) > 0$. Let B' denote the set of all $b \in B_1$ such that $a_0 + b \notin A_1$, and let A' denote the set of all integers $a_0 + b$ such that $b \in B'$ and $a_0 + b \leqq g$. Finally let $A_2 = A_1 \cup A'$ and $B_2 = B_1 \cap \overline{B'}$. Then $C_2 \subset C_1$ and $B_2(g) < B_1(g)$.*

Proof. Note that $0 \in A_2$ and $0 \in B_2$, so that the sum C_2 is well defined. If $h \in C_2$, then $h = a + b$, $a \in A_1 \cup A'$, $b \in B_1 \cap \bar{B}'$. If $a \in A_1$, then $h = a + b \in C_1$ since $a \in A_1$, $b \in B_1$. If $a \in A'$, then $a = a_0 + b_1$ for some $b_1 \in B'$, and we have $h = a_0 + b + b_1$. Here $a_0 + b \in A_1$ since otherwise we would have $b \in B'$. Since $b_1 \in B_1$, we again have $h \in C_1$. Finally $B_2(g) < B_1(g)$, since the definition of a_0 ensures that $B'(g) < 0$.

Lemma 11.14 *For A_1, B_1, A_2, B_2 as in Lemma 11.13, if A_1, B_1 satisfy* (11.14) *then*

$$(11.16) \quad A_2(m) + B_2(m) \geq \theta m \quad for \quad m = 1, 2, \cdots, g.$$

Proof. From the way A', B', A_2, B_2 were chosen we have

$$A_2(m) = A_1(m) + A'(m),$$

$$B_2(m) = B_1(m) - B'(m),$$

$$A'(m) = B'(m - a_0),$$

$$A_2(m) + B_2(m) = A_1(m) + B_1(m) - (B'(m) - B'(m - a_0)),$$

for $m = 1, 2, \cdots, g$. Therefore (11.16) holds for all m for which $B'(m) = B'(m - a_0)$. Consider any $m \leq g$ for which $B'(m) > B'(m - a_0)$. Then $B_1(m) - B_1(m - a_0) \geq B'(m) - B'(m - a_0) > 0$, and we let b_0 denote the smallest element of B_1 such that $m - a_0 < b_0 \leq m$. Therefore

$$(11.17) \quad A_2(m) + B_2(m) \geq A_1(m) + B_1(m) - (B_1(m) - B_1(m - a_0))$$

$$= A_1(m) + B_1(m - a_0)$$

$$= A_1(m) + B_1(b_0 - 1).$$

Now $m - a_0 < b_0 \leq m \leq g$, so we can apply Lemma 11.11 with $b = b_0$ and $z = m$ to get

$$A_1(m) \geq A_1(b_0) + A_1(m - b_0).$$

We also have $m - b_0 < a_0$ so Lemma 11.12 shows that

$$A_1(m - b_0) \geq \theta(m - b_0).$$

Thus we can reduce (11.17) to

$$A_2(m) + B_2(m) \geq A_1(b_0) + \theta(m - b_0) + B_1(b_0 - 1).$$

But $b_0 \in B_1 \subset A_1$ so we have $A_1(b_0) = A_1(b_0 - 1) + 1$. Using this and (11.14) we have,

$$A_2(m) + B_2(m) \geq A_1(b_0 - 1) + B_1(b_0 - 1) + 1 + \theta(m - b_0)$$
$$\geq \theta(b_0 - 1) + 1 + \theta(m - b_0)$$
$$\geq \theta m.$$

Theorem 11.15 *For any positive integer g let A_1 and B_1 denote fixed sets of non-negative integers $\leq g$. Let 0 belong to both sets A_1 and B_1, and write C_1 for $A_1 + B_1$. If for some θ such that $0 < \theta \leq 1$,*

$$A_1(m) + B_1(m) \geq \theta m, \quad m = 1, 2, \cdots, g,$$

then $C_1(g) \geq \theta g$.

Proof. If $B_1(g) = 0$, then B_1 consists of the single integer 0, $C_1 = A_1$, and $C_1(g) = A_1(g) = A_1(g) + B_1(g) \geq \theta g$. We prove the theorem for general sets by mathematical induction. Suppose $k \geq 1$ and that the theorem is true for all A_1, B_1 with $B_1(g) < k$. If $A_1(m) + B_1(m) \geq \theta m$ for $m = 1, 2, \cdots, g$, and if $B_1(g) = k$, then Lemma 11.10 or Lemmas 11.13 and 11.14 supply us with sets A_2, B_2 such that $B_2(g) < k$, $C_2 \subset C_1$, and $A_2(m) + B_2(m) \geq \theta m$ for $m = 1, 2, \cdots, g$. Therefore, by our induction hypothesis, we have $C_2(g) \geq \theta g$, which implies $C_1(g) \geq \theta g$.

Theorem 11.16 *The $\alpha\beta$ theorem. Let A and B be any sets of non-negative integers, each containing 0, and let α, β, γ denote the Schnirelmann densities of A, B, $A + B$ respectively. Then $\gamma \geq \min(1, \alpha + \beta)$.*

Proof. Let A_1 and B_1 consist of the elements of A and B, respectively, that do not exceed g, an arbitrary positive integer. Then $A_1(m) \geq \alpha m$ and $B_1(m) \geq \beta m$ for $m = 1, 2, \cdots, g$. If we take $\theta = \min(1, \alpha + \beta)$, the conditions of Theorem 11.15 are satisfied and we conclude that $C_1(g) \geq \theta g$. Since $C_1(g) \geq \theta g$ for every positive integer g, we have $\gamma \geq \theta = \min(1, \alpha + \beta)$.

Problems

1. What is the Schnirelmann density of the set of positive odd integers? The set of positive even integers? The set of positive integers $\equiv 1 \pmod 3$? The set of positive integers $\equiv 1 \pmod m$?

2. Prove that the analogue of Theorem 11.1 for Schnirelmann density, namely, $d(A) = \inf n/a_n$, is false.

3. Prove that the analogue of Theorem 11.16 for asymptotic density is false. *Suggestion:* take A as the set of all positive even integers, and consider $A + A$.

4. Prove that if $d(A) = \alpha$, then $A(n) \geq \alpha n$ for every positive integer n. Prove that the analogue of this for asymptotic density is false.

5. Establish that Theorem 11.16 does not imply Theorem 11.15 by considering the sets $A = \{0, 1, 2, 4, 6, 8, 10, \cdots\}$, $B = \{0, 2, 4, 6, 8, 10, \cdots\}$. Theorem 11.16 asserts that the density of $A + B$ is $\geq \frac{1}{2}$, whereas Theorem 11.15 says much more.

6. Exhibit two sets A and B such that $d(A) = d(B) = 0$, $d(A + B) = 1$.

7. For any two sets A and B of non-negative integers, write $\alpha = d(A)$, $\beta = d(B)$, $\gamma = d(A + B)$. Prove that $\gamma \geq \alpha + \beta - \alpha\beta$.

8. Consider a set A with positive Schnirelmann density. Prove that for some positive integer n

$$nA = (n + 1)A = (n + 2)A = \cdots = I,$$

where I is the set of all non-negative integers, and $nA = A + A + \cdots + A$ with n summands.

General References

J. W. S. Cassels, *An Introduction to Diophantine Approximation*, Cambridge Tract 45, 1957.

Harvey Cohn, *A Second Course in Number Theory*, New York, John Wiley and Sons, 1962.

H. Davenport, *The Higher Arithmetic*, London, Hutchinson's University Library, 1952.

L. E. Dickson, *History of the Theory of Numbers*, Washington, Carnegie Institution of Washington, 1919; reprinted, New York, Chelsea, 1950.

L. E. Dickson, *Introduction to the Theory of Numbers*, Chicago, University of Chicago Press, 1929.

L. E. Dickson, *Modern Elementary Theory of Numbers*, Chicago, University of Chicago Press, 1939.

G. H. Hardy and E. M. Wright, *An Introduction to the Theory of Numbers*, 4th ed., Oxford, Clarendon Press, 1960.

B. W. Jones, *The Arithmetic Theory of Quadratic Forms*, Carus Monograph 10, New York, John Wiley and Sons, 1950.

D. H. Lehmer, *Guide to Tables in the Theory of Numbers*, Washington, Bulletin, National Research Council, No. 105, 1941.

W. J. LeVeque, *Topics in Number Theory*, vols. I and II, Reading, Mass., Addison-Wesley, 1956.

T. Nagell, *Introduction to Number Theory*, New York, John Wiley and Sons, 1951.

Ivan Niven, *Irrational Numbers*, Carus Monograph 11, New York, John Wiley and Sons, 1956.

O. Ore, *Number Theory and its History*, New York, McGraw-Hill, 1949.

Hans Rademacher, *Lectures on Elementary Number Theory*, New York, Blaisdell Publishing Company, 1964.

J. V. Uspensky and M. H. Heaslet, *Elementary Number Theory*, New York, McGraw-Hill, 1939.

I. M. Vinogradov, *Elements of Number Theory*, translation of 5th Russian edition, New York, Dover, 1954.

Special References

Chapter 2

D. N. Lehmer, "On the congruences connected with certain magic squares,"
Trans. Amer. Math. Soc., **31**, 529–551 (1929).

Chapter 5

J. Hunter, *Number Theory*, Edinburgh, Oliver and Boyd, 1964.

L. J. Mordell, "On the equation $ax^2 + by^2 - cz^2 = 0$," *Monatsh. Mathk*,
Bd. **55**, 323–327 (1951).

Th. Skolem, "A simple proof of the solvability of the Diophantine equation
$ax^2 + by^2 + cz^2 = 0$," *Norsk Vid. Selsk. Forh.*, Trondheim **24**, 102–107
(1952).

H. S. Vandiver, "Fermat's last theorem, its history, and the nature of the
known results concerning it," *Amer. Math. Monthly*, **53**, 555–578 (1946).

Chapter 9

Harry Pollard, *The Theory of Algebraic Numbers*, Carus Monograph 9, New
York, John Wiley and Sons, 1950.

Abraham Robinson, *Numbers and Ideals*, San Francisco, Holden-Day, 1965.

Chapter 10

S. Ramanujan, *Collected Papers*, Cambridge Press, 1927.

Chapter 11

E. Artin and P. Scherk, "On the sums of two sets of integers," *Ann. Math.*
(2) **44**, 138–142 (1943).

F. J. Dyson, "A theorem on the densities of sets of integers," *J. London
Math. Soc.* **20**, 8–14 (1945).

H. B. Mann, "A proof of the fundamental theorem on the density of sums of
sets of positive integers," *Ann. Math.* (2) **43**, 523–527 (1942).

Answers

1. (a) 77, (b) 1, (c) 7, (d) 1.
2. $g = 17$, $x = 71$, $y = -36$.
3. (a) $x = 9, y = -11$, (b) $x = 31, y = 44$, (c) $x = 3, y = -2$.
   (d) $x = 7, y = 8$, (e) $x = 1, y = 1, z = -1$.
4. (a) 3374 (b) 3660.
5. 128.
7. 6, 10, 15.
17. 1; $n(n + 1)$.
18. $a; b$.
25. $x = 100n + 5$, $y = 95 - 100n$, $n = 1, 2, \cdots$, will do.
27. $a = 10$, $b = 100$ is a solution in positive integers. All solutions are given by $a = \pm 10$, $b = \pm 100$; $a = \pm 20$, $b = \pm 50$; $a = \pm 100$, $b = \pm 10$; $a = \pm 50$, $b = \pm 20$; with all arrangements of signs. There are 16 solutions in all.
28. $a = 10$, $b = 100$, $c = 10, 20, 50,$ or 100; $a = 20$, $b = 50$, $c = 10, 20, 50,$ or 100; and all permutations of these, 36 answers in all.

Section 1.3

16. p, p^2; p, p^2, p^3; p^2, p^3.
17. p^3, p.
18. $2|\alpha_j$; $3|\alpha_j$; $\alpha_j \leq \beta_j$; $\alpha_j \leq \beta_j$; for all j, $1 \leq j \leq r$ in each part.
24. Counterexamples for false statements are
    (1) $a = 2, b = 6, c = 10$.
    (8) $a = 8, c = 4$.
    (10) $p = 5, a = 2, b = 1, c = 3$.
    (13) $a = 2, b = 5$.
25. All n not of the form $p - 1$ where p is an odd prime.
39. $a, a, \cdots , a$ or $a, a, \cdots , a, 2a$ or $a, 2a, 3a$.

Section 2.1

1. 7, 24, 41, 58, 75, 92.
2. 0, 18, 36, 3, 21, 39, 6, 24, 42, 9, 27, 45, 12, 30, 48, 15, 33.
3. 1, 5, 7, 11 (mod 12); 1, 7, 11, 13, 17, 19, 23, 29 (mod 30).
4. $y \equiv 1$ (mod 2); $z \equiv 1$ (mod 6).
5. $x \equiv 5$ (mod 12).
10. $m = 1, 2, 3, 4, 5, 6, 7, 8, 9, 10, 11, 12.$
        $\phi(m) = 1, 1, 2, 2, 4, 2, 6, 4, 6, \ \ 4, 10, \ \ 4.$
11. $x = 5.$
13. 1, 9, 3, 81, 243, 27.
14. $x = 9 + 11j.$
16. $a = 2, 3, 4, 5, 6, 7, 8, 9, 10.$
    $x = 6, 4, 3, 9, 2, 8, 7, 5, 10.$
25. 1.
26. 6.
27. 0, 1.
35. Primitive solutions with $a \leq b \leq c$ are $a = b = 1$, c any positive integer.
36. Solutions such that $(a, b, c) = 1$, $c \geq |b| \geq |a|$ are
    $a = -b = \pm 1, c = 1$ or 2;
    $a = -1, b = 2, c = 3;$
    $a = b = \pm 1$ with any $c > 0;$
    $a = 1, b = 1 - c$ with any $c > 2;$
    $a = 2, b = -2n + 1, c = 2n + 1$ with any $n > 1.$

Section 2.2

4. $x(x + 1)(x + 2) \cdots (x + m - 1) \equiv 0$ (mod m).

Section 2.3

1. (a) no solution
   (b) no solution
   (c) $x \equiv -82$ (mod 400).
2. (a) 5,   (b) 0,   (c) 5.
3. $x = 106.$
4. $23 + 30j.$
5. $x \equiv 33$ (mod 84).
6. $60j - 2.$
7. $\dfrac{73}{105}, \dfrac{4}{7}.$
12. $x \equiv 42$ (mod 125).

Section 2.4

1. 1, 2.
2. 960.
3. 2640.
4. 1920.
5. 6720.
10. n odd.
11. n even.
12. $n = 5^k$, $k = 1, 2, \cdots$ will do.
13. 35, 39, 45, 52, 56, 70, 72, 78, 84, 90.
15. 3, 1, 2, 4.

Section 2.5

1. $x \equiv 1, 2, 6 \pmod 9$
   $x \equiv 1, 3 \pmod 5$
   $x \equiv 1, 6, 11, 28, 33, 38 \pmod{45}$.
2. No solution.
3. $x \equiv 1, 3, 5 \pmod{503}$.
4. $x \equiv 1, 3, 5, 14, 16, 27, 122, 133, 135 \pmod{143}$.

Section 2.6

6. No solution.
7. $x \equiv 4 \pmod{5^3}$.
8. $x = 7, 15, 16, 24 \pmod{36}$.
9. $x \equiv 15 \pmod{3^3}$.
10. No solution.
11. $x \equiv 23 \pmod{7^3}$.

Section 2.7

1. (a) $x^5 + x^2 + 5 \equiv 0 \pmod 7$,
   (b) $x^2 + 3x - 2 \equiv 0 \pmod 7$,
   (c) $x^4 - x^3 - 4x + 3 \equiv 0 \pmod 7$.

Section 2.8

1. (a) $(4x + 1)^2 \equiv 2 \pmod 5$
   (b) $(x + 1)^2 \equiv 4 \pmod 7$
   (c) $(4x + 7)^2 \equiv 8 \pmod{11}$
   (d) $(2x + 1)^2 \equiv 5 \pmod{13}$.

Section 2.9

1. 2, 2, 3, 2, 2.
2. 5.
3. 4.
4. 1, 3, 6, 3, 6, 2.
   1, 10, 5, 5, 5, 10.
7. $p - 1$. 0.
8. (a) 4, (b) 0, (c) 4, (d) 1.
9. $x^2 \equiv 1$, $x^2 \equiv 2$, $x^2 \equiv 4$, $x^2 \equiv 8$, $x^2 \equiv 9$, $x^2 \equiv 13$, $x^2 \equiv 15$,
   $x^2 \equiv 16 \pmod{17}$

Section 2.10

1. (a), (e), (f), (h), (i).
3.

	7	−2	17	30	8	3		1	4	5	0	2	3
7	8	17	30	7	3	−2	1	2	5	0	1	3	4
−2	17	8	3	−2	30	7	4	5	2	3	4	0	1
17	30	3	−2	17	7	8	5	0	3	4	5	1	2
30	7	−2	17	30	8	3	0	1	4	5	0	2	3
8	3	30	7	8	−2	17	2	3	0	1	2	4	5
3	−2	7	8	3	17	30	3	4	1	2	3	5	0

Section 2.11

6. 8.
13.

$\oplus$	0	1	2	3	4	5	6
0	0	1	2	3	4	5	6
1	1	2	3	4	5	6	0
2	2	3	4	5	6	0	1
3	3	4	5	6	0	1	2
4	4	5	6	0	1	2	3
5	5	6	0	1	2	3	4
6	6	0	1	2	3	4	5

$\odot$	0	1	2	3	4	5	6
0	0	0	0	0	0	0	0
1	0	1	2	3	4	5	6
2	0	2	4	6	1	3	5
3	0	3	6	2	5	1	4
4	0	4	1	5	2	6	3
5	0	5	3	1	6	4	2
6	0	6	5	4	3	2	1

23. 0, 1, 6, 10, 15, 16, 21, 25.
    0, 2, 3, 4, 5, 6, 8, 9, 10, 12, 14, 15, 16, 18, 20, 21, 22, 24, 25, 26, 27, 28.
24. (a) and (c) are integral domains; (b) is an integral domain if and only if
    m is a prime.

Section 3.1

1. $1, -2, 3, -7, 0.$

4. $\left(\dfrac{-1}{11}\right) = -1,\ \left(\dfrac{-1}{13}\right) = +1,\ \left(\dfrac{-1}{17}\right) = +1,$

$\left(\dfrac{2}{11}\right) = -1,\ \left(\dfrac{2}{13}\right) = -1,\ \left(\dfrac{2}{17}\right) = +1,$

$\left(\dfrac{-2}{11}\right) = +1,\ \left(\dfrac{-2}{13}\right) = -1,\ \left(\dfrac{-2}{17}\right) = +1,$

$\left(\dfrac{3}{11}\right) = +1,\ \left(\dfrac{3}{13}\right) = +1,\ \left(\dfrac{3}{17}\right) = -1.$

5. $x \equiv \pm 1 \pmod{11},\ x \equiv \pm 5 \pmod{11},\ x \equiv \pm 2 \pmod{11},$
   $x \equiv \pm 4 \pmod{11},\ x \equiv \pm 3 \pmod{11}.$
   $x \equiv \pm 1 \pmod{11^2},\ x \equiv \pm 27 \pmod{11^2},\ x \equiv \pm 2 \pmod{11^2},$
   $x \equiv \pm 48 \pmod{11^2},\ x \equiv \pm 3 \pmod{11^2}.$

6. $1, 2, 4 \pmod 7,\quad \pm 1, \pm 3, \pm 4 \pmod{13},\quad \pm 1, \pm 2, \pm 4, \pm 8 \pmod{17},$
   $\pm 1, \pm 4, \pm 5, \pm 6, \pm 7, \pm 9, \pm 13 \pmod{29},\quad \pm 1, \pm 3, \pm 4, \pm 7, \pm 9, \pm 10,$
   $\pm 11, \pm 12, \pm 16 \pmod{37}.$

7. (d) 2,   (h) 2.

8. (a) 2,   (b) 0,   (c) 4,   (d) 0,   (e) 2,   (f) 0.

Section 3.2

4. (b), (c), (d), (e), (f).

5. $\left(\dfrac{7}{227}\right) = +1,\ \left(\dfrac{7}{229}\right) = -1,\ \left(\dfrac{7}{1009}\right) = +1,$

$\left(\dfrac{11}{227}\right) = +1,\ \left(\dfrac{11}{229}\right) = +1,\ \left(\dfrac{11}{1009}\right) = -1,$

$\left(\dfrac{13}{227}\right) = -1,\ \left(\dfrac{13}{229}\right) = -1,\ \left(\dfrac{13}{1009}\right) = -1.$

6. Yes.

7. $p = 2,\ p = 11,$ and $p \equiv 1, 5, 7, 9, 19, 25, 35, 37, 39, 43 \pmod{44}.$

8. $p \equiv \pm 1, \pm 3, \pm 9, \pm 13 \pmod{40}.$

9. Odd primes $p \equiv 2, 3 \pmod 5.$

10. $p \equiv 1, 3 \pmod 8.$

Section 3.3

1. $\left(\dfrac{-23}{83}\right) = -1,\ \left(\dfrac{51}{71}\right) = -1,\ \left(\dfrac{71}{73}\right) = +1,\ \left(\dfrac{-35}{97}\right) = +1.$

2. (b).

3. (c).

10. $p = 2$ and $p \equiv 1 \pmod 4$.

11. 2 and p^a for $p \equiv 1 \pmod 4$ and $a = 1, 2, 3, \cdots$.

12. $n = 2^{a_1}p_2^{a_2} \cdots p_k^{a_k}$, $a_1 = 0$ or 1, $p_j \equiv 1 \pmod 4$, $a_j = 1, 2, 3, \cdots$.

Section 4.1

1. 529, 263, 263, 263, 87.

2. 24.

3. (a) all x such that $x - [x] < \frac{1}{2}$,
   (b) all x,
   (c) all integers,
   (d) all x such that $x - [x] \geq \frac{1}{2}$,
   (e) all x such that $1 \leq x < 10/9$.

5. (a)

$$e = \begin{cases} \sum_{i=1}^{\infty} \left[\dfrac{n}{p^i}\right] \text{ if } p \text{ is odd,} \\ n + \sum_{i=1}^{\infty} \left[\dfrac{n}{2^i}\right] \text{ if } p = 2, \end{cases}$$

(b)

$$e = \begin{cases} \sum_{i=1}^{\infty} \left(\left[\dfrac{2n}{p^i}\right] - \left[\dfrac{n}{p^i}\right] \right) \text{ if } p \text{ is odd,} \\ 0 \text{ if } p = 2. \end{cases}$$

Section 4.2

1. 7.

2. 12

3. 2, 1, 12, 24

4. 6.

8. $\sigma_\kappa(p_1^{e_1} \cdots p_r^{e_r}) = \displaystyle\prod_{i=1}^{r} \dfrac{p_i^{k(e_i+1)} - 1}{p_i^k - 1}$.

10. $f(n) = n$ will do.

13. $x = p^{n-1}$ will do, where p is any prime.

16. 6, 28, 496.

Section 4.3

1. $n = 33$ will do.

3. 1.

7. $\displaystyle\sum_{d|n} \mu(d)\sigma(d) = (-1)^k p_1 p_2 \cdots p_k$.

Section 4.4

1. $x_n = a^n x_0$.
$$x_n = \begin{cases} b^{n/2}x_0 \text{ if } n \text{ is even,} \\ b^{(n-1)/2}x_1 \text{ if } n \text{ is odd.} \end{cases}$$

2. $x_n = n.\ x_n = 1.\ x_n = (3^n - (-1)^n)/4.\ x_n = (3^n + (-1)^n)/2.$

3. 0, 1, 1, 2, 3, 5, 8, 13, 21, 34.

11. (b) $-[-n/3]$ if n is odd.
(d) $S_3 = \{1\}$, $S_9 = \{2, 3, 5, 7\}$.

12. $n = 1\ 2\ 3\ 4\ 5\ 6\ 7\ 8\ 9\ 10$
$f(n) = 0\ 1\ 2\ 4\ 6\ 9\ 12\ 16\ 20\ 25$
$f(5+3) - f(5-3) = f(8) - f(2) = 16 - 1 = 15 = 5 \cdot 3$, for example.

13. $x_n = 1 + 2^{n-2} - (-2)^{n-2} = \begin{cases} 1 \text{ if } n \text{ is even,} \\ 1 + 2^{n-1} \text{ if } n \text{ is odd.} \end{cases}$

Section 5.2

2. $x = 1 + 7t,\ y = -1 + 10t.$

9. $(b_1 - b_2, c_1 - c_2)|(d_1 - d_2).$

Section 5.3

1. (a) $x = 8, y = 4;\ x = 5, y = 9;\ x = 2, y = 14.$
(b) $x = 6, y = 3.$
(c) $x = 2, y = 7.$
(d) $x = 2, y = 5.$
(e) no solution.
(f) no solution.
(g) no solution.

10. $ab.$

Section 5.4

1. (a) $x = 1 + u,\ y = -2u + 3v,\ z = u - 2v,$
(b) $x = 10 + u,\ y = -2u + 3v,\ z = u - 2v,$
(c) $x = 1 + 2t,\ y = 6 + 15t - 2v,\ z = -2 - 5t + v,$
(d) $x = 2 + 2t,\ y = 15t - 2v,\ z = -5t + v,$
(e) $x = t,\ y = -11 + 3t + 5v,\ z = -11 + 3t + 6v.$
(f) no solution.

Section 5.5

1. $x = 3,\ y = 4,\ z = 5,$ $\qquad x = 4,\ y = 3,\ z = 5,$
   $x = 15,\ y = 8,\ z = 17,$ $\qquad x = 8,\ y = 15,\ z = 17,$
   $x = 5,\ y = 12,\ z = 13,$ $\qquad x = 12,\ y = 5,\ z = 13,$
   $x = 21,\ y = 20,\ z = 29,$ $\qquad x = 20,\ y = 21,\ z = 29,$
   $x = 7,\ y = 24,\ z = 25.$ $\qquad x = 24,\ y = 7,\ z = 25.$

3. (a) $x = 3k,\ y = 4k,\ z = 5k,$
   $\quad\ x = 4k,\ y = 3k,\ z = 5k.$
   (b) none.

5. $n \equiv 0, 1, 3 \pmod 4$.

Section 5.10

1. $N(100) = 12,\ P(100) = 0,\ Q(100) = 0,$
   $N(101) = 8,\ \ P(101) = 2,\ Q(101) = 8,$
   $N(102) = 0,\ \ P(102) = 0,\ Q(102) = 0.$

Section 5.13

1. (a) all $n = 2^e p_1^{e_1} \cdots p_k^{e_k},\ e \geq 1,\ e_i$ even if $p_i \equiv 3 \pmod 4$.
   (b) all $n \equiv 0, 2, 6 \pmod 8$.
   (c) all integers.
   (d) all non-negative even integers.

2. All perfect squares.

9. (a) $x = 2,\ y = -3,$ $\qquad x = -2,\ y = 3,$
   $\qquad x = 4,\ y = -1,$ $\qquad x = -4,\ y = 1,$
   $\qquad x = 6,\ y = -5,$ $\qquad x = -6,\ y = 5,$
   $\qquad x = 8,\ y = -5,$ $\qquad x = -8,\ y = 5.$
   (b) no solution.

10. 1.

Section 5.14

2. (a) $x^2 + xy + 3y^2,$ $\qquad$ (c) $2x^2 + xy + 6y^2,$
   (b) $x^2 + xy + 2y^2,$ $\qquad$ (d) $x^2 + xy + 3y^2.$

4. $x^2 + xy + 5y^2.$

Section 6.1

6. $a = b = d = 1,\ c = 0$ will do.

Section 7.1

1. $17/3 = \langle 5, 1, 2 \rangle$, $3/17 = \langle 0, 5, 1, 2 \rangle$, $8/1 = \langle 8 \rangle$.
3. $\langle 2, 1, 4 \rangle = 14/5$, $\langle -3, 2, 12 \rangle = -63/25$, $\langle 0, 1, 1, 100 \rangle = 101/201$.

Section 7.2

1. The following conditions are necessary and sufficient. In case $a_j = b_j$ for $0 \leq j \leq n$, then n must be even. Otherwise define r as the least value of j such that $a_j \neq b_j$. In case $r \leq n - 1$, then for r even we require $a_r < b_r$, but for r odd, $a_r > b_r$. In case $r = n$, then for n even we require $a_n < b_n$, but for n odd we require $a_n > 1 + b_n$, or $a_n = 1 + b_n$ with $b_{n+1} > 1$.

Section 7.3

1. $(1 + \sqrt{5})/2$.
2. $(3 + \sqrt{5})/2$, $(25 - \sqrt{5})/10$.
3. (a) $1 + \sqrt{2}$, (b) $(1 + \sqrt{3})/2$, (c) $1 + \sqrt{3}$, (d) $3 - \sqrt{3}$.
4. $h_n/h_{n-1} = \begin{cases} \langle a_n, a_{n-1}, \cdots, a_2, a_1, a_0 \rangle & \text{if } a_0 \neq 0, \\ \langle a_n, a_{n-1}, \cdots, a_4, a_3, a_2 \rangle & \text{if } a_0 = 0. \end{cases}$

Section 7.4

1. $\sqrt{2} = \langle 1, 2, 2, 2, \cdots \rangle$, $\sqrt{2} - 1 = \langle 0, 2, 2, 2, \cdots \rangle$,
$\sqrt{2}/2 = \langle 0, 1, 2, 2, 2, \cdots \rangle$
$\sqrt{3} = \langle 1, 1, 2, 1, 2, 1, 2, \cdots \rangle$, $\dfrac{1}{\sqrt{3}} = \langle 0, 1, 1, 2, 1, 2, 1, 2, \cdots \rangle$.

Section 7.6

1. $1/1$, $3/2$ will do.
2. $3/1$, $22/7$ will do.

Section 7.7

1. $c = 1, 2, \cdots, 2[\sqrt{d}]$.

Section 8.2

1. $\log 9$ (base 10).

Section 8.3

5. 1, 2, 3, 4, 6, 8, 12, 18, 24, 30.

Section 9.2

1. $x - 7$, $x^3 - 7$, $x^3 - 3x^2/2 + 3x/4 - 1$, $x^4 - 4x^3 - 4x^2 + 16x - 8$. 7, $\sqrt[3]{7}$, $1 + \sqrt{2} + \sqrt{3}$ are algebraic integers.

Section 9.4

3. Yes; no, for example $\alpha = \frac{1}{2}(1 + i\sqrt{3})$.

Section 9.5

6. $\alpha = (1 + 7i)/5$ will do.

7. The suggestion also works in case $m = -2$. The other special cases can be handled by such numbers as: $\dfrac{1 + 4\sqrt{-3}}{7}$, $\dfrac{9 + 4\sqrt{2}}{7}$, $\dfrac{27 + \sqrt{3}}{11}$, $\dfrac{4 + 10\sqrt{5}}{11}$.

Section 10.4

1. $n = 1, 2, 3, 4, 5,\ 6,\ 7,\ 8,\ 9, 10, 11, 12.$
$p(n) = 1, 2, 3, 5, 7, 11, 15, 22, 30, 42, 56, 77.$
$n =\ 13,\ 14,\ 15,\ 16,\ 17,\ 18,\ 19,\ 20.$
$p(n) = 101, 135, 176, 231, 297, 385, 490, 627.$

2. $n = 1, 2, 3, 4, 5,\ 6, 7,\ 8,\ 9, 10, 11, 12.$
$\sigma(n) = 1, 3, 4, 7, 6, 12, 8, 15, 13, 18, 12, 28.$
$n = 13, 14, 15, 16, 17, 18, 19, 20.$
$\sigma(n) = 14, 24, 24, 31, 18, 39, 20, 42.$

Section 10.6

2. $p(35m + 19) \equiv 0 \pmod{35}$.

Section 11.1

1. (a) $\frac{1}{2}$, (b) $\frac{1}{2}$, (c) $\frac{1}{3}$, (d) $\frac{1}{4}$, (e) $\frac{1}{m}$, (f) 0, (g) 0, (h) 0, (i) 0, (j) 0.

15. $\frac{1}{11}$.

Section 11.2

1. $15/(2\pi^2)$.

2. $\dfrac{6}{\pi^2} \displaystyle\sum_{j=1}^{10} \dfrac{1}{j^2}$.

3. $8/\pi^2$.

Section 11.4

1. $1/2, 0, 1/3, 1/m$.

Index